The Lead, Copper
& Barytes Mines
of Shropshire

LOGASTON PRESS
Little Logaston Woonton Almeley
Herefordshire HR3 6QH
logastonpress.co.uk

First published by Logaston Press 2009
Copyright © Michael Shaw 2009
Copyright © illustrations as acknowledged 2009

ISBN 978 1906663 09 4

Typeset by Logaston Press
and printed in Great Britain by
Bell & Bain Ltd., Glasgow

*Cover illustration: Abandoned mine trucks in the
Forty Yard Level at Snailbeach Mine in 2004 (I.A. Cooper)*

The Lead, Copper & Barytes Mines of Shropshire

by
Michael Shaw

Logaston Press

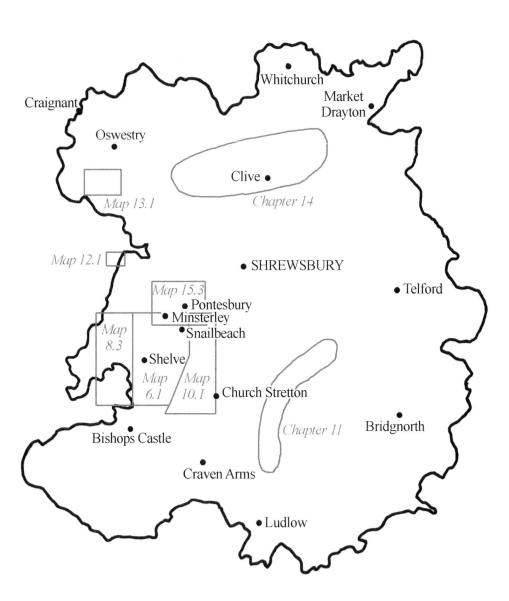

Craignant

Whitchurch

Market
Drayton

Oswestry

Map 13.1

Clive

Chapter 14

Map 12.1

SHREWSBURY

Map 15.3

Telford

Pontesbury
Minsterley
Snailbeach

Map
8.3

Shelve

Map
6.1

Map
10.1

Church Stretton

Chapter 11

Bridgnorth

Bishops Castle

Craven Arms

Ludlow

Contents

Acknowledgements

Any work of this nature builds on (or digs below perhaps in this case) the research and activity of many others. As always it is impossible to name all of them but some must be mentioned. Corporately, past and present members of Shropshire Caving and Mining Cub have provided an enormous body of material, and their publications and library contain a vast amount of information. Andy Cuckson (Snailbeach), David Poyner (Corvedale), Ivor Brown and Ian Cooper, Peter Eggleston and Kelvin Lake (for recent photographs) perhaps should be picked out for specific mention. Andy Yapp and Nick Southwick are to be thanked for the use of material from the Shropshire Mines Trust collection. The staff at Shropshire Archives have been unfailingly pleasant and professional, not only doing what they are paid for but also on occasions directing me to material I might otherwise have missed. Mr C. Pearce of Shropshire Photographic Society must be thanked for giving that society's consent for the publication of photographs taken by members, some now deceased; the individuals are credited below their photographs. One unpublished, non-mining related source deserves mention and that is the vast archive of Lily Chitty (she was related to Heighway Jones, who features large in the following pages), a well respected amateur archaeologist who noted a huge amount of detail in her notebooks and on her maps; much information on local archaeology, copper and copper mining is from this source. I would also like to thank, in some cases posthumously, the authors of the books and reports I have consulted. I trust that I have always acknowledged my sources.

Introduction

Human beings have been intent on the search for metal ores ever since they first discovered how to use them, but it was the Romans who first began systematic mining in Shropshire, and evidence of their activities still exists in many places in the county. It was in the nineteenth century, however, that the search for the mineral resources needed to support industry intensified to the extent that any likely or even unlikely site was acquired for exploration by generations of entrepreneurs: these were decades of boom and bust, and there were some winners and, predictably, many losers. New technologies of all kinds were developed to make the most of potential opportunities: railways, ropeways, mills and smelthouses; but, as ever, the brunt of the work was borne by men, and the mines both provided employment and dealt in tragedy in the relentless (and often fruitless) quest for mineral wealth. The story of Shropshire's mines contains all the elements of the history of Britain's industrial past, and many clues to that history are still to be found — most of them in the form of written records, and the remains of mines. There are a few people living who were born before lead mining ceased to be significant, a few more who might just remember the last copper scratchings and a number who do remember barytes mining, though it has been over sixty years since it effectively ended.

The book opens with a gazetteer which lists the mines, their period of activity, the metals and minerals produced and other core details, not least the various spellings under which the mine might be mentioned over time. It also provides a page number link to the mine's main entry in the book. The following four chapters cover the pre industrial age history of the mines, the geology of the area, the metals and minerals extracted, the process of opening and operating a mine and transhipping its products and details the main people involved. These are meant as general introductions; much more information on these and related subjects will be found in appropriate specialist publications though an attempt has been made to highlight areas where Shropshire was noteworthy.

Subsequent chapters then cover each ore field, looking in detail at the individual mines. Shropshire contains some of the best metal mining remains outside Cornwall and some of the best lead mining remains in the country. The most extensive remains are at Snailbeach and the highest percentage survival is at Tankerville, in each case from the latter stages of the mines' lives: the 1870s at Snailbeach and the 1880s at Tankerville.

Both are now under the care of the Shropshire Mines Trust. These remains are the most spectacular, but ruins of many of the hundred or so mines covered in this book still exist. Gritt sett (Grit and Ladywell mines) has four engine house ruins of a wide variety of dates from *c*.1783 to 1875; the first housed one of the earlier engines in the ore-field and is one of the oldest survivors in the country.

There are powder magazines at Snailbeach, Grit, Gatten, Buxton and Bog, only the last being anywhere near complete. Four of the area's smelters have substantial remains, two at Pontesford and one each at Snailbeach and Pontesbury, all of their buildings now being used for other purposes. In addition to standing remains, a number of foundations (sometimes with low walls) especially of engine houses remain, including those at Pennerley, Roman Gravels, Ritton Castle, East Roman Gravels and Westcott. Tips, sometimes white with spar and sometimes grassed over, remain at a substantial number of sites and are often the only clue as to the whereabouts of the mine. Shafts, fenced or filled, survive, as do a number of adits, these latter often used as water supplies for cattle.

Other remains of the lead mining industry survive and may be preserved (or at least excavated and recorded), including the smelter sites at Pontesford and Snailbeach. Hopefully other sites with lesser remains will be recorded before the remains disappear totally. The future is much bleaker for barytes industry remains. They are not considered worthy of preservation and are more likely to be cleared as environmental improvement (grant aided) than to be excavated and recorded. This fate threatens all the country's barytes mines, preparation plants (like Malehurst) and the premises of the end users in the chemical industry. It is to be hoped that some coherent recording can be funded and carried out. Meanwhile underground exploration, the gathering of historical information, and the collation and publication of the results of those labours will hopefully carry on.

Other buildings not directly related to any one mine also survive. It would be impossible to list them all but some are certainly worthy of note. Chapels, for example; the miners, like their fellows in other parts of the country, felt ignored by the Church of England (often with considerable justification) and took to non-conformity. The Stiperstones area was almost littered with chapels, some of which still serve their original purpose, as at Lordshill and Snailbeach. Others have been replaced by newer chapels and the original buildings have been converted into dwellings, as at Perkins Beach; at least one, Potter's Pit, is disused but was complete at the time of writing, while others e.g. The Paddocks have disappeared altogether. Then there are Public Houses. The Stiperstones Inn and the Miners Arms at Priestweston at least are very much alive and kicking but many others are now dwellings. The sad roll call includes the Tankerville Arms at Hope, the Gravels Inn at The Gravels, the Miner's Arms at The Bog, the Cross Guns at Crows Nest and during the writing of this book the More Arms at White Grit and the Bath Arms at Minsterley have closed and in the latter case been demolished, bringing to an end the pubs named after mining landlords. Many miners' cottages survive, most bearing no trace of their origin, but one is still to be found (protected rather than preserved) in Crowsnest Dingle. Several stood in a bleak location at Blakemoregate on the Stiperstones and one of these survives, although it is no longer occupied. Foundations and garden walls abound, especially on the slopes and dingles on the west of those hills.

Where trials are known of they are included but there were clearly many others, some of which have left slight scars. Some of these are known of from leases and have been included in the gazetteer if the location is known, but many have left no record at all. The entire upland area of the county was probably turned over in a search for mineral wealth at some time between 1660 and 1990.

The choice of mines included and the names used for them is of necessity somewhat arbitrary. Often I have used the names used in other published sources; these may not be the earliest names but may be the best known. One interesting feature is the naming of a new or failed mine after a successful one e.g. West Snailbeach (Rorrington) and Central Snailbeach (Crowsnest). This seems to have started in about 1858 with the use of West Snailbeach and carried on through the rest of the century.[1] Company names also provide endless scope for confusion. Prior to the series of Companies Acts in the mid nineteenth century anyone could use the word 'company' and it meant no more nor less than that and had no legal significance. The names these concerns used sometimes changed for no apparent reason — for instance Messrs Stainsby, Horton and Jones might trade under that name or as Stiperstones Mining company. These companies were partnerships usually run on a 'cost book' basis and should not be confused with joint stock companies which could have identical names. The Joint Stock Acts of the mid nineteenth century defined business names; prior to that they had been vague and variable. In this book, when the information is known, the full word 'company' has been used for these earlier cost-book enterprises and the uppercased 'Company' or more usually 'Co' has been used for names with legal significance.

Units of measurement cause their own share of confusion. Imperial units have been used where appropriate to original sources and contemporary usage, so that the 40 Yard Level at Snailbeach is always called that (not the 36.58 Metre Level). The mines in this book measured distance in fathoms, yards or feet. Imperial weights have been used for the same reasons.

Each mine has been dealt with using documents and reports that are often unique to it. Dates are problematic as, for instance, work may have been carried out on site for a long time before a lease was drawn up and possibly, though not always, signed. Other information, for instance from the much used official returns, gives figures for the previous trading year. This should go some way to explaining conflicting dates between mine entries, though I have tried to tie them all up.

Plans of mine sites have been included if there is at least some good information as to the layout and a significant amount of the mine is still visible. Mine sections are occasionally used as examples of the type of information available but as this book is not primarily an underground history, it has not been overloaded with them. Many more exist, either published, for example in the British Geological Survey reports, or in the archives, notably as abandonment plans, which exist for a substantial number of mines and are kept in Shropshire Archives. Where they do exist they offer a considerable amount of information as at a given date. I have tried to paint comparable pictures of each mine so that likes can be compared, but given that much of the source material is partial, lost, destroyed or conflicting, some entries are much more complete than others.

When official returns are cited they come from the 'Memoirs of the Geological Survey of Great Britain and the Museum of Practical Geology in London' which were first published in 1845 and continued until the early 1880s. The task of recording returns was then taken under the wing of the government, which published titles such as 'Summaries of the reports of the Inspectors of Mines to Her Majesty's Secretary of State, and the Mineral Statistics of the United Kingdom of Great Britain and Ireland, including Lists of Mines and Mineral Worked'. These government reports carried on until 1913, after which date statistics were collected in a more general way and do not give the same mine by mine information. Some entries are incomplete and do not contain either production or employment figures. On occasions these specifically cover a period of inactivity, while at other times they just confirm the continued existence of the mine. Limited they may be — nothing before 1845 or after 1913 and no ownership notes until 1859 — but these articles are nevertheless immensely useful. I have not worked through these from the original documents but am much in debt to Roger Burt's team at Exeter University for collating and publishing them.

More certainly remains to be discovered. Papers relating to the Lawrence law suits over the Leigh Level were extant in the 1970s but are at present mislaid. A country house library has been in the process of relocation for the duration of the writing, though as the catalogue is excellent all is not lost. Libraries I have not visited and personal collections will contain important material too, so perhaps this book should be seen as an interim report.

This is a book for the intelligent observer rather than the specialist mining historian, though for the latter much previously unpublished material has been used and the known histories of most mines have been extended. Underground descriptions have generally been omitted; there are competent publications detailing the underground layouts and levels in the BGS publications and on the accessible remains in Shropshire Caving and Mining Club (SCMC) Accounts, supplemented by reports in their newsletter *Below!* and the Annual Journals. Limited underground visits for the public are available on open-days at Snailbeach and at other places by arrangement through the SCMC, possibly the Shropshire Mines Trust, and other similar organisations for persons holding appropriate insurance cover and having adequate equipment and training.

Any book on mining must include a warning about the dangers inherent in the sites, especially in the mine shafts. The reference to a mine in this book is no suggestion that the site is accessible.

Basically this book is what seems to be called a labour of love though it has not always been referred to quite so affectionately when I have been bogged down at Bog, bothered at Wothercott and Cotherton or shelved at Shelve.

The Gazetteer

This list includes all the usual names of the known mines and trials and most of the alternative names used. It also includes drainage levels which served more than one mine and smelthouses and barytes mills which were sited away from the mines. Some minor spelling variants have been omitted as have alternative spellings of placenames where that spelling does not seem to have been used for the mine which shared it. In some cases names were used for more than one mine or have been used incorrectly for so long as to have become treated as fact. One other class of names is included for the sake of avoiding further confusion — mines which have appeared in various sources as being in Shropshire but are not, for which simply a correct location is given. Several mines cross the border either above or below ground and a few are wholly in Wales but have been included because they relate in some significant respect to Shropshire.

The use of these names is not to imply that they were the names that the mine owners, miners or landlords used. In many cases these are not known and convenient 'handles' have been invented which could of course be the ones originally or subsequently used during the mine's life.

Some mine names e.g Lord's Hill and Crowsnest not only appear as one word or two but also with or without the apostrophe. Some of the former have been noted but none of the latter; the apostrophe has been included if it is used in the name on current Ordnance Survey maps. Where these do not help the form of the name used in British Geological Survey publications has been used. Potter's Pit is rendered thus in the most recent BGS publication but as Potterspit on the c.1880 OS 6in. to the mile map; the former has been used here. Many shafts' names grammatically should have had apostrophes but frequently did not, they have therefore all been omitted. But where a spelling is used in an historical source I have retained that where it adds interest unless the use would cause confusion.

Some names require comment. Dingle: several mines used this name both in Shropshire and Wales. Myttonsbeach was sometimes called Dingle as was Crowsnest and there was a Dingle Shaft at Grit. In this book the name has been used for a calcite mine at Middletown, Montgomeryshire.

Shel(ve)field, Shelve and **Shelve Gravels** are dealt with in chapter 8 where the confusion is tackled.

For **Venture/Ventnor, Wentnor,** see the Perkins Beach and Ritton Castle entries in chapter 7.

Grid references given are for a central or obvious part of the mine unless otherwise noted. Locations are included in the gazetteer to give a general indication only; grid references are (hopefully) precise.

Dates shown in the gazetteer are what they say: approximate. More complex approximate dating will be found in the mine's entry, but rarely are precise opening or closing dates known. Closing dates have tried to take into account any working of the tips for named minerals but not the working of those tips for roadstone or hardcore. A period in the gazetteer's date column is not a suggestion of any continuity.

Gazetteer

Principal Entries

Name	metals mined	approx dates	location	GR	page entry	notes
Adstone	copper	prob 19th c	W. edge of Long Mynd	SO 391941	p.218	Trial
Batholes	lead	pre 1785-1880s	Hope Valley	SJ 339006	p.141	
Benree	lead	1850s and 60s	Shelve	SO 344987	p.143	Trial ?
Blackhole	lead	?pre 1695-1813	Stiperstones	SO 367999	p.95	possibly 2+ Trials
Blackwood	not known	17th c and later	Corvedale	?	p.231	possibly 2+ Trials
Bog	lead, silver, zinc, barytes	?pre 1680s-1932	Stiperstones	SO 356978	p.98	
Bower Yard smelter		pre 1788	Ironbridge Gorge	SJ 670034	p.257	
Bromlow	lead	pre 1749 -1860s	W. of Hope	SJ 321019	p.171	
Broseley smelter		1731-1750s	Ironbridge Gorge	SJ 673033	p.257	
Bulthy	lead, barytes	pre 1836-1923	Breidden Hills	SJ 310131	p.235	
Burgam	lead, barytes	1860s-1962	Stiperstones	SO 358997	p.111	
Buxton	lead?	c.1840	W. of Stiperstones		p.112	possible site only
Calcot	lead, barytes	pre 1826-1919	Corndon Hill area	SO 298973	p.172	In Wales
Callow Hill	lead	c.1613-1914	N. of Snailbeach	SJ 386048	p.113	
Cardington	various	17th c to 1870s	E. of Long Mynd		p.199	several small mines & trials
Carreghofa	lead, silver, copper	pre 1195?-1850s	Oswestry area	SJ 264219	p.241	sometimes in Wales, as now
Cefn Gunthly	lead, barytes	1827-1921	S. of Stiperstones	SO 331950	p.188	
Central Snailbeach	lead	1850s-1875	Stiperstones	SJ 369016	p.114	
Chittol Wood	copper	c.1860	S. of Stiperstones	SO 348950	p.201	
Churchstoke	lead, barytes	Roman?-19th c?	Corndon Hill area	SO 286937	p.173	In Wales
Clive	copper, cobalt	17th c -1870	N. Shropshire	SJ 514239	p.247	
Coalport smelter		?1760 -1810	Ironbridge Gorge	SJ 686032	p.68	
Coldyeld	barytes	early 1940s	E. of Stiperstones	SO 364965	p.217	Trial
Cothercott	barytes	1908-35	N.W. Long Mynd	SJ 415003	p.201	
Craignant	lead	?	Oswestry area	SJ 247346	p.242	In Wales
Crickheath Hill	copper, lead	pre 1799-1870s	Oswestry area	SJ 274232	p.242	
Crowsnest (see also Central Snailbeach)	lead	pre 1761-1811	Stiperstones	SJ 369015	p.95	possibly 3+ substantial Trials
Cwmdyla	barytes	1895-1913	Corndon Hill area	SO 291965	p.174	In Wales
Dingle	calcite	20th c	Breidden Hills	SJ 301127	p.239	In Wales
Drepewood	copper	c.1709 - ?	Nr. Clive		p.247	
East Roman Gravels	lead, silver, zinc, calcite, barytes	pre 1790-1920s	Hope Valley	SJ 337002	p.143	

East Wotherton	barytes copper	pre 1793-1890	Well N.W. of Corndon Hill	SJ 279004	p.185	
Far Gatten	barytes	?	E. of Stiperstones	SO 388985	p.209	
Gatten	copper, lead, barytes	pre 1870-1948	E. of Stiperstones	SO 386992	p.208	
'Gibbons's' mines	lead, zinc	c.1787-1790	near Oswestry		p.246	various sites west of Oswestry
Grit, East and White	lead, zinc, calcite	Roman?-1940	Shelve	SO 327980	p.148	
Hawkstone	copper	pre 1737	N. Shropshire	SJ 587293	p.249	
Hayton's Bent	copper	1680s-1920	Corvedale	SO 516811	p.229	
Hazelor	copper	pre 1860	E. of Long Mynd	SO 462929	p.211	
Heathmynd	ochre	c.1830-1874	S. of Stiperstones	SO 336941	p.195	one word or two
Hogstow Hall	lead	19th c ?	Stiperstones	SJ 361014	p.98	Trial
Huglith	copper, barytes	18th c -1945	E. of Stiperstones	SJ 404016	p.211	
Knolls	barytes	c.1937-c.1943	E. of Stiperstones	SO 374974	p.217	Extensive trial
Ladywell	lead	1790s?-1900	Shelve	SO 328992	p.157	
Larden	copper?	pre 1882	Corvedale	SO 574934	p.232	Trial?
Lee Brockhurst	copper	pre 1925	N. Shropshire	various	p.254	Trials
Linley	lead, copper	Roman?- 19th c?	S.W. of Long Mynd		p.217	Several possible mines and trials
Little Postern	copper?	pre 1882	Corvedale	SO 539821	p.231	
Llanymynech	lead, copper, zinc	Bronze Age-1870	Oswestry area	SJ 266222	p.243	In Wales
Llynclys Hill	lead, copper, zinc, ochre, limestone	c.1851-1886	Oswestry area	SJ 274238	p.245	
Lyd Hole	copper	?	N. of Long Mynd	SJ 416053	p.218	Trial
Lyth Hill	copper	Roman? -19th c?	S.W. of Shrewsbury	?	p.218	Various trials
Maddox Coppice	lead	?	N. of Snailbeach	SJ 382031	p.116	Trial
Maesbury Mill		1860s-70s	Oswestry area	SJ 304257	p.269	
Maesbury smelter		1837	Oswestry area	?	p.265	
Malehurst smelters		pre 1783-1796	Nr. Minsterley		p.258	Two smelthouses
Meadowtown	lead, barytes	pre 1792-1860s	W. of Hope	SJ 314015	p.175	
Medlicott	copper	pre 1839	W. edge of Long Mynd	SO 400946	p.218	Trial
Middleton (Hill)	lead, barytes	pre 1820-1886	N. of Corndon Hill	SO 303994	p.175	Probably more than one trial and one mine
Middletown Hill	lead, feldspars, barytes	pre 1729-1870s	Breidden Hills	SJ 306134	p.234	
(Middleton/Middletown, both spellings are used with or without Hill, apparently indiscriminately, for Middleton Hill, Chirbury and Middletown Hill, Montgomeryshire)						
Moelydd	?	?	Oswestry area	SJ 252252	p.246	
Myndtown	copper, barytes	?- 20th century?	W. edge of Long Mynd	SO 389888	p.218	

Myttonsbeach	lead, barytes	1830s-70s	Stiperstones	SO 368005	p.117	
Nether Heath	lead, barytes	1728-35	Stiperstones	SJ 361008?	p.117	
New Piece	?	c.1786	Breidden Hills	SJ 296136	p.239	Trial?
New Venture	lead, barytes	1860s?-1930s	Stiperstones	SO 367999	p.125	
Nick Knolls	lead, calcite, barytes	pre 1844-1956	E. of Hope Valley	SJ 343008	p.160	
Nipstones	barytes, ?lead	pre 1890-1920s	Stiperstones	SO 354968	p.118	
Norbury	copper	pre 1839-c.1914	S.W. of Long Mynd	various	p.219	Trials and small mines
Norbury Hill	barytes	1920s	S.W. of Long Mynd	SO 359943	p.219	Tried for copper in 19th century
North Roman Gravels companies existed, but the mine may not have done, 1875-87					p.160	
Oxenbold	copper?	pre 1882	Corvedale	SO 588922	p.232	Trial
Pennerley	lead, silver, zinc, barytes, calcite	1724 -1956	Stiperstones	SO 353989	p.119	
Pentirvin	lead?	?	W. of Hope	SJ 330015	p.176	
Perkins Beach	lead, barytes	1840s-1930s	Stiperstones	SO 364997	p.125	
Pim Hill	copper, cobalt, vanadium	1640s-c.1900	N. Shropshire	SJ 488215	p.250	
Pitcholds	lead	c.1700?-1874	S. of Stiperstones	SO 330929	p.195	
The Pitts	?copper	c.1800	E. of Stiperstones	SJ 407014	p.211	possible site of copper trial, see Huglith
Pontesford Hill	copper	?	Nr. Pontesbury		p.52	Various trials
Pontesford smelter, Snailbeach Co		1784-1870s	Nr. Pontesbury	SJ 409062	p.260	W. of the road to Pontesford Hill
Pontesford smelter, White Grit Co		pre 1832-post 1880	Nr. Pontesbury	SJ 410062	p.261	E. of the road to Pontesford Hill
Potter's Pit	lead	1850s-1902	Stiperstones	SO 355993	p.128	
Radlith Wood	copper	pre 1902	N. of Long Mynd	?	p.218	Trial ?
Ratlinghope	copper	pre 1839	W. edge of Long Mynd	SO 396964	p.218	At least two trials
Rednal	copper, cobalt, iron, manganese	1827-1870	N. Shropshire	SJ 367247	p.251	
Reilth	lead	c.1836	W. of Bishops Castle	SO 279874	p.195	
Rhadley	lead, barytes	1825-1940	S. of Stiperstones	SO 344957	p.195	
Ridge Hill	barytes	1915-31	N.W. of Corndon Hill	SO 279980	p.176	
Ritton Castle	lead	pre 1820-1870s	W. of Stiperstones	SO 341977	p.129	
Rock	lead, barytes	c.1820-1940s	Stiperstones	SO 347963	p.130	
Roman Boundary	lead	pre 1869-1889	Hope Valley	SJ 333002	p.161	
Roman Gravels	lead, zinc, silver, barytes, calcite	Roman - c.1910	Hope Valley	SO 334998	p.161	

Ropeways (one from Bog Mine & one from Huglith Mine)		1918-1948	to Malehurst near Minsterley		p.280	Bog had branches from Buxton Quarry and Perkins Beach Mine
Rorrington	lead, barytes	1720s?-1920s	N. of Corndon Hill	SO 305998	p.178	
Roundhill	lead, silver, barytes, calcite, ?copper	pre 1836-1940s	W. of Stiperstones	SO 351995	p.131	
Roundtain	?lead, barytes, calcite	1820s-1920	Corndon Hill area	SO 292947	p.181	In Wales
The Sallies	barytes	1937-48	E. of Stiperstones	SJ 396001	p.219	
Sandford	copper	1667	not known	not known	p.20	
Santley	lead	c.1831	E. of Hope Valley	SJ 342003	p.168	Trial
Scott Level	lead	?	Snailbeach	SJ 373022	p.98	Trial?
Shelve	lead	pre 1801-1930s?	Shelve	SO 339991	p.168	
Shelve Pool	lead, barytes	1872-1901	Shelve	SO 332979	p.169	
Shelve Trial	lead	?	Shelve	SO 331985	p.157	Trial
Shipton	?lead	1790s-1830s	Corvedale	SO 563922	p.231	Trial
Shuttocks Wood	copper	? - c.1914	S.W. of Long Mynd	SO 373923	p.219	
Snailbeach	lead, zinc, silver, barytes, witherite, calcite	Roman-1970s	W. edge of Stiperstones	SJ 375022	p.71	
South Roman Gravels	lead, barytes, calcite	1860s-1940	E. of Hope Valley	SO 342996	p.169	
Spendiloes	copper	?1711 - ?	Nr. Clive	SJ 520236	p.247	
Squilver	barytes	c.1944	E. of Stiperstones	SO 377974	p.217	Extensive trial
Squilver Hill	lead, barytes	?1714-1874	S. of Stiperstones	SO 327932	p.198	
Stapeley	lead	1860s	N. of Corndon Hill	SO 309992	p.151	Several trials
Stiperstones Trials	lead		E. of Snailbeach	?	p.116	At least three trials
Tankerville	lead, silver, zinc, barytes, witherite, calcite	1830s-1920s	Stiperstones	SO 355994	p.133	
Todleth Hill	?lead	1820?	Corndon Hill area	SO 288946	p.182	In Wales
Treflach	copper	c.1800	Oswesrty area	SJ 263256	p.246	
Venus Bank	lead	19th c?	W. of Stiperstones	SJ 352011	p.98	Trial
Vessons	lead	c.1853	Stiperstones	SJ 381021	p.73	See note in cross referenced entries below
Wenlock	copper	1390s	Much Wenlock?	?	p.232	
Westcott	copper	1850s-1890s	E. of Stiperstones	SJ 403015	p.222	
West Middletown	feldspars	1850s	Breidden Hills	SJ 300128	p.239	In Wales
Weston (Cliffdale)	lead, barytes	1720s-1936	N. of Corndon Hill	SO 302977	p.182	Part in Wales
Weston Heath	copper	pre 1728-?	N. Shropshire	SJ 55x27x	p.254	Trials?
Wixhill	copper	1697-1860	N. Shropshire	SJ 559287	p.254	

6

Whitcliffe	lead	1751	Ludlow	SO 50x74x	p.198	
Whittingslow	lead	?	S.E. of Long Mynd	SO 428894	p.218	Trial
Wilderley	copper	1914-7	N.W. of Long Mynd	SJ 412005	p.223	
Wotherton number 2	barytes	1865-1920	well N.W.of Corndon Hill	SJ 277005	p.185	
Wrentnall	copper, barytes	18th c-1925	E. of Stiperstones	SJ 417031	p.226	
Yorton	copper	?1710 -1860s	N. Shropshire	SJ 499238	p.254	
Boat Level		1720s-1930s	Stiperstones	SO 358001 (mouth)		
Leigh level		1820s-1920s	Hope Valley	SJ 331035 (mouth)		
Wood Level		1790s- 1940s	Hope Valley	SJ 336004 (mouth)		
Abbey Mill		1830s	Shrewsbury	SJ 497124	Known period of barytes milling	
Cliffdale Mill		1863-1926	Hope Valley	SJ 364026		
Hanwood Mill		1890-1925	Hanwood	SJ 441094	period of barytes milling	
Malehurst Mill		1925-48	Nr. Minsterley	SJ 385061	period of barytes milling	
Minsterley Mill		1893-1907	Minsterley	SJ 372000	period of barytes milling	
Sutton Mill		19th-20th c Shrewsbury		SJ 503107	unknown period of barytes milling	

Sites only noted in the Shropshire Sites and Monuments Record (SMR) held by Shropshire County Council

Bettws-y-crwyn	lead or copper	post medieval	S.W. Shropshire	SO 171835	SMR ref.10634. Three prospection pits noted
Nantmawr	lead?	post medieval	Oswestry area	SJ 246251	SMR ref.7323. Series of shafts sunk along a vein
Plowden	?copper, ?barytes	post medieval	S.E. of Long Mynd	SO 393876	SMR ref. 10636. Adit and spoil noted during field work. This may be one of the two sites nr. Hillend on p.218
Sutton	?copper	post medieval	E. edge of Shrewsbury	SO 492103	SMR ref.5485. This was almost certainly a coal mine
Little Wenlock	?copper	1860s-70s		SJ 630083	SMR ref.4003

Cross Referenced Entries

Name	Cross reference & notes
Benthall smelter	see Broseley smelter
Bergam	one of several alternative spelling of Burgam
Bog Rock	part of Bog. Probably Rock but possibly Nipstones as John Lawrence distinguishes between South Bog and Bog Rock mines
Burgham, Clun	see Burgam. Mistake on abandonment plan for Burgam
Brownhill	alternative name for Gatten
Cefn or Cevn: Guntly, y Gunla	alternatives or misspellings of Cefn Gunthly
Cefn Brew Mine: Landysilio Salop.	appears in correspondence re Bulthy Mine, probably should refer to Cefn Briw, which is in Powys
Cefn-y-Castell	alternative name for Middletown Hill
Chittol	alternative for Chittol Wood
Cliffdale	see Weston
Crest Wood	see Wotherton
Cross's	see Buxton
Crowsnest Dingle	sometime alternatives for Central Snailbeach or Crowsnest
Cuthbarcote	alternative for Cothercott, possibly a misspelling
Cathercott	alternative for Cothercott, possibly a misspelling
Cwm Dingle	part of Weston
East Grit	part of Grit
East White Grit	see Grit
East Tankerville	part of Perkins Beach sett
Eardiston	alternative for Rednal
Foxhole	part of Grit, also a trial level at Snailbeach, half a mile north of Chapel shaft
Further Gatten	presumably Far Gatten
Gatten/ing Lodge	alternatives for Gatten
Gravels	earlier name for or later alternative for Roman Gravels (or East Roman Gravels depending on context)
Great Roundtain	alternative for Roundtain
Grinshill	part of or alternative for Clive
Grit Hill	possibly an alternative for Grit or Benree or possibly a separate, otherwise unrecorded undertaking
Gritt	alternative spelling of Grit
Harmer Hill	alternative for Pim Hill
Hill sett	mining area incuding Myttonsbeach
Hope	as above entry for Gravels
Hope Valley	see East Roman Gravels; geographical description or ref to Hope Valley Co mines
Hoskin's Shaft	see Pennerley
Hyssington	see Middleton Hill, Shropshire
Lady Eleanor	has appeared in official returns for Shropshire, it is actually in Flintshire
Lane End	see Rednal
Leeds Rock House	alternative for Rock
Leviathan mining co	a name used by an unknown Shropshire mining company when writing 'anonymously' to the *Mining Journal* re the lead trade Feb/Mar 1843
Linley Consols	company said to have operated Cefn Gunthly and Rhadley
Lloyd Hole	alternative for Lyd Hole

Lordshill/Lords Hill	part of Snailbeach (also, probably incorrectly, Lord Hill)
Lower Batholes	alternative for Batholes
Middletown	alternative for Middletown Hill
Middleton	often a now unused alternative for Middletown (Hill) but see Middleton Hill
Minsterley	see East Roman Gravels and Snailbeach
Mitchels Fold	alternative for Stapeley
Mucklewick	see Middleton Hill, Shropshire
New Central Snailbeach	later name of Central Snailbeach
North Snailbeach	Company operating Bulthy and Middletown Hill
North Tankerville	see Roundhill. The sett went through mostly barren ground to the Hope Valley north of Batholes sett
New Bog	see Nipstones
New West Snailbeach	may be Roundhill or Rorrington
Nipstone Bog/Rock	alternative for Nipstones
North Central	Ladywell and Grit
Old Batholes	part of Batholes
Old Churchstoke	see Roundtain
Old Grit	part of Grit
Old Snailbeach	alternative name for Snailbeach
Ovenpipe	earlier name for Tankerville
Perkins Reach	Perkins Beach, probably a misspelling
Potter's Pipe	alternative for Potter's Pit
Priest Weston	see Weston
Pultheley	part of Cefn Gunthly
Radley	alternative spelling of Rhadley
Rehadley	alternative spelling of Rhadley (1907 official return)
Rhadley Stiperstones	alternative for Rhadley
Rock House	alternative for Rock
Roman	alternative for Roman Gravels (see 1858 prospectus)
Roman Gravels Boundary	alternative for Roman Boundary
Rorreton	Rorrington, probably a misspelling
Rorrington Hill	see Rorrington
Rossington	Rorrington, probably a misspelling
Roundton	alternative for Roundtain
Rownton Hill	alternative for Roundtain
Sawpit	part of Roman Gravels
Scutt Level	alternative for Scott Level
Sellatyn	see Craignant. There are small lead mines which have been said to be in Shropshire but are just over the border in Wales
Shelve deep Level	see Shelve
Shelfield	alternative for Roman Gravels or South Roman Gravels or possibly Roundhill. South Roman Gravels is at Shelfield. There were Shelfied setts on the More and Tankerville estates, More presumably at Shelfield and Tankerville associated with Roundhill
Shelve Gravels	presumably Roman Gravels
Shelvefield Gravels	alternative for Roman Gravels
Shelvefield	alternative for East Roman Gravels or possibly South Roman Gravels though this could be a misspelling of Shelfield
Snailbach	Snailbeach as on Baugh's map of the county of 1808
Snail Bitch	Snailbeach, spelling used on a commemorative china mug of 1853
South Bog	alternative for Rock and possibly Rhadley, the sett at one time included both
South Salop	Company working Ladywell and Grit

South East White Grit	possible alternative name for Rhadley
Stapeley Hill	alternative for Stapeley
Stiperstones Consols	Company running Heathmynd, Pitcholds and Squilver Hill
Stiperstones	Company running Bog, New Venture, Pennerley and Potters Pit
Tankerville Great Consols	Company running Bog, Pennerley and Tankerville
Threapwood	alternative for Drepewood
Upper Batholes	alternative for East Roman Gravels
Upper and Lower Lawnt	site near Bentlawnt purchased by Wotherton Barytes and Lead Mining Co. Ltd., and conveyed at their liquidation to Shropshire Mines Ltd. during the First World War. Never mined, it may well have been acquired in connection with the extension of Leigh level which passed under it.
Wentnor	alternative for Ritton Castle
Ventnor	Perkins Beach Valley, often used as a mine name locally when it refers to the lower part of the valley i.e. Perkins Beach Mines, Top Ventnor refers to New Venture Mine
Venture	alternative for New Venture possibly a corruption of Ventnor
Vessons	usually refers to the part of Snailbeach mine which was in the Tankerville estate, but for a few months in 1853 was a separate mine
Wagbeach Level	see Snailbeach
Watercress Level	see Nether Heath
West Felton	see Rednal
West Grit	part of Grit
West Roman mine	sett south of Roman Boundary; there is no evidence of mining on this sett
West Roman Gravels	alternative for Rorrington or Roman Gravels as the context requires
West Snailbeach	alternative for Rorrington
West Stiperstones	alternative for Ritton Castle
West Tankerville	Company running Batholes, East Roman Gravels and Roman Boundary
Weston/Western Hill	alternatives for Weston, also well known as Cliffdale
White Grit	part of Grit
White Grit East	small mine in Grit sett
Whotherton	alternative spelling for Wotherton
Wood	alternative for East Roman Gravels
Wotherton	see East Wotherton
Wotherton number 1	see East Wotherton

1   An Overview of Shropshire Mining

Bronze Age

Nature having delivered complex largesse, it remained for man to discover and exploit it. His first appreciation of metal was probably of copper in the near east before 9000 BC which, by 6000 BC, he had learned how to smelt and cast. This required a temperature of about 1150°C which could only be achieved using a flue or a forced draught from bellows. At some point, probably by accident, alloying was discovered and bronze (copper alloyed with tin or, less commonly, arsenic) became widely used as it had much greater hardness than pure copper. It was usually made with about 10% tin and often a little lead, this latter to help the molten metal flow into the mould. Bronze technology reached Britain about 2500 BC via Ireland.

Metal working in the British Isles during the Bronze Age was apparently dominated by itinerant founders who travelled extensively with their packhorses. Many of the artefacts found in Shropshire, as elsewhere, came from some distance, often from Ireland. Our knowledge of this industry, and with it our assumptions about local mining, come via three routes.

Firstly there were the mines. Bronze Age copper mines are known in various parts of Britain and Ireland, significantly, for the point of view of this study, at the Great Orme, Llandudno and Alderley Edge in Cheshire. Shropshire is near enough to be within the influence of these two areas and it was crossed by important trade routes. There is also reason to believe that Bronze Age copper and possibly lead mining took place at Llanymynech, which straddles the Shropshire/Wales border.

The second source is the metal products themselves. They exist as archaeological finds of three sorts — grave goods, items lost or discarded and the scrap hoards of the itinerant bronze founders. These latter seem to have been buried by the founders, presumably to be available for recycling on their next visit to the area. Several of them have been found in or near the copper mining areas of Shropshire and strongly suggest a local industry — notably those found at Asterton Prolley Moor on the western edge of the Long Mynd and at Red Castle at Hawkstone. Bronze Age artefacts, axes, palstaves, trunnions and the like are liberally scattered throughout the county.

The third source are moulds for casting tools and weapons. One of the finest such moulds in England was found at Whalleybourne near Longden Common, Shropshire, in 1961 (Fig. 1.1). It is of the early Bronze Age (1900-1700 BC) and has matrices on all

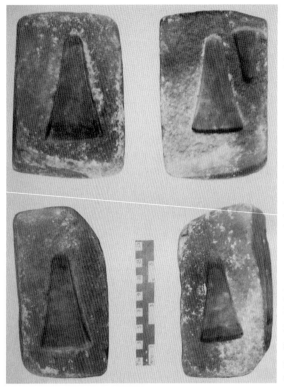

Fig. 1.1 The Bronze Age Whalleybourne mould

four faces for six objects in total: five axes and a rod or awl (the next most complex English mould of the period has just two matrices). It is made of a carboniferous grit which could have come from any one of a large number of sites either on the mainland or in Ireland. It was found in a flooded stream bed and may well have been washed down from up to a mile away. The (used) mould is now stored, along with bronze items from various local hoards, in Rowley's House museum, Shrewsbury awaiting the opening of Shrewsbury's new museum.

From the above it seems very probable that Bronze Age copper mining took place in the county, a view reinforced by finds of local stone axes[1] at or near potential copper mining sites and finds of other period tools on track-ways near such sites.

To produce bronze, tin is also required and, although optimists in the 18th century prospected for it, tin is not mineable in Shropshire. The evidence for Cornish tin being imported into the county is, not surprisingly, circumstantial. But numerous axes made from various Cornish stones have been found, notably in Shropshire's copper areas. On one of the ancient track-ways there is a place called Tinlie (SJ 431013) whose name could contain a reference to the import of the metal.[2] Little analysis of finds (and as far as I know none of ores) has been done, but what evidence there is suggests that the metal of some of the items from hoards at Asterton and Edgebold, near Shrewsbury, could be from the same source.[3] There is a reasonable suggestion that two palstaves found near Llandrinio (Powys) at separate times in the 19th century could have been cast in the same mould and possibly made locally.[4] The situation at Red Castle, Hawkstone, is similar, for copper existed in the locality and items cast from the same mould were excavated there in a founder's hoard.

Though it is reasonable to believe that itinerant Bronze Age founders would have been aware of and capable of exploiting local copper ores, it is clear that they carried and acquired scrap metal on their travels and that scrap bronze was imported from the continent. It is also clear that as the Bronze Age progressed the amount of metal in circulation increased, increasing the likelihood that additional local sources had been found and exploited, but early mining is not an activity which has always left much trace. For every Great Orme mine 70m deep there must have been hundreds of places where copper ore outcropped or where shallow mining took place, only for all traces to be subsequently destroyed. In Shropshire the most likely places for Bronze Age copper mines are the west edge of the Long Mynd, at Hawkstone and in the Llanymynech area. The presence of founders' hoards and moulds makes it fairly certain that smelting took place in the county though no conclusive archaeological evidence has yet been found.

Iron Age

Around 500 BC saw the start of the Iron Age. This did not in any sense mean an end to bronze working but signalled a great increase in all metal working, reflected particularly in the development of the higher temperature technology needed to smelt iron. Iron Age period bronze working is known to have taken place at Llanymynech,[5] where not only was copper ore available and almost certainly worked, but lead ore also. Metal working would have increased generally in the county and by the end of the period, when the Romans came (AD 43), there must have been a thriving national metal mining and processing industry.

The Romans

The Romans are believed to have come to these shores searching principally for gold and silver. They did find some gold (as at Dolaucothi in south-west Wales) and some silver from argentiferous (silver bearing) lead ores — though not significantly in Shropshire. What they did find in quantity was lead. The Roman lead industry was up and running, at least in the Mendips, within six years of their arrival. They also mined copper, though the evidence is less definite and views as to where the mines may have been vary.

Amongst the most spectacular relevant Roman archaeological finds are lead pigs. Eighty or so of these dating from circa AD 49 into the 3rd century have been found in the UK although not all now survive. Three of the known survivors have been found at mining sites in Shropshire; a further two or three are said to have existed but either did not or are now lost.

Of the survivors one was found in 1767 probably 3 miles north-west of Bishops Castle. It is now at Linley Hall near Bishops Castle, having travelled there via Mr. Probert's private museum at Copthorne and Birmingham University Geological Museum (Fig. 1.2). A second was found in 1796 at Snailbeach Farm and is now at the British

Fig. 1.2 Roman pig found near Bishop's Castle in 1767 showing the main inscription IMP.HADRIANI.AVG, now at Linley Hall. (Drawing M. Newton)

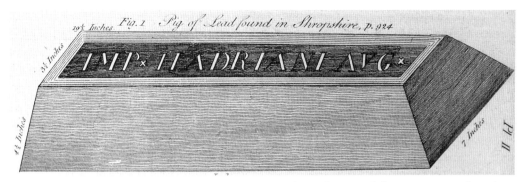

Fig. 1.3 Engraving from the Gentleman's Magazine *of 1798 of the Roman pig found at Snailbeach Farm in 1796 showing the inscription 'IMP.HADRIANI.AVG', now in the British Museum*

Museum (Fig. 1.3). A third was found in 1851 at the Roveries Snead, one mile west of Linley Hall and is now in Liverpool Museum. Of the others, a fourth was supposedly found in 1851 at Snailbeach, but it is unlikely that this report is accurate and, if the pig did exist it has been lost. A 'fifth' has been claimed but it has not been heard of since it left Mr. Probert's museum upon the sale of its contents in 1827. It may in fact be a mistaken suggestion as to what happened to the first one mentioned above. A further one was said (by mining promoters) to have been found in the bottom of the open workings which are assumed to be of Roman date at Roman Gravels Mine.[6]

The first three of the above pigs have the inscription 'IMP.HADRIANI.AVG' cast into their tops (the bottom of the moulds). In addition the first carries a small mark which may read 'MIN' and a branch brand and hammer stamped on its rim, possibly the marks of an Imperial officer at the mines. On the now lost fourth pig the main inscription was said to have been 'IMP.HADRIANI.AVG.LEG XX'.

In addition to the pigs found in the county a number found elsewhere possibly emanate from Shropshire. Significant amongst these are one found at Stocksbridge in Hampshire in 1793, now in the British Museum, and datable to 60 AD, and one found at Chalon sur Saône in France, datable to 195 AD. Two pigs in Rome and others, now lost, of 20 dredged up from the bottom of the river at Runcorn in the 19th century could also be from Shropshire. However any or all of the pigs mentioned in this paragraph could have been cast from lead from the similar ores found in mines in Flintshire. The survival of such a number of these pigs hints at the extent of the Roman industry both in the county and in the country as a whole. At one time national production was so high and its costs so low that production limits were placed on British lead to protect the Spanish mines. In addition to pigs, what were claimed to be Roman spades and candles have been found underground during later mining operations. One such Roman mine was discovered during 19th-century works at the aptly named Roman Gravels Mine; for a contemporary account of its Roman work see appendix 2.

Much of the world's silver comes from lead ores and because of this the Roman lead mines were initially worked under the control of the military, possibly by slaves or convicts. It is thought that if little silver was present in the lead, control would have passed at some stage into civilian hands. If this was the case then all Shropshire's mines would have been civilian as the silver content of the lead rarely exceeded 0.06%, which was below the economic limit for extraction until modern times.[7]

There are several Roman villa sites in the county and those which are in or near the lead areas have attracted suggestions of metal working associations, none more so than that at Linley. The villa was partially excavated in the 19th century and a strong case has been made for the villa being in part used for processing ore. As an archaeologist has said: 'We can make a good guess that the other buildings [i.e. beyond what was excavated in the 19th century] were for the accommodation, ore processing and smelting.'[8]

In addition to deep and opencast mining, the Romans (and later miners) used hushing. A dam would be built as high up on a hillside as water could be made available. When sufficient head had built up the dam was breached and the water scoured the area below either revealing sources of ore or washing ore out from shallow trenches to be collected at the bottom of the hill. Some authorities are convinced not only that this method was used near Linley but that the remains are there to be seen, at least on aerial photographs.[9] If the Romans did seek lead where they are believed to have hushed, they would have been disappointed. Being to the east of the Pontesford Linley Fault, virtually no lead would have been present, though a little copper would have been, and was later worked nearby. The fault, in crude terms, divides lead bearing areas from copper areas. That lead to the west of Linley Hall was worked by the Romans is evidenced by the finding of two of the lead pigs nearby. The various finds make it clear that the Romans probably worked mines at Snailbeach, Gravels and possibly Grit in the south of the county.

The other area of Roman mining interest was around Llanymynech, partly in Shropshire and partly in Wales, where coins were found in one of the former workings. Lead and copper would both have been worked, with ores perhaps being shipped via the River Severn to *Uriconium* (Wroxeter).[10] Small quantities of silver were present and worked in medieval times but the Romans are believed to have not known of it or not bothered with it. Copper was probably mined by the Romans at many other locations in the county for anywhere previously mined was likely to have come to the Romans' notice — especially as gold could be associated with copper ores. Such locations probably include Hawkstone, Clive, Wenlock, Lyth Hill and the western edge of the Long Mynd; in the latter area finds of Roman coins have added a slight degree of weight to the suggestion.

Cupellation (see chapter 3) is a process for separating silver from lead or lead ore. It had been developed prior to Roman times and it was presumably they who introduced it to this country, and evidence for Roman cupellation has been found at Wroxeter where lead ore is known to have been processed to obtain silver and scrap coinage was very probably also dealt with to recover its silver content.[11]

In addition to the cupellation hearth a copper alloy casting jet and an iron matrix for producing relief designs in sheet brass have been found. There was evidently a significant metal industry at Wroxeter. Archaeological evidence of 3rd-century cupellation has also been found at Brompton Fort near Montgomery.[12]

Dark Ages

As in so many fields the departure of the Romans in the 4th century leaves something of a void. Any mining which did take place is probably indistinguishable from Iron Age mining, and almost all evidence would have been destroyed long ago. Lead technology would not however have been lost, and although scrap Roman lead would have been reused some lead would probably have been mined. It was certainly still used, for the Venerable Bede, writing around about AD 700, records its use for church roofs in the north of England. The Domesday Book refers to mines in some parts of the country but not in Shropshire. Shelve is referred to indirectly, however, and Lily Chitty asks why this should be — is it because of the lead mines?[13]

The Middle Ages to 1600

After the Norman Conquest references to Shropshire's mines — principally 'Shelve'[14] — increase. The first is from 1163 when Drogo paid rent of £6 13s. 4d. to the king for lead mines in the county. In 1180 King Henry II demanded an additional sum of £55 on top of his usual income from the Royal Forest of Stiperstones. This sum, which represents the value of lead raised in what were described as his mines, was demanded from Nicholas Poncier who worked the mines on a lease. By 1181 Madoc ap Einion had the mine. By 1182 the mines were described as Mines Royal, presumably worked by employees rather than on a lease. Between 1178-84, lead from the royal mines at Shelve was sent via Gloucester and Bristol for use in the rebuilding of Amesbury Nunnery. The King's 'share' in 1180, at £55, would have been about 160 cart loads. In 1181, 60 cart loads were sent from Shrewsbury to Gloucester at a cost of £26 13s. 4d. In 1182, 110 loads were produced which cost £3 8s. 9d. for carriage. In 1183, 30 loads, £10 10s. plus 18s. 9d. carriage. In 1184, £4 11s. of lead plus 8s. 3½d carriage, probably 13 loads. 1185 saw 60 cart loads, 30 with 18s. 9d. carriage and the remainder with £2 6s. 3d. carriage, the latter being from the mine to Gloucester. Carriage from Shelve to Shrewsbury cost 11d. per load. It is not possible to be dogmatic about the weight of a cart load but later in the middle ages (and after) a carrat (i.e. a cart load) or fother was about a ton. This gives a price between 1180-5 of about 7s. a ton with river carriage at 7½d. a ton.[15]

The mine(s) seem to have been held by the king until after the death of Henry II when they reverted to Robert Corbett of Caus who had previously forfeited them, hence his ability in 1220 to gives tithes of the lead — 10% of the lead produced went to Shrewsbury Abbey. That tithe was confirmed by his son Thomas some three years later after he had succeeded to his father's estates. The tithe was again confirmed between 1234 and 1239 by Thomas Corbett and Ralph Maidstone, bishop of Hereford. The last mention of this tithe is a further confirmation by Thomas in 1270, the document in this case being signed in the monk's infirmary at the abbey. It is probable that the abbey received the tithe in kind and put it on their roof (Fig. 1.4).[16]

Shelve lead was again used by the king, this time Edward I, to roof his castle at Builth in 1278 when three wagon loads were sent there.

Fig. 1.4 The roof of the tower of Shrewsbury Abbey is apparently the oldest in situ *one in the country. Right: evidence of repairs carried out in 1646 applied in the lead. (Author, November 2006)*

Lead was also used locally. Not all that much is known but the bailiff's accounts for Shrewsbury for the 1260s survive and include tolls on lead carried through the town gate. Reyner de Lodelowe owed tolls on 100 fothers in 1262 and 115 fothers in 1263 and John Bernard on 7 cartloads in 1264 and no doubt this was typical. This was not the only metal industry in the town as the same sources record the activity of 'bronze potters' and brass workers in Coleham, but there is no reason to believe that these used any local metal as they would have produced their wares from imported brass or bronze sheet.[17] Thirty cartloads of lead from Shrewsbury are recorded as going to Hanley Castle in Worcestershire.[18]

There is one further reference of interest in connection with Shrewsbury Abbey. In 1402 four men were appointed to look into the revenues taken by Abbot Thomas (after the death of Abbot Nicholas in 1399) which allegedly should have reverted to the king. These included £6 13s. 4d. for a pit which Richard Maydins held at Winsley (Wyndesley). The editor of the printed edition of the Abbey Cartulary assumes this to be a lead mine, in my view erroneously, for the underlying geology of the area makes it clear that it would almost certainly have been a coal pit.[19] Even so it is of interest as it underlines the importance of local coal, not least for the smelting of lead. The verdict, given at Bridgnorth in 1403, cleared Abbot Thomas.

In the 12th century international politics briefly impinged on the mining in the county. King Richard I, 'the Lionheart', was held to ransom on his way back from the crusades. To raise this ransom all possible sources of wealth were examined and a small contribution was made by a lead mine at Carreghofa (Carreghwfa) near Llanymynech,[20] then in Shropshire but now in Wales. The silver content of the ore must have been

Fig. 1.5 Short cross penny from Shrewsbury Mint in 1194 or 5. (Oxford University Press and the British Academy)

sufficient to justify mining it and extracting the silver. Shrewsbury mint[21] was reopened at Michaelmas 1194 'to make pennies from the silver obtained from the new mine' which had opened three months earlier. It seems that the mine and the mint were both closed again about a year later. The mine was near the eponymous castle on the disputed border and may have provided the lead to repair the depredations due to its having been 'wasted' by the Welsh 1162 and subsequently recovered[22] by the English. By 1202 the castle had both been lost to the Welsh and again recovered. A further Pipe Roll of 1212 apparently implies that the mine could still (or again) have been functioning then. No more is heard of the mines until modern times (see chapter 13). In 1333 Edward III sent men to report on a possible gold mine in the county, but their findings are unknown.

It would be unlikely that lead mining ever totally ceased but later medieval references are scarce. The Corbetts of Wattlesborough and the Staffords of Caus Castle had a joint mining venture in 1378-9, presumably in the Upper Heath/Gravels area where the estates abutted. However no further activity is known of until leases were granted by the Staffords for mining in Hogstow Forest (including Nether and Upper Heath and probably the Snailbeach area) in the 1550s, shortly before Lord Stafford sold his estates to the Thynnes (later Marquis of Bath, see Snailbeach) and those who were to become the Tankerville and Lloyd families who controlled various mines individually and jointly as the 'joint Lordship'.[23]

The level of mining activity probably did not change much until the Black Death in 1348 which must have disrupted all aspects of life, at least temporarily. Building would have stopped in the short term and slowed down for a longer period. Labour would have been scarce for a considerable period and costs would have risen and remained high. There may have been some recovery before the Reformation with church building carrying on and some military demand for fortifications for the Wars of the Roses. After these wars, and even more so after the Reformation, the bottom must have fallen out of the lead market. The 'King's Works' reveals just how much lead was being recovered both from monastic and military buildings. The lead mining industry may not have fully recovered until after the Restoration of the Monarchy in 1660.

One other tantalising reference exists to mining in the county, this time for copper and silver. In 1394 James 'mynour' of Derbyshire was permitted to work a copper mine which belonged to the Prior of Wenlock Abbey, but activity appears to have finished by 1397. This is not quite the end of the story of that mine, as it was cited in the lawsuit referred to below.

The mid 16th century saw considerable changes and mining began to take on something akin to its modern form. Techniques began to change, especially in Germany, recorded in and spread by the publication of the first significant book on metallurgy and mining, Agricola's *De Res Metallica* in 1556. Progress spread to this country with the arrival of German miners and was marked by an increased royal interest in their noble metals, for instance Queen Elizabeth I took the Earl of Northumberland to court in 1568 to seize his copper mine at Newland near Keswick, which also produced some gold. The case centred round the crown's right to claim a mine if it contained precious metal. In the case reference was made to gold being found in a copper mine at Wenlock or on the lands of the prior of Wenlock, in the reign of Richard II.[24] Quite what the evidence for the gold was is not known but it almost certainly never existed.

It is from this period that the first references occur to mining near to Snailbeach (or what was to become Snailbeach) when a lease was granted in 1552 to one John Clifton to mine lead in Hogstow Forest. The Lawrence family, who were still involved in coal mining into the 1850s, began their involvement in Shropshire's lead mines in about 1580.[25]

From the 17th century

At the beginning of this period the amount of mining carried on in Shropshire was very limited. Callow Hill was being worked or prospected in 1613. This and one reference to copper mining at Pim Hill are the only indications of activity prior to the Civil War. The war no doubt created demand for ammunition and roofing material but must have disturbed any mining that existed and made investment a dubious proposition. Shot was being cast at Leighton, just upstream from the later site of Ironbridge, no doubt using both local ore and scrap lead.

Various factors in the late 17th century resulted in an increase in industrial activity across the board. These included a rise in confidence upon the restoration of the monarchy, a decline in state intervention exemplified by the removal of royal monopolies, an increasing amount of capital available, a reduction in interest rates, the introduction of gunpowder in mining and an upsurge in building, not least of prestige houses which needed metal for roofs, cisterns and plumbing. Progress was not of course uniform, with foreign and domestic events influencing mining prosperity. Within England the South Sea Bubble in 1720, when public speculation was followed by a crash, saw confidence in investment damaged. A probable direct, though delayed, result of this was the withdrawal of the London Lead Company from its local ventures at Weston, Broseley and Nether Heath. A succession of wars in Europe throughout the first half of the century either created or lost markets, or involved blockades of Britain's exports or our customers' imports. It is not surprising that the 18th century was just as much a financial roller-coaster as more recent centuries, the early 1750s, mid '60s, early '70s and early '90s all being periods of easy credit interspersed with more difficult times.

Copper

The copper industry was never very significant in Shropshire. There was activity prior to the Civil War (see Pim Hill entry) and in 1667 when the Society of Mineral and Battery Works gave licences to work in the parish of Sandford, Shropshire. There was a flurry of investment from the late 1680s which saw small mines developed at least at Hayton's Bent, Hawkstone, Wixhill, Pim Hill, Weston Heath and Clive. The lifting of the Royal monopolies in 1689 and 1693 no doubt had a significant effect on this; previously any copper mine was likely to have been declared a Mine Royal due to the possibility of gold or silver being present in association with the copper ores.

Another factor that gave impetus to home production was the successful application of coal to the smelting of copper. This led initially to developments in the Bristol area and subsequently in Swansea. European wars between 1697 and 1713 further boosted UK industry as imports became threatened. Even so, little copper mining seems to have taken place in Shropshire between the early 18th century and the mid 1860s. Then the success of the Alderley Edge mines in Cheshire led to some proprietors becoming active at Rednal and Clive. This boom had ended by 1870, some small quantities of copper having been obtained at various places including Clive, Rednal, Westcott and various mines on the western flanks of the Long Mynd and around Oswestry. Like other metal prices, that of copper slumped in the 1880s, which led to the effective end of copper mining in the county, although an expensive but unsuccessful attempt was made at Wilderley during the First World War and UK Mineral Developments Limited looked at Clive, Pim Hill and Rednal (and possibly others) in 1917/8. Some work was carried out at Hayton's Bent mine, near Ludlow, in the early 1920s.

The Official Returns, which run from 1845 to 1913, only show production of the metal or its ores in 1866-8 and 1878, the latter year's 325 tons of ore being the only three figure sum and 65% of all the ore officially recorded from the county. This 325 tons produced just 4 tons of metal and is the only copper ever recorded from Wotherton mine or from that area of the county. This is not, however, the full story as many other mines worked and produced at least small amounts of ore but gave no details of such on their government returns, if they made any.

Lead

The greater quantity of lead ore available in the county meant that the industry followed a very different pattern to that of copper. The late 17th century saw much activity. Snailbeach continued on a small scale, Grit mine was developed by the Mores of Linley from the 1670s, a mine, which must have been Bog, was working in the Manor of Ritton and Kinnerton in the 1680s, and in 1693 (at least) lead ore was being purchased by the London Lead Company from somewhere in the county for their works at The Cupola in Bristol.[26] It is probable that other mines were working, although no records are known. The wars, lack of technology and capital and the booms and busts of the early and mid 18th century kept mining on a fairly small scale.

In the later part of that century the development of steam power and other technology led to a need for greater capital, which in turn led to larger partnerships exemplified by the restructuring of the Snailbeach company in 1782. The 1790s through to 1815 saw massive destabilisation due to the French Revolution and the Napoleonic wars, and an associated increase in demand both from home and foreign markets. This was not met by an increase in output from the mines, and consequently led to a large increase in lead prices. The end of these wars saw the loss of many foreign markets and was followed by the American war of Independence which saw even more markets lost.

The early 1820s saw financial instability and bank collapses and it was the middle of the decade before prices recovered — but not for long, for there was a depression from 1829 to 1833. The rest of the 19th century was a succession of booms and busts, with booms in the 1860s, early '70s and mid '90s in each case followed inexorably by the next bust. From the middle of the century imports of lead ore began to become important, outstripping home production from 1866 onwards. Nationally and locally, 1815 to the 1880s saw the peak of the industry. Annual production in the county reached its maximum of almost 8,000 tons of ore in 1875. Levels remained quite high until 1883 at nearly 6,500 tons, but in the following year only 3,800 tons was produced. The 1870s boom saw the peak of the Shropshire industry with massive investment; again, Snailbeach mine provides one of the best examples. By 1889 the county's production had fallen below 2,000 tons for the first time since records began, and it carried on generally falling until 1910, since when the total production has been perhaps 600 tons in all. Most of that was in 1911-3 though some lead was mined as a by-product of barytes throughout the inter war years. Attempts were made right up to the 1960s to revive the industry, but to no avail. The final chapter was written at Burgam mine by two men and a wheelbarrow between 1959 and 1963, where production seems to have been in single figures of tons per annum.

In terms of national production Shropshire tended to produce about 4% of the total; from 1872 to 1883 this increased from around 9 to over 12% (in 1883), thereafter reverting to about 4% until the end of the century when it began its terminal fall. In all some 236,000 tons of lead ore were produced in the county during the period that appropriate records were kept, over half of which was from Snailbeach.

The price of pig lead fluctuated continuously. From the 1690s when it fetched from about £9 a ton it generally rose to the late 1780s when it passed the £20 mark. With the exception of a boom from 1788-1814 (maximum £41) and a slump from 1829-1833 (minimum £13) it remained not too far from this level until the late 1870s. It then declined to the mid 1890s back to the 1690s level of around £9. Prices recovered by the turn of the century but never climbed high enough to make Shropshire's mining economical again.

With the exception of barytes, which is dealt with in the next chapter, the other substances mined were produced in such small quantities as not to impinge on the overall history of the area, any relevant notes being included in the following chapter and individual mine entries.

Clearly the mining industry in no way stood alone; it spawned and supported to varying degrees other industries and communities. Most obvious amongst the latter is Snailbeach, which only came into being because of mining. Minsterley and Pontesbury grew to a significant extent on the industry and numerous small places enjoyed some degree of prosperity because of it. Several industries grew on the back of mining. The local building trades, for example, would have been kept busy. Metal working industries from the local blacksmith to firms the size of the Coalbrookdale Company and Harveys of Hayle in Cornwall supplied the mines with engine parts, major tools, pumping and lifting equipment. Smaller sundries like candles and hand tools were needed and there were several ropewalks in the area, some of whose products undoubtedly were sold to mines. All in all the number of people earning at least some of their living from the mines was several times the number directly employed.

One ancillary industry which changed out of all recognition during the mining period was explosives. When gunpowder first appeared in the area in the late 17th century it possibly would have come from military sources, but by the early 18th it was being sold by mercers. One who died in 1711 in Cleobury Mortimer had some in the inventory of his property, and although this is unlikely to have ended up at a mine covered in this book, no doubt other mercers in the area supplied it. By the mid 19th century the handling of explosives had been tightened up by Acts of Parliament, including the Gunpowder Act of 1860 and the Explosives Act of 1875. These set out requirements for storage which led to all law-abiding mines building a magazine, which has left interesting buildings in some places. The walls of such a magazine had to be robust and the inside thoroughly dry and lined with timber. The external walls were often doubled with a walkway between and doors out of alignment, and roofs were lightweight, thus encouraging the force of unintentional explosions upwards to provide a degree of safety. The explosives also had to be stored separate from detonators, and the magazines were licensed and liable to inspection. Examples from this period are to be found at Snailbeach, White Grit and Bog and at Buxton. This latter kept explosives primarily for the quarry but the mines did use them too. By the end of the period of mining each mine had its own locked cupboard in place of a magazine away from main buildings, and this cupboard was annually licensed and inspected.

2   The Products

Geology

No understanding of mining can ignore the geology which explains the presence of the mineral, but this book is not the place for more than the briefest of sketches of this subject.

In very basic terms the metals etc. covered by this book are vein minerals having been deposited by a series of hydrothermal movements of mineral rich solutions filling fissures along fault lines in suitable rocks. The process of deposition seems to not yet be fully understood and various models exist, some requiring a large igneous body, probably — as under Cornwall — of granite, whilst others see the mineralisation quite differently from the Cornish (and apparently any other) model and suggest that such a body of rock is not necessary and probably does not exist.[1] There is also the possibility of secondary hydrothermal activity affecting some of the barytes veins. The fissured strata into which the vein material moves, known as country rock to the miners, has a significant effect on the degree, if any, of vein mineral formed, only certain strata being subsequently fruitful to miners, either being of sufficient hardness to permit the precipitation of minerals and/ or being of rock which has reacted chemically with the mineral rich solutions.

Of principal significance to this study are two sets of rocks separated by the Pontesford Linley Fault. To the west are the flags, shales and ashes of the Ordovician period (492-435 million years ago).[2] The Mytton Flags are the principal ore bearing rocks, the sources of the overwhelming majority of the county's lead. This rock outcrops in two bands each a few miles long, less than a mile wide and about a mile apart, running more or less north/south. They are separated by the Shelve anticline. The eastern of the two outcrops, i.e. that immediately east of the summit ridge of the Stiperstones and containing Snailbeach, Tankerville, Pennerley, Bog and a few smaller mines, contains much lead and is also the better source of barytes. The western of the outcrops, which runs from Batholes to Grit via Gravels, also contains much lead but only a relatively small amount of barytes. To the west of the Mytton Flags are the Hope Shales which are barren and beyond these the volcanic Whittery, Hagley and Stapeley Ashes which have a little lead and substantial quantities of barytes.

East of the Pontesford Linley Fault, barytes cohabits with copper in various red or purple Precambrian (more than 570 million years ago) sandstones, grits and mudstones of the Oakwood and Bridges Groups. The barytes in this area is frequently pink due to the presence of iron in the country rock. The copper in this area is in solution, having been washed down and coated other rocks, rather than primary deposition, a process that is still occurring as large areas of Huglith mine have been coated with malachite in the 60 years since closure. Huglith is the area's principal mine. It has veins which run through the Oakwood Grits between disturbed ground to the north-east and the Habberley Fault to the south-west. The other major mines in this area, Cothercott and Wrentnall, are located in the same or similar strata.

Small amounts of copper, lead, barytes and associated minerals have been mined outside these areas, notably along the edge of the Long Mynd, again in Precambrian rocks, in the Breidden hills mainly in Ordovician shales and going into the Silurian shales above and in parts of the north of the county.

The copper in the north of the area, as at places in Cheshire and Staffordshire, seems to have been formed in the tertiary period (66-2 million years ago) when copper-rich solutions rose through Triassic (250-205 million years ago) sandstones until stopped by an impermeable layer of Keuper marls which caused them to crystallise out in suitable areas of sandstone.

Lead was the pre-eminent metal found, and associated with it were zinc and silver. The other group of metals mined, found in various combinations with copper, were cobalt, vanadium, manganese and iron, all but copper in very small or negligible quantities. Apart from metals, major extraction of earthy (and a few other) minerals took place, principally of barytes and calcite but supplemented by feldspar, fluorspar, greenstone, mundic (pyrites), ochre, pitch/tar, fireclay, gravel, stone, shale, witherite and limestone.

Fig. 2.1 One of the higher profile lead products were rainwater hopper heads and cisterns. The cistern shown here was made by Robert Hill in Swan Hill, Shrewsbury and is now outside Shrewsbury library. (Author)

Metals associated with Lead Mines

Lead

A soft silvery metal noted for its density and its workability, it was one of the first metals men worked. The Romans made great use of it for roofing and for water-pipes. At the beginning of mining in the county it would have been mainly used for domestic vessels and a little for alloying. As time progressed its use for roofing, plumbing and ammunition developed. As the 18th and 19th centuries progressed a large number of industrial uses emerged, not least in the electrical industries where lead was used in batteries and cable coverings. Printers' metal and (low grade) pewter were other products which used significant quantities. One high profile use in the 18th century was what must be called decorative plumbing, the making of items such as cisterns and hopper heads by Robert Hill in Swan Hill, Shrewsbury (Fig. 2.1).[3] Lead for plumbing was a major use. During the second half of the 19th century a large quantity of plumbing requisites were manufactured at Burr Bros.' lead works in Coleham, Shrewsbury, along with shot and paint products (Fig. 2.2). Burr's used much of the output of the Pontesford smelters. Lead from Shropshire was also good for glass manufacture, being free of pyrites.

Ore prices depended on various factors, notably the metal content, the purity of the resulting metal, local transport or smelting costs and demand, and varied with the national price of pig lead. Most lead was produced from galena, lead sulphide, which often contained 75% metal, and the best price was obtained either for ore producing very pure metal or for ore containing a high silver content such as was never found in Shropshire. Smaller quantities of silver or other metals in the ore made the resulting metal harder or increased the refining costs, hence the lower price.

Fig. 2.2 Though T.W. & G. Burr's lead works at Burrs Field, Kingsland, Shrewsbury did not close until 1895, no photographs of it have surfaced. The only known illustration is this billhead of 1849 which gives an idea of the scale of the enterprise in its early days. (Reproduced courtesy of Mr. Guy Bridges)

Zinc

Another soft silvery metal, though neither as soft, dense or malleable as lead, zinc is also a much more difficult metal to smelt because the metal evaporates at a lower temperature than is required for the breakdown of the ore. The primary (virtually only) use of zinc until the 19th century was in the production of brass. This latter was first produced by the Chinese and then the Romans and others by adding zinc oxide produced from the ore calamine (zinc carbonate or silicate, though usually the carbonate) to copper ore and melting the two together, the zinc vapour combining with the melting copper to form the alloy. Early zinc items are rare though a zinc coffin base from the 1st century AD was recently excavated from an Essene (of Dead Sea Scroll fame) tomb at the Qumran caves overlooking the Dead Sea. The Romans appear to have worked brass at *Uriconium* (Wroxeter) and there are suggestions that it may have been made at Llanymynech in the Iron Age.

Zinc was historically produced by one of two methods. The simpler was to scrape residues off the flues of lead furnaces, part of the residue being condensed zinc. The 'proper' production of zinc was by using condensers designed for the purpose, a process developed in India certainly by the 14th century.

The first commercial European plant for the production of zinc was built by William Champion at Walmley near Bristol in 1747 when, using a furnace similar to those of the local glass works, he smelted calcined calamine from the Mendips. From 1758 a process using black jack, also known as zinc-blende or sphalerite (zinc sulphide), was available. This involved roasting the ore at high temperature and was little used until calamine became less readily available in the early 20th century. Zinc ore, interestingly black jack not calamine, was being produced in Shropshire as early as 1780, probably being sent to brass works in Birmingham and Macclesfield. Prior to this the ore had been a waste product, some of it tipped and some used as road-stone; in each case much of it was subsequently recovered.

Zinc ore production was well established in the county by 1860 and continued to supplement the mines' income from lead until the end of lead production. Zinc production died out at a similar period and for a similar reason to that of lead, namely competition from larger and more efficient foreign mines. The last recorded zinc ore production in the county was 18 tons in 1924 from Bog mine.

By the 19th century other uses had been found for zinc. It became very important for corrosion protection as in the galvanising of iron, as was being advertised in Kelly's Shropshire *Directory* by 1863. Zinc plate work was a local trade, with at least one firm, M&S Jones of Mardol, being listed in the same directory. The growing electrical industries demanded increasing quantities of the metal as the century progressed. It was also used as its oxide or in its pure state in conjunction with barytes in paint manufacture. It had several medicinal uses, not least as the pink calamine lotion still used to treat skin conditions.

Shropshire produced about 20,000 tons of zinc concentrates — the ore prepared for smelting. The annual figures vary greatly, exceeding 800 tons four times but more often around 400. Once, in 1872, the proportion of national production exceeded 4%.

Lead and zinc ores are almost always found together, with the zinc-blende generally deeper than the lead. Tankerville Estates, who retained their mineral rights until recently, considered prospecting for zinc in the later years of last century, but nothing came of it.

Prices for zinc-blende were almost always lower than for galena, although during the 19th century they rose from generally about a quarter to two-thirds of the price, ranging from £2 a ton to a brief maximum of £10 in 1899. During Shropshire's mining period they never reached this level again, being down to £5 by 1913.

Silver

Silver's main uses are in bullion and as jewellery. Galena, Shropshire's principal lead ore, contains at least traces of silver and some contains worthwhile amounts; most of the world's silver comes from galena.

The percentage of silver in the lead to make extraction viable has gradually reduced over the years with improving understanding and technology. Shropshire's lead generally contained just about the minimum viable amount so not surprisingly little silver was produced. The economic absolute minimum by the late 19th century was about 3 ounces per ton (about 0.015% silver) and even this was only profitable if silver prices were high. Official statistics show less than 1,900 ounces were produced outside the period 1872-1883, when in the rest of the country 63,700 ounces were produced. Tankerville and Roman Gravels mines produced the most, but six other mines produced silver in lesser quantities. The first recorded silver in the county was in 1854 when Roundhill and Snailbeach each produced about 100 ounces. The last recorded production was from Bog mine in 1909 and 1912, with a total of 375 ounces. In the period before statistics were recorded there is no way of telling how much silver might have been produced.

Metals associated with Copper Mines

Copper
One of the first metals to be worked by man and one of the most important. When alloyed with tin or arsenic it formed bronze, which being harder than pure copper enabled tools and weapons to be much more effective that anything that had gone before. It has been mined over a large part of the county but with little success. The copper content of the local ores rarely seems to have exceeded 10%, at which mining is barely viable.

Cobalt
One of the prizes of 18th and 19th century British mining would have been a native supply of cobalt for the ceramic industry where it is used as 'the' blue pigment. Significant quantities were never found in this country, but a little was found at Clive and trials took place at Pim Hill.

Manganese
A very little manganese was produced at Rednal mine though when or where it was used is not recorded.[4] Kelly's *Directory* for 1870 records a manganese mine proprietor

living near Llanymynech. Wad or earthy manganese was noted but probably not mined at White Grit in the 1850s. Prior to the 1880s manganese was primarily used in factories at Liverpool or Glasgow for bleach, glass or ceramics, later it became important when alloyed with steel or other metals for numerous specialised uses.

Vanadium
Pim Hill mine is known to have produced some of this uncommon metal[5] which is used in steel making and, in very small quantities, in steel alloys.

Iron
Vast quantities of iron were produced from Shropshire mines in the coal areas but very little from the mines covered here. The only exceptions were Rednal and Clive.[6] Passing reference is made elsewhere (see fireclay below) to some of the Snailbeach Company proprietors' involvement in ironstone mining at Bentley Ford mine.

Earthy Minerals etc.
If the metals mined in Shropshire needed little comment, some of the earthy minerals are nowhere near as well known and warrant more of an introduction.

Barium Minerals
Effectively there were two of these, barytes and witherite, the most significant of which, by a considerable margin, was barytes. Although the substance is now generally known as barite, the older form has been retained here because it is what the mines called it throughout the 150 years that it was mined. It was widely called heavy spar (thus distinguishing it from calcite, light spar, which was much less dense but similar in looks), and was also called cawk or caulke, heavy gypsum, ponderous spar and marmor metallicum (marmor = marble). Chemically it is barium sulphate. It became important in the middle of the 19th century, supplementing lead and zinc production at several mines and becoming the major mineral extracted in the former lead mining area for the first half of the 20th century. Witherite on the other hand is a fairly uncommon mineral, until very recent times only ever mined in Britain. A few mines in the north had workable veins, the last, Settlingstones near Hexham in Northumberland, closed in 1969, bringing world production of the mineral temporarily to an end. Outside these northern mines occurrences were sparse, a little was found in Flintshire and, over the years, 941 tons at Snailbeach, a few tons at Tankerville and a little at White Grit. Recently the mineral has been found in China[7] and world production has restarted. These two minerals effectively provide the world's supply of barium chemicals, for although other minerals exist they have not been found in commercial quantities, with two exceptions. One of these is barytocalcite, which was worked for a few years at one mine in the Pennines, probably exists at Snailbeach and has been found at Rorrington mine, though not worked. The other exception is barium chloride, which was extracted as a brine from a Northumberland colliery.

Soluble barium compounds are poisonous, poisonous enough to be a significant component of some rat poisons and insecticides. Despite this, the inertness of some barium compounds, especially barium sulphate, enables them to be used diagnostically for barium meal in humans. Barium itself, the eighteenth most common element and therefore occurring widely throughout the world, unlike lead and zinc does not present a toxicity problem. Very few food crops absorb the compounds and any small amounts pass through the body harmlessly; the only food which does contain any quantity is brazil nuts and they present no hazard.

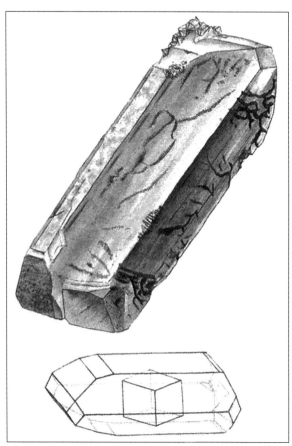

Fig. 2.3 Plate 98 from J. Sowerby's British Mineralogy *of 1804. This is one of the earliest reproductions of a barytes crystal from Shropshire. The specimen belonged to 'Mr. Professor Hailstone' of Cambridge. It was given to him by John Probert who had a private museum at Copthorne Shrewsbury (the house is now flats adjoining the Royal Shrewsbury Hospital, Mytton Oak Road). Unfortunately Mr. Sowerby did not know (or did not record) which mine this came from*

Barytes

Barytes occurs in a variety of forms, both crystalline and non crystalline. The latter forms, described as earthy, platy or fibrous, are more desirable commercially as they are easier to grind. It is a heavy material having a density similar to that of lead. In Shropshire, and generally throughout the world, it is a vein mineral, and in colour varies from clear to opaque white to various shades (and bands) of brown, pink, green, blue and black, the colours being either superficial or throughout the material. The pink and brown stainings are due to iron and generally reduce the value, while the black is due to mineral pitch which renders it more or less worthless. The green and blue staining are due to the presence of copper and can be bleached out. Crystalline barytes can be of similar colours and various shapes and the crystals can under ideal conditions reach a large size. The more attractive forms, even non crystalline ones, can be polished and sold for jewellery and as decorative items; a particularly fine red, brown and white banded form found in Derbyshire is sold as 'oak-stone'.

The first written references to what was to become known as barytes come from Italy in the mid 17th century where it was noted that under certain circumstances it fluoresced; it was known as Bologna stone. At about the same time it appears to have been identified as a separate substance in Derbyshire lead mines and by the end of the century its difference was recognised by the mineral collector John Woodward, who described it as a 'coarse talky spar'. In the early 1720s it was referred to as a 'ponderous white stone found in the lead mines' and by the end of the decade as 'heavy spar' when at their Nether Heath mine the London Lead Company discovered 'several very large, strong veins of heavy spar of which we sent up to London'.[8] What they sent it to London for is not known but it would be nice to think that it went to a state of the art laboratory where scientists pondered over its nature, properties and possible potential in the ceramics industry. It is in this field that the first major use is noted. By 1750 sulphuric acid had been produced from it but still without any idea what mineral it was. It was finally recognised as a previously unknown substance in the 1770s in Sweden by Carl Wilhelm Scheele. Josiah Wedgwood is famed, *inter alia*, for his scientific approach to ceramic manufacture; he kept copious records of kiln temperatures and firing problems and of a vast number of experimental ceramic bodies. Included in the products he tried was barytes which, by the early 1770s finally provided 59% of the constituents of Jasper-ware, a further 2% being witherite (though he could not have called it that). This is well known in ceramic circles but seems to have been lost in many mining history circles, but then Wedgwood was very careful about security and did not let any of this research reach the ears of his competitors. Industrial secrecy about both barytes and witherite was still an issue in 1831 when Leonard Abington visited Snailbeach to try to buy barytes and witherite on behalf of his employer Joseph Mayer and wrote from there to his wife saying, 'I have found out one of the workmen and have got him here with a jug of ale and am by this means possessed of all the information I could desire previous to my going to the mine.' He added: 'I shall return to Shrewsbury tomorrow and shall call on Mr. Whitney to try if I can strike a bargain with him for a small lot. If I should succeed in doing this I shall of course disguise the real consignment of it.'[9]

The first English reference acknowledging barium in its make up was from 1789 when James Watt junior wrote of the 'application of muriated barytes, in schrouphylous [scrofulous] cases, by Dr. Crawford'.[10] By 1791 its use in bleaching had been noted, though it was to be many years before this became an important use due to the relative difficulty of producing useful chemicals from the barytes. The metal, barium, was finally isolated and recognised as an element in 1808 by Sir Humphry Davy. Its name, and by extension that of its compounds comes from the Greek *barys*, the word for heavy. By 1822 it was in use in paints, though this use was not without its critics, and as late as 1870 Kelly's *Directory* of Shropshire (and no doubt others) carried an advertisement from Thomas Hubbard, paint manufacturer, warning the public that 'several paint grinders have been selling zinc paint adulterated with sulphate of barium'.

It was being mined at Wotherton in the late 18th century and being ground in Shropshire by the mid 1830s, though it was also still being considered a 'gangue' material and accordingly dumped as waste from some of the lead mines then and until the 1850s. Many of these tips were later reworked and the barytes, amongst other useful products, recovered.

Witherite

This mineral is basically barium carbonate. Like barytes it can be massive or, less commonly, crystalline and is whitish to pale yellow or pink in colour. The crystals are rhombic and six sided and as they often occur in pairs can appear pyramidal. It is more valuable than barytes, principally because it reacts readily with acid which makes it cheaper and easier to process and form the various useful compounds, a particularly important matter in the earlier days of its use. It is also about 15% richer in barium oxide (77% compared with 66% for barytes), the most useful of the barium compounds, and in some cases the quality of the compounds produced is higher, notably blanc-fixé (see below).

It was first described and analysed in 1784 by Dr. William Withering of Birmingham who called it 'Terra Ponderosa aerata' thus distinguishing it from 'Terra Ponderosa vitroliata' barytes.[11] Ten years later it was named witherite in his honour. Small quantities were first found in Lancashire but greater quantities were subsequently found at Snailbeach mine and in the north Pennines. The material was called yellow spar by the miners (at least at Snailbeach) because that was the colour of the mineral in the mine with a candle behind it; this manifestation of its translucency was the way that it was distinguished from the much more common barytes or heavy spar.[12] At Snailbeach it sometimes shows pink. It may well not have been recognised here until Arthur Aikin, a noted early geologist, visited in the summer of 1811 and published his findings that autumn. In national terms the county's production is insignificant.

Witherite has little use in itself, although it is used to control efflorescence in bricks and tiles. Its principal use is as a source of the same barium chemicals as barytes. Unlike barytes, the quality of witherite is always judged by its purity, rather than the fineness of its grinding. It has not been used to the same extent as a filler as has barytes, partly because of its higher cost and partly no doubt because it is more reactive and significantly poisonous, although during the war successful experiments were made using it as an extender in paints and varnishes. The carbonate in its refined form is used in pottery glazes and in enamelling iron and steel.

The Barytes Industry

Production figures for the county (or for the country) are not available before 1857 but it is reasonable to assume that they were small and very variable. In 1857, 1,000 of the nation's 12,500 tons were apparently dug in Shropshire. Production remained erratic until the mid 1870s, none at all being recorded in several years either for county or country. The proportion of national output from Shropshire was often small but 1864 proved an exception when the county produced 497 tons which was 99.4% of the recorded national output, a percentage never approached since.

From 1874 the county's production increased erratically from around 2,000 tons to nearly 14,000 in 1913. A peak of almost 19,000 tons was dug in 1916 and 76,000 during the whole of the First World War.[13] Figures are then not available until 1921 when 7,000 tons were dug. The low point of the inter-war period was 1926 with 5,700 tons.

Production picked up again by 1930 and was usually between 10,000 and 20,000 tons until figures again cease, this time for good in 1938 when 10,125 tons was produced. Production will certainly have increased during both wars but tailed off sharply with the closure of Huglith mine in October 1945. In 1944 a British Geological Survey publication dealing with the nation's barium mineral resources considered Shropshire's position to be 'not very promising'.[14] Gatten and Sallies mines continued production into 1948, limited production came from Snailbeach mine until 1950, and Nick Knoll mine is said to have closed in 1956.

The only significant amount of barytes extracted after that was in 1957 from Snailbeach; the material was needed as a nuclear shield after 'the incident' at what was then Windscale Nuclear Power Station. J.L. Burden of Jackfield Mines Ltd. did some prospecting and picked over tips at most mines in the 1960s, and may have obtained some barytes. Small quantities were sometimes produced from the white tips at Snailbeach, where for instance 8 tons was noted in official returns for 1965. Very small quantities have been moved from some mine sites (notably Cothercott) since, as part of prospecting exercises, none of which have led to a resumption of mining. For much of the time that barytes has been produced Shropshire has been a major player, often contributing between a quarter and a third of national production. Between the wars only Ayrshire always bettered Shropshire's output and Northumberland pushed Shropshire into third place in 1926. The statistics for 1854–1939 production show Shropshire as producing more than any other English or Welsh county and more than the whole of Scotland, at over a quarter of the national total.[15]

The First World War marked a watershed for the barytes industry in the whole country. The position is well summed up by J.C. Shepherd, the first manager of Malehurst Mill, writing in the *Industrial Chemist* for February 1927:

> Prior to the war the main supplies of barytes came to this country from Germany, which controlled almost the entire barytes market of the world. There were few producers in this country, but their output was negligible and the standard of their product unreliable.
>
> With the war came a serious shortage in barytes, and an increasing necessity for it, both as a pigment and for the manufacture of barium salts for explosives, etc. This gave the barytes mines in Great Britain a great impetus and put it into a position which it could not maintain after the close of the war.
>
> The war period had done nothing towards improvements in methods of production or grinding, and at the conclusion it was not very long before consumers were turning their attention to and buying the foreign product. Their point of view was regrettable but reasonable.
>
> The foreign product was uniform in both colour and grinding, and the grinding was really good, whereas the home product was poorly ground and variable in colour, and therefore could not be depended upon. Nothing had been done towards the scientific investigation of the product.

Malehurst set out to remedy this situation (see chapter 15).

The famously difficult trading conditions of the 1920s did not leave the Shropshire barytes industry unscathed. In February 1923 Viscount Sandon, the Conservative MP for Shrewsbury, asked a question in Parliament of the secretary for mines: 'was he aware of the problems of cheap imports and rail tariffs facing the Shropshire Barytes industry?' If the question seems to have produced little result, the *Shrewsbury Chronicle* carried features and letters on the subject for the next three weeks. Unfortunately they are mainly anonymous and couched in general terms and do not add much to the knowledge of individual mines. They do, however, clearly demonstrate the problems facing the industry. German and Spanish prices were quoted, and were below English production costs; prices between 12s. and £3 a ton are quoted comparing with £1 12s. to £4 15s. for British prices (though these are taken from different sources and compare 1923 with 1925 respectively). There was a plea on behalf of the producers that the railway companies be asked to reduce their freight charges and treat barytes as Class A, like coal, rather than Class B as other higher value minerals. By 1926 the same newspaper carried an upbeat assessment of the Shire industry again from Viscount Sandon, but by 1927 and each year thereafter unemployment in the mines is reported. By 1930 Viscount Sandon's successor was asking the Lord Privy Seal about unemployment in the industry.

Uses of Barium Compounds

Barytes is chemically inert which is both a strength and a weakness. Its inertness combined with its density gives a material which has acid and nuclear resistant properties, making it useful in a variety of ways, the best known of which is for barium meals; its opacity shows clearly on x-rays and its inertness means that it is safe despite being inherently poisonous. It is also used in specialist bricks, plasters and concretes and although these are much more difficult to use than standard products, they have a very important place in hospital and industrial premises where radioactive products are used. The combination of inertness and density also make it a very useful filler and extender in a considerable range of products including paints (where it has other 'better' uses, see below), linoleum, leather, foam-backed carpets, car sound proofing, golf balls, artificial marble and ivory, textiles, ceramics, road surfaces, paper and card. Many of these obviously require fine white barytes.

In the past coloured barytes has had many uses including some of the above but now its main use is for drilling muds in the oil and natural gas industries. This accounts for 86% of the UK's use. The barytes is ground and mixed to a slurry with clay, which is pumped down the drill holes where it lubricates the drill bit, 'floats' the (lighter) shavings of rock to the surface, and by virtue of its density reduces the risk of a blow-out if a pressurised pocket of gas is struck. In the past non-white barytes has also been used in coal washing plants at mines, where, when mixed to give the required density, it enables grades of coal to be sorted — low ash coals will float whilst high ash discard will sink. The material has also been used as a furnace lining. A further use of low grade barytes occurred in the Second World War, when at least four barytes miners in Shropshire tried to enlist but were rejected as they were in a reserved occupation. The barytes was not only used chemically (see below) but also as a heavy filler in bombs and shells in the way that depleted uranium was used in the Balkans in the 1990s.

In addition to these uses of ground barytes there are a large range of uses of higher quality material, most of which involve other barium chemicals being produced from it. Ground barytes is roasted in a kiln with coal or coke to produce water soluble barium sulphide and this is the starting point for a number of products. When zinc sulphate is added to the solution, lithopone or Orr's White is produced, and used as a non-poisonous substitute for white lead in paints. One of the by-products of this process is barium sulphate, chemically the same as the initial barytes, but of higher quality and used accordingly.

If soda ash is added to the sulphide, barium carbonate (chemically the same as witherite) is produced. This can then be roasted with pitch to produce barium oxide (baryta). When this oxide is treated with phosphoric acid barium peroxide is the result. For many years this was used in the Brin's Process for the production of oxygen and subsequently it was used to produce hydrogen peroxide (see below). If the above mixture is further treated with sulphuric acid the result is the top quality form of barium sulphate called blanc-fixé. This is used in bleaching and as a pigment and filler in top quality white paint, as a base for coal tar dyestuffs and in cosmetics, greasepaint and toothpaste.

Barium oxide is also used in the production of barium itself and gave its name to baryta photographic paper, used late in the 19th century.

Barium chloride is produced from the sulphide by treatment with calcium chloride, and is the starting point for other compounds used in sugar refining, soap manufacture and tanning.

Barium nitrate and barium chlorate are used to produce one of the green colours for fireworks and flares. During the Second World War they were also used in shell primers, incendiary bombs and tracer bullets. Barium chloride is a water softener and has medical uses. Barium chromate, otherwise lemon chrome or chrome yellow, is a yellow pigment; a blue pigment can also be produced from barium chemicals. In the glass industry small quantities of various compounds improve the fluidity of the molten glass enabling finer castings to be made; other compounds add brilliance to the glass.

Barium peroxide was for many years one of the more common starting ingredients of the process to produce hydrogen peroxide. Though this product is more associated with blondes and bleaches, in the right concentration it can be used as a rocket propellant and an explosive; the German V1 and V2 rockets and the Me163 Komet fighter were so propelled. Since the 1930s this chemical process has gradually been replaced by an electrolytic one.

Barium itself is a soft silvery-coloured alkaline earth metal. Sources differ as to its melting and boiling temperatures, varying from 830°C to 1140°C for the former, and 1,560°C to 1,737°C for the latter.[16] It is very reactive and may burst into flame in the presence of moisture. It is difficult to produce and has no uses on its own. It is used in a limited number of alloys: with nickel for sparking plug wires, with magnesium, aluminium and nickel in radio valves and conductors in electronic apparatus and to produce Frary metal with lead and calcium — a low friction alloy used in bearings which has the advantage over the similar Babbit metal that it can be cast. Investigation has also taken place into the use of barium to replace tin in solder, though the necessary large scale production of the metal could be a problem. It has its place in history as the nuclear physicist Otto Hahn noted that when he bombarded a uranium atom with neutrons a barium atom was produced (due to nuclear fission), and a barium atom was the first atom to be photographed.

A key issue as to which of its wide range of uses the barytes from any particular mine could be put to was the impurities that it contained. Apart from the obvious point that stained material was not a useful base for the white product there were more subtle issues. For coal washing it had to be free from low density matter, e.g. calcite or shale, for roasting to produce barium sulphide it needed to be nearly free of silica (especially in the presence of lime) though not silicates, and it also needed to be free of alkalis, iron and manganese compounds, fluorite and calcite. (Snailbeach mine had problems with silica and calcite as impurities in their product towards the end of the mine's life.) For use as a drilling mud it must also be free of low density matter and be fairly free of iron, otherwise its purity is not significant. The vast growth of this use, however, was too late for Shropshire's mineral pitch stained barytes which was not much use for anything else. Impurities were not the only problem. If very finely ground, barytes became a wet slurry and especially if it contained clay, it could cause mechanical difficulties in some of the milling processes.

Shropshire has long ceased to be involved in barytes mining but the 20th century's steady increase in demand has had to be supplied. The last English mines — Closehouse and Silverband in the Pennines — closed around the turn of the century, our barytes needs then being met by imports from China, Morocco and Turkey. Reserves have been identified in the UK; a site in Scotland is estimated to hold 6 million tons, and extraction has recently begun there. (This makes an interesting contrast with the estimated total production from this country and Ireland to date of about 5.5 million tons, of which Shropshire contributed over 10%.) Prospecting has been carried out in Shropshire at The Sallies mine site, Snailbeach and most recently (1990s) Cothercott. In the last case material of suitable quality was located but mining it was felt to be unviable and no planning application to extract it was made. Other veins are from time to time noted e.g. at Criggion quarry near the onetime Bulthy and Middletown mines in the early 1970s, but this was not of commercial interest.[17]

Other Earthy Minerals

The quantity of other products mined was small by comparison to the barium minerals. Several of them, however, helped to prolong the lives of certain mines and none of them are without interest.

Commercially the most important of them is **calcite**, also known as spar, light spar, calspar and calcspar.[18] This is crystalline calcium carbonate — limestone. In its most commercially desirable form it is white, but it also exists in various colours and some dark coloured material was described and sold by Snailbeach mine in the mid 1930s as 'black and white' spar. Though calcite has uses in the chemical industry Shropshire's production seems to have been used for pebble-dashing buildings, on driveways and by monumental masons. The small scale production of this material was probably the very last true extractive activity connected with lead mines of the county, as small quantities regularly left Snailbeach mine into the 1980s, reworked from the 'white tip'. Most calcite production is recorded in the 20th century, typical being the hundred or so tons a quarter from Snailbeach mine in the 1930s and 40s.

Various minerals known as feldspars were mined in the area. **Feldspar** is defined as 'any group of alumino-silicate minerals which contain calcium, sodium or potassium'.[19] **China stone**, a hard rock containing feldspar, was also found. Green and white feldspar, china stone and **greenstone** (which may have been the green feldspar) were obtained by quarrying and mining at sites in the Breidden Hills (see entry for Bulthy and Middletown mines). These minerals were all used in the ceramic industry at Stoke on Trent. The china stone and feldspars were used in ceramic bodies and the feldspars also in glazes. Production certainly ran from about 1850 to 1875, though by 1860 the china stone was considered inferior to the Cornish product because it was harder to grind and damaged the mills.

One other small scale extraction of feldspar occurred. A farmer at The Gravels found nodules of feldspar on his land, employed up to 11 men and paid the Earl of Tankerville, his landlord, 6d. a ton royalty. He would have liked to have worked the field in front of the Gravels Inn but could not get consent. Feldspar was encountered in local mines and the farmer was probably working the tips, in this case presumably East Roman Gravels , as they were in the Tankerville Estate. This activity probably took place in the early years of the 20th century with the product being used in scouring soaps.[20]

There are references to feldspar being worked at Snailbeach in the 1920s, with a dedicated siding on the Snailbeach Railway, but this is considered to be a mistake for calspar.

Enormous quantities of **limestone** were mined and quarried throughout several areas of the county but little other than the decorative calspar in conjunction with non-ferrous metal mining. The Llynclys Lead and Copper Mining Company (Limited) in 1871 issued a prospectus which suggested that limestone would be mined. Whether it was and if so whether it was used for agricultural lime, building or as a flux for steel making is not known.

Fluorspar, or fluorite, is calcium fluoride. Like barytes and calcite it is a gangue mineral and was discarded as waste until the later 19th century. It is uncommon in Shropshire, Snailbeach being the only mine where commercial production is recorded. 900 tons, which was nearly 30% of total UK output for the period, was mined between 1874 and 1879. It is, however, worth noting that on at least one occasion a considerable tonnage sold as fluorspar did not fetch the usual fluorspar rate, and was probably purple calcite. The mineral has also been noted at Rorrington mine. Until the beginning of the 20th century its main use had been in the production of hydrofluoric acid and the manufacture of glass; subsequently it became important as a flux in steel making. A purple and yellow form found only in Derbyshire is well known as Blue-John and is used for ornamental purposes.

Quartz is an oxide of silicon, a very common and widespread mineral with innumerable uses. The Stiperstones ridge that runs from the north of Snailbeach south to Bog is formed of quartzite (a very pure white quartz sandstone), and was extensively quarried mainly for road stone. It contained no useful minerals but was worked at Snailbeach where, in the early 20th century, the Halvans Company sold it, crushed for the manufacture of refractory bricks for use in furnace linings.

Clearly much stone was excavated and brought to the surface; in some cases this was utilised for building, either by the mine or by local sale. This and the similar production of **gravel** was a by-product of the mining. Gravel production appears in the returns for Perkins Beach mine in 1935 and 1936. The other widespread mine connection with stone was the use of tips as road-stone and hardcore; this went on probably into the 1970s. By the time the 'white tip' at Snailbeach was reclaimed such material was considered contaminated and either covered *in situ* or tipped elsewhere.

The English Barytes Company sent several tons of **shale** from their mine at Bulthy to their Derbyshire works for an unspecified purpose, possibly paint, sometime between 1914 and 1922.

Ochre, or iron oxide, was dug at a number of mines within the remit of this book and at others in the coal measures in the east of the county, famously at the Tar Tunnel near Coalport in the Ironbridge Gorge. Heathmynd mine is recorded in an 1869 publication as being a functioning ochre mine.[21] It is used as a pigment and ranges in colour from orange to brown to purple. Ochre was also produced by The Llynclys Lead and Copper Mining Co. Ltd. from their mine at Llanymynech.

Pitch was not extracted to any extent in the non-ferrous mining area but was present in several barytes mines as a contaminant. At Snailbeach, and no doubt other places, it is remembered as being used to waterproof boots. In the 1820s, a vein at Pontesbury was mined though nothing is known of this operation.[22] Just north of this area it was extracted from a tar spring and from impregnated sandstone at Pitchford and was found in much greater quantities at various places in the east Shropshire coalfield, notably Tarbatch and the Tar Tunnel, both near Coalport.

In 1694 Messrs. Eele, Hancock and Portlock obtained a patent for producing pitch from bituminous rocks which they extracted both from Benthall and from Row Brook, Pitchford, and seem to have operated into the early 18th century. By the mid 18th century cures for leprosy and to expel poison from the wounds made by a mad dog, ease swelings, bruises and septic wounds, curing rickets and help knit broken bones were claimed in advertisements. Medical claims continued to be made into the mid 19th century when various people, including T. Boyce of Claremont Street, Shrewsbury, produced 'British Oil'. 'Betton's British Oil' was produced by a competitor. It is not known when extraction at Pitchford ceased.[23]

Fireclay, a form of clay with refractory properties generally found in coal measures only warrants a mention here as some of the Snailbeach proprietors, notably John Job, were granted a licence to search for minerals at various sites in Cardington in 1870. A year later a 21-year lease was granted to work ironstone and fireclay at Bentley Ford, Frodesley. The South Shropshire Haematite Iron Ore and Coal Co. Ltd. was formed to work this.

Iron pyrites, sometimes known as mundic and colloquially called fool's gold, was recorded at a few mines but there was probably never enough for it to have been worked commercially. **Copper pyrites**, as 'allum of vitriol', was sought in Rushbury and Eaton probably without commercial (or any other) success in the 1660s and occurred in other mines where it was probably lumped with iron pyrites as mundic. Much was found in the coal mining area of east Shropshire and it gained considerably in importance after the early 19th century when it replaced sulphur as the principal raw material for the production of sulphuric acid. It is possible that disruption in Sicilian production in 1839, which caused a sharp rise in the mineral's price, may have affected Shropshire's prospecting and production.

Some materials were found whose identity has been all but forgotten. One such, remembered by a long retired miner, was found at Tews Shaft, Bog mine; he thought that it could possibly have been used for making gramophone records, though this proved not to be the case. These were made at one time from a hydrocarbon mineral called montan wax commercially found in the Czech Republic and California; it is very unlikely to have been present in Shropshire. However barytes was sent to the Imperial Gramophone Record Co. in Tunbridge Wells. One substance removed and sold from Bog mine, at least in 1761, was called **Gout**, but what was it? That which had been sent for sale was described in a letter as being 'verry bad' and quite white, which appears to have been undesirable.[24]

What was not found

Almost by definition mining entrepreneurs are optimists, as are shareholders, so it is hardly surprising that various substances were looked for but not found. Of these the most valuable was **gold**. One of the earlier references to mining in the county is in the episode in 1333 when John Inge and Henry of Wisbech were instructed to report to Edward III, who had been informed that a mine of lead, copper and gold existed under the land of Robert Brown in Shropshire, but their report does not appear to have survived.[25] A law case in the 16th century refers to gold being found in a copper mine in the lands of the prior of Wenlock in the reign of Richard II (see p.232), and gold was also claimed at Drepewood mine in 1709 (see Clive). The fact that Shropshire was not far from the Dolgellau area gold mines encouraged the optimists, but the only other reference to the metal being found in the county is a report from October 1735 that a man had found gold in a quarry at Newport. Nothing further is known of this and it may have been pyrites (fool's gold).

If the search for gold was optimistic, that for **tin**, at least in the 18th and early 19th centuries was not; after all, lead, copper and tin were all found in Cornwall, so why not in Shropshire? Many leases up to the end of the 19th century include the metal. When members of the Caradoc and Severn Valley Field Club visited Snailbeach Mine in 1896 they had what were said to be tin veins pointed out to them during their underground visit.[26] However it was never found although some geologists suspect that very deep below the lead veins it could exist.

Despite a series of authors claiming that **arsenic** was present in Snailbeach lead ore, it was not.[27] An analysis published in 1870 confirms that no significant quantity was present.[28] The cause for the confusion is either the fact that lead fumes were also poisonous or that the long and often convoluted flues to the lead smelters were not dissimilar to those used in the production of arsenic, principally in Cornwall. If any arsenic is to be found in Snailbeach slag it would suggest the not unlikely possibility that lead ores from elsewhere in the country were mixed with their own. Where this was done it was to improve the smelting quality and output.

"There's nothing to worry about. It's only another of those Harwell professors looking for uranium in the Stiperstones"

Fig. 2.4 The suggestions of uranium in the area caught the public's imagination, Shrewsbury Chronicle *31 October 1958*

In 1878 the *Mining Journal* informed its readers that **platinum** was found at Pim Hill mine. This is clearly incorrect. Perhaps the reporter remembered that Pim Hill did produce an uncommon metal and got it wrong; the metal was actually vanadium.

Since the Second World War radioactivity scares have not been unknown. The *Shrewsbury Chronicle* for 14 October 1958 reports that locals believed that the water flowing out of Boat level (see chapter 15), which drained various mines including Pennerley, was radioactive. The water was tested and no trace of radioactivity found. A retired miner is convinced that prospecting was carried out for **uranium** in a field near Pennerley mine and that traces were found. Two things could be behind these claims. One is that Pennerley was noted for geothermal activity — it had a vein known as the warm water vein and at times the mine was so hot that mining had to be stopped. The other could be confusion over blende — zinc-blende or sphalerite. This is the principal local zinc ore but there was local belief that blende was pitch-blende — uranium ore — and that Bog mine was rich in it.[29] During the First World War a surveyor recorded minute traces of radioactivity, with hindsight no doubt due to radon. There is no reason to believe that radioactive elements have existed in the county in geologically recent times in other than minute quantities.

3   The Process

Land ownership

In the medieval period all land belonged to the crown or the church. Secular land was held from the crown by tenants in chief who gave military or other feudal service in return. Below these were other tenants who gave the tenants in chief service, and so on down the line. The key tenant was the lord of the manor, who controlled mining on secular lands. The church controlled the rest, usually through the monasteries. (This provides a very simplistic view of pre-Reformation land-tenure, but sufficient for this story.) By the late 17th century when the county's mines really began to develop the church had, after the dissolution of the monasteries, lost much of its former lands, including virtually all interest in mining, and the feudal system had gradually developed into a system nearer to that of today where freehold effectively meant total control, although most land was owned by a relatively small landed class.

Leases would be granted to enable a named person or group of people to mine a specified area, either for an annual rent (dead rent) or, more usually, for a royalty of a proportion of the produce, or both. For prospecting a take note, sometimes called a tack note or licence, would be issued for a shorter period, usually between six months and two years, with an option of a full lease being available if required. The royalty (the name reflecting the former crown ownership) on metal or metal ores would typically be one seventh part, though on potentially poorer sites a lesser figure would be agreed, one 12th and one 14th parts not being unknown. More complex arrangements existed; for example, the Bromlow Mining Company was granted a lease from the Wakemans with one 12th royalty up to 500 tons p.a., one 15th up to 1,000 and one 18th thereafter, though deals like this were uncommon in metal mines.

As the 19th century proceeded the 'earthy' minerals increased in importance, and the royalty on these usually became a fixed amount per ton. Royalties could be paid either in kind or in cash, the latter becoming of increasing importance after the legal judgement in the case of Rowll v Gell in 1776, which determined that royalties taken in money were exempt from poor and highways rates whilst those taken in kind were not.[1] The assessment of the royalty and the volume or weight upon which it was based were also dealt with in the lease, proper weigh-bridges being required in some cases, and access for the landlord or his representative to be present at the weighing was always a condition. The mine entries that follow do not usually include details of the royalties and lease conditions unless these are worthy of note.

Not surprisingly, the system of mining leases followed the farm lease practice. The lease would be for a fixed term, 21 years being the most common although this was rather a short period, not permitting enough time for long term development especially for works such as drainage levels. Conversely, the life of most plant and equipment seems to have been 25 to 30 years, so anything longer than the next most common period of lease, 31 years, would have been too long in most cases. At the expiry of the period a new lease would have to be negotiated or the land would have to be handed back to the landlord. In practice, however, work on site would often start before a lease or even a tack note was granted and continue after the expiry, with no apparent concern about a new lease or note. The lease would endeavour to ensure that all possible produce, including timber for fuel, buildings and plant, hay for horses, coal and stone, was purchased from the landlord. The landlord's mine agent would be guaranteed access to inspect the mine, mine plans and account books at all reasonable times, and the lessees would have to carry out the work in a competent manner. Conditions would be imposed giving rights to the landlord to repossess the mine in the event of (most commonly) three months unwarranted inactivity. The lease also stipulated the conditions the miners must accept, such as to fence pits and to fill in old workings, to minimise interference with other tenants'

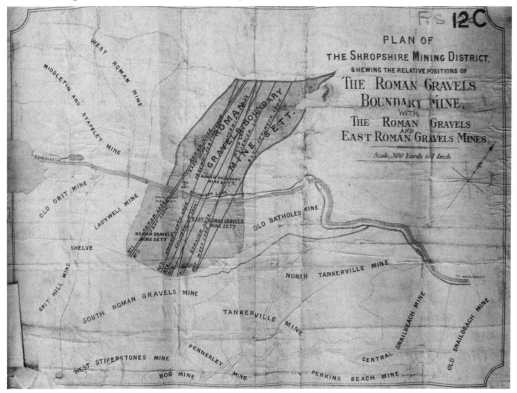

Fig. 3.1 Sett names are both a help and a hindrance. The above undated mid 19th-century plan names various setts, some of which were mined, others apparently not. (SA 1509/44a)

land and access, and not to damage or pollute water supplies. It would often also make requirements as to continuity of use, the numbers to be employed, and the amount of capital to be spent over a set period, and it would almost always specify the condition in which the land and mines were to be left upon the expiry of the lease. This latter clause was to enable the landlord to re-let the mine as a going concern, but it was also advantageous for the departing tenant as he would be able to try to dispose of plant to a new tenant rather than having to dismantle it and try to sell it off-site.

Sometimes the landlord would take a stake in the mine company and occasionally, notably in the 20th century, he would work the mines 'in hand' — this was usually for humanitarian reasons in an endeavour to provide work for his tenantry (and to get the rents of their cottages and small holdings paid). The landlords are the only group of people involved in the mining process who almost never lost out; their rents and royalties were usually paid, although the royalties fluctuated wildly. The adventurers and later shareholders often gained massive short term profits but more frequently took massive losses, and rarely long-term profit. A few speculators, some at least criminal, made large sums. The miners generally got a living though often not a well paid one, but in the not unknown event of the liquidation of a mine the miners frequently did not get the monies that they were owed.

The land area covered by a lease came to be referred to as a sett. The use of the word seems to date from the early 19th century; prior to that the area was specified by the parish or the manor, the vagueness of which probably caused problems at the time and certainly leaves some mine histories uncertain.

Finance

Having acquired the right to mine the land, capital was required. Until the passing of a series of Acts of Parliament from the Joint Stock Companies Act of 1844 to the Companies Act of 1862, a specific Act of Parliament was required if the liability of the members of the company was not to be unlimited. Given the cost of obtaining such Acts it is not surprising that such companies were rare beasts. Few were ever involved in Shropshire mines, the most notable of the ones that were being the London Lead Company (see chapter 4).

Partnerships were the usual way of sharing costs and rewards, Snailbeach being a very good example of a well run and effective one. Until about 1870, most mines were 'cost book' companies. These were partnerships which were nominally illegal outside areas which had specific local legislation, such as Cornwall with its Stannary Courts and Derbyshire, where mining was regulated by various ancient laws and customs. A cost book was the simplest method of accounting; the adventurers paid their shares and the money was spent on developing and equipping the mine (for an example see the mine entry for Cefn Gunthly). The proceeds of the sales of ore were shared out on a regular basis and the costs incurred collected from the members.

It does not take much imagination to see that this method of finance offers no long-term stability, nor did it prove adequate for capitalising a state of the art mine with steam pumping and winding and a transport infrastructure. It also favoured production as against development thus leaving mines 'cherry-picked' with often large quantities of ore undeveloped. It was the realisation that this type of finance, coupled with the expense of limiting individuals' liability, was hampering the nation's development by making the raising of large sums of capital unnecessarily difficult that led to changes in legislation. Without this, major national infrastructure projects such as main line railways and dock construction and improvement would have been much less likely to proceed. This new outlook also had its effects on mining.

The introduction of limited liability led to a degree of centralisation of venture capital and although much Shropshire mining still relied on local funds, money was also available from all over the nation. In some respects Shropshire was an unusual case and much of this available venture capital was not needed. Mine development proceeded slowly until the 1820s when some outside capital came in, the amount increasing until the early 1860s when it decreased again for a few years. Even so *The Mining Journal* for 5 February 1870 could report that 'Nearly all the Shropshire mines are worked by individuals or private companies, the Shropshire district being so rich and so little speculative that the aid of the capital of the general public is rarely enquired or sought after'. These individuals and private companies, bolstered by an increasing amount of external funding, made much heavy investment in the mines, especially in the 1870s and into the 1880s, but the subsequent slump in lead prices rendered much of that investment unprofitable. That abortive boom has left some of the most spectacular remains, notably at Snailbeach and Tankerville.

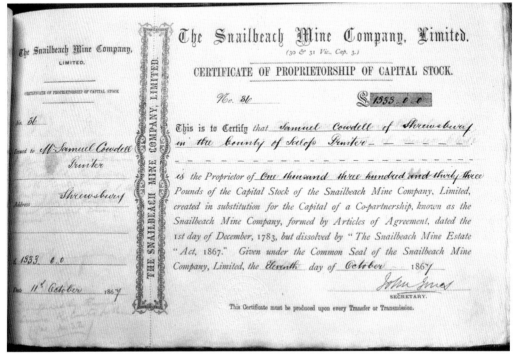

Fig. 3.2 The various Companies Acts which established limited liability required a more ordered system than the former cost book partnerships, reflected here in a typical printed share certificate, this one for Snailbeach. (SA 800/25A)

Mining

Prospecting

At one level mining is very simple — you dig a hole and get ore out. The first miners relied on finding outcrops of the ores they recognised and this method of prospecting was very successful, certainly well into the 19th century. From the late 1830s onward many minerals were discovered whilst digging railway earthworks, but this did not play much part in the area covered by this book. This *ad hoc* approach began to be challenged from the late 18th century with the rise in the study of geology. Shropshire was prominent in the development of this science, with several leading exponents living locally, including Robert Townson, Arthur Aikin and Thomas Blunt, and national figures such as William Smith and Sir Roderick Murchison visiting, studying and publishing their findings. This scientific approach gave prospectors the tools to make reasonable estimates as to where a particular mineral might be found thus making trial excavations less risky. From the early 19th century core borings could be made, a much quicker and cheaper way of establishing the presence or absence of what you hoped to find. This process was invented by Irishman James Ryan in about 1804 and produced a cylinder of rock which enabled the thickness and dip of the strata to be precisely known. It should have revolutionised prospecting, but a combination of conservatism and cost-cutting meant that earlier, much inferior methods were retained because they offered a short-term saving. In the end the device was only used for ventilation in coal mines and then only in certain areas of the country, notably south Staffordshire. Ryan's other claim to fame is that around 1820 he opened the country's first school of mining on the Welsh border near Bulthy, but it was not a success and its location is now unknown.

Once the mineral was located mining could proceed either by sinking shafts or by digging adits. The latter had the advantage of being initially self-draining but were severely limited in the amount of ground they could open up and of course could only be used where the lie of the land permitted. Shafts were expensive (unless you could dig down a vein) and needed drainage provision and winding power for both men and mineral. They could be vertical or inclined. Until mechanisation shafts usually went vertically until they met the vein which they then followed down at the appropriate angle; this later became a major problem. After mechanisation vertical shafts became the norm unless a convenient gradient, often not related to a vein, could be achieved all the way to the surface, as at Huglith and Bog. Drainage could be provided in one of three ways: by digging a drainage level if economic, by pumping by steam, electric, hydraulic or horse power or by lifting the water out using the system also used for the ore. Winding could be done by windlass, horse gin, steam or, towards the end, electricity.

Winning the ore

If a mine was lucky, development work itself could be productive, although most veins do not go down vertically and a sloping shaft becomes increasingly difficult to work as it goes down. Steam pumping engines, introduced from the mid 18th century, necessarily worked vertically but the pump rods could have to work at an angle. The frictional losses involved were high, and there was a lot of wear and tear on the parts; many of the more successful mines dug vertical shafts away from the veins and dug crosscuts to meet them to avoid the expensive problems of angled shafts. Winding from such a shaft was also problematic. Whether the ore was lifted in a kibble, as in most of the lead mines, or trams were raised in a cage, as in a few modern barytes mines, friction and wear and tear took their expensive toll.

Horizontal galleries would run from the shaft and from these, depending on the layout of the veins the ore would be stoped. Ultimately complex layouts of shafts, stopes, winzes and rises would result, stretching considerable distances from the principal shafts. With the exception of Huglith, which had an endless rope system, even the larger mines used narrow gauge man propelled trams to shift the ore. The smaller mines used barrows right up to the end — at Burgam in 1963.

Having located the ore various techniques were used to extract it. Galena in an area of soft(ish) rock could be won just with a pick, but in a harder matrix more force would be needed. As mentioned above, one of the keys to the expansion of mining was the introduction of gunpowder in the late 17th century. With it came a need for drilling and for great care. Holes would be drilled by one miner with a steel bit and another with a large hammer. The resulting pattern of holes would be packed with powder using copper rammers to avoid the risk of sparks, fuses would be inserted and the holes stopped up and the charges ignited. Several hours were needed to allow the dust and fumes to dissipate before the ore could be extracted. The fuses would have consisted of a straw filled with powder, known as germans. These were still used in Shropshire mines well into the 20th century despite the widespread introduction of electric firing. This latter process is remembered by miners as being complex (getting the charges to detonate in the right order) and difficult to rectify if things did not go to plan. Other explosives including dynamite and gelignite replaced gunpowder from the later 19th century. Before the days of explosives three methods of breaking up the rocks were used. The first was the use of picks, as mentioned above. Fire setting was used in ideal circumstances from Roman times onward. A very hot fire would be built up against the rock face and this would be rapidly quenched, the resultant stresses causing the rock to split, although the problems of draught and of access are obvious. The third method was lime or chemical blasting. Holes were drilled and packed with quick lime, the holes were stopped with clay except for a tube which came out and then up, water was poured into this tube and the resulting chemical reaction fractured the rock. The ore was extracted and then trammed, barrowed or sledded to the foot of a shaft for winding to the surface or taken along an adit to daylight.

Drainage

Water was a killer, literally and metaphorically. Nationally a large number of mines have been rendered uneconomic due to flooding and vast sums have been expended pumping out old mines for further development. Early mining stopped when the amount of water present exceeded the capacity of the winding gear to clear it. Short drainage levels could be dug into adjoining valleys in some cases but the unproductive costs were considerable unless they could follow a vein to daylight. As the 17th and 18th centuries progressed capital and confidence increased and in various parts of the country long levels, often called soughs, were dug to de-water large areas of productive ground. Gradually the county caught up, with the digging of Boat Level and Wood Level. The former was about 2 miles long and drained Pennerley mine, later being extended to Bog and rendering an earlier level redundant. It later drained Roundhill, Tankerville, Potter's Pit and Burgam mines. As its name suggests it was used as an underground canal to shorten the road journey from the mines to the River Severn at Shrewsbury or to the smelthouses. Wood Level, 1.5 miles long, was dug from the Hope Valley to drain (Roman) Gravels Mine and later Grit mine. The development of drainage levels continued with the Leigh Level begun in 1825, then abandoned, reworked between 1916 and 1922 and then again abandoned.

The breakthrough for draining mines occurred in the early years of the 18th century with the develop-ment of the atmospheric steam pumping engine by Thomas Newcomen. The first in the world was installed at a coal mine at Dudley in the West Midlands in 1712. Their use spread slowly because of the

Fig. 3.3 *An angle bob for changing the direction of pump-rods etc., this one at Cwm Cipwrth. (I. Cooper)*

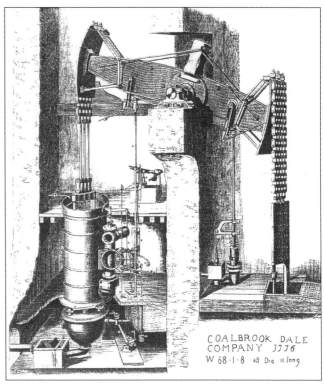

Fig. 3.4 *The advent of the steam pumping engine changed the face of mining. This example was built by the Coalbrookdale Company for use in an east Shropshire colliery and later moved to Derbyshire. The illustration is from* The Engineer, *1880*

47

difficulty of raising the capital cost and meeting the cost of coal to fire them, for they were not particularly efficient. Steam pumping engines were at work in the area by 1775 (on the Pontesbury coalfield) and others followed both in the metal mines and the coal-fields, the local coal making this economic earlier than in several more important metal mining areas. Improvements in efficiency were made by Messrs. Boulton and Watt (Fig. 3.5) who sold several engines in Shropshire. The steam engine kept on improving until challenged in the late 19th century by electric pumps of which there were a few, principally in the barytes mines.

A competitor to the steam pump was the hydraulic engine. These engines relied on a head of water to provide power. In a simple sense a waterwheel is a hydraulic engine though the description is not usually used. It could have some other similar device where buckets, when filled, hauled a chain as they descended, discharged their water into a drainage level and came back up the chain empty, or where full buckets tipped a beam which worked pump rods in the same manner as a steam pumping engine. Simple hydraulic engines appear to have first been used in mines in the UK in the early years of the 18th century. The first, and probably only one at a mine covered by this book was operational at Bog by 1760, though precisely which type is not known. However, many waterwheels were used.

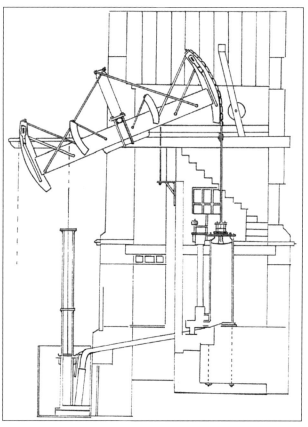

Fig. 3.5 Drawing from the Boulton and Watt archive of the steam engine supplied to Grit Mine (now known as Old Grit)

Fig. 3.6 The remains of one of the last Shropshire horse gins at Broseley Deep Pit clay mine in 1945. (coll. D. Trumper)

Animal power was also used for draining, either men with a windlass or horses and a horse gin (engine or ingin) (Fig. 3.6). Both were cheap to install but very limited in capacity. Some remained in use in the county at small pits into the 20th century and at least in the case of windlasses, within living memory.

Winding
Having won the ore it had to be got out of the mine, and for this winding gear of one form or another was used. Some of the drainage methods outlined above were also used for this purpose. Sometimes ore could be trammed or barrowed out of adits, often having been raised below ground. When the first steam pumps were introduced the mechanics of (and capacity for) using them for winding had not been developed, but once this had been achieved life became easier and outputs grew. Many of the mines in this book used one engine for both purposes. Horse gins and windlasses were used extensively but they put a limit on both the depth and the output of a mine (Figs. 3.6 and 3.7).

It was not only the ore which had to be got up out of the mine, but the men too. For generations this was done by ladders, not too bad in a shallow mine, but as they

Fig. 3.7 The simplest form of lifting tackle, the turntree or windlass, here seen in 1906 on Moss Rake, Bradwell, Derbyshire. (Peak District National Park Authority collection)

49

got deeper, it was not uncommon for it to take up to two hours a day for the men to go to and from the working face. In many cases men would, often unofficially, be wound out in kibbles (Fig. 3.8); unsurprisingly, fatalities were common. With increased winding power available the larger mines installed cages, often used for both men and ore.[2]

Dressing

Obviously an element of selection was exercised by the miners in what material was dug and what of that was brought out. Waste matter underground can be divided into two classes: country rock and gangue. Country rock is that which surrounds the mineral veins; in many of the lead mines it is Mytton Flags, which form the basic relevant geology of the area. If a mine was lucky this country rock could be used for building or road making, if not they tried to dig as little of it as was possible, what was dug being used to fill worked-out parts of the mine and known as deads. Gangue materials are the minerals in the veins which you do not want. For a long time barytes, calcite and blende were in this class and where they could be easily separated, they would be used as 'deads'; otherwise they would be taken to the surface and ultimately tipped. Subsequently, many of these tips have been reworked.

Once material had been got out of the mine, the ore would be dressed. This process would obviously vary from mineral to mineral. Metal ores would be sorted by hand and the ore itself would then follow one of a number of similar paths, a variant on the following. The ore would be crushed (originally with hammers but later by horse, water or

Fig. 3.8 An underground turntree and kibble in 19th-century workings in Busy Bee Vein, Minera, Wrexham. (P. Appleton)

Fig. 3.9 The simplest form of transport for ore and spoil was the man and barrow, here seen at the very end of the county's mining in the early 1960s at Burgam. The miner is Ivor Brown, now a notable mining historian. (coll. I. Brown)

50

steam powered machines) and would then be screened, lumps that would not pass through the screen being returned to the crusher. From the screen the mechanical separation of the ore from other material would begin in jigs or jiggers, and from these it would go through a wet process called buddling where the greater density of the ore enabled it to be separated from any remaining oddments. This jigging and buddling process could be repeated depending upon local need. The ore was now ready for transport to the smelter and the waste products would be tipped.

Barytes was sorted and graded; its treatment thereafter depended on the mine and on the customer. Most of it was crushed and sold, usually bagged or in kegs as powder or, less commonly, as gravel. Cothercott and Bulthy had mills on site, but most mines sent their barytes to their own off-site mills. Most of the mineral was bleached to remove some of the impurities. Milling was taking place at Abbey Mill Shrewsbury by 1836 and continued in the county until the closure of Sallies and Gatten mines in 1948 when Malehurst mill closed (for barytes). The remaining small production from Snailbeach was sent out at best just jigged.

Initially barytes was ground using ordinary millstones at mills which would at other times have ground corn. As the industries required a finer product finer stones were needed; the best of these were French Buhr-stones through which the barytes could be passed two or three times, though even then the fineness of imported German barytes was not equalled. By the time that Malehurst mill was being equipped in the mid 1920s the Raymond Mill was state of the art, though Cothercott, which was being finished at the same time, was still fitting Buhr-stones.

Fig. 3.10 Dressing area and tip run at Wilderley mine in 1917. (coll. IBGMT)

51

The little witherite produced was sorted and sold crude to the chemical industry. Calcite was sorted, jigged and crushed to a suitable size for chippings. The other minerals would have been sorted and sold for further processing by specialists or for immediate use in the case of gravel and stone.

Smelting

The different metal ores clearly needed different treatment, which they generally got in different places. Copper and zinc ores were not smelted in Shropshire. The copper went, by river and sea until the coming of the railways, to Bristol and later Swansea. The zinc ores for zinc metal production would probably have gone to the Bristol area, while that for use in brass manufacture will have gone to various places — some of the earliest recorded production from Llanymynech went by canal to Macclesfield and Birmingham between 1795 and 1804. Other zinc ore is known to have re-joined the copper ore at Swansea for brass production. Some of the zinc metal may have returned to the county to the local galvanising industry.

It is a distinct possibility that the accidental smelting of galena is what sparked metallurgy. Lead smelting did not necessarily need a large capital investment, even to produce it from the ore, and production from scrap lead was, and is, widely carried out. The earliest known smelting sites in the county are small, crude stone 'boles' on the brows of west facing hills, such as Pontesford Hill. There is debate over the reason for this location. One school of thought is sure that it was to obtain a good draught from the prevailing winds, another that they were high up so that the toxic fumes would blow over the hill-top wastelands and not over the crops. Both may be true, or it may just be that the boles at lower levels have all disappeared. Such boles probably predate the Romans and may have remained a regular feature into the 18th century. The process did not require high temperatures and the initial smelt could be carried out using wood as a fuel layered with the ore. This would melt some of the lead and leave a quantity of rich slag such as has been found at various sites in Shropshire. Charcoal was required in addition to wood to recover the metal from this slag.

By the Civil War lead shot is known to have been cast at Leighton for the royalists at Worcester.[3] The shot was produced on a site which also contained a blast furnace for iron, though how industrialised the lead industry was there is not known.

Some of the county's ore was probably being smelted industrially by 1710 when the Earl of Powis built a smelter at Pool Quay near Welshpool, Montgomeryshire. This smelter was primarily for lead from the earl's Llangynog mines in the same county but it may well have smelted some ore from Weston mine. This smelter closed in 1762.

The first dated large scale smelting in the county was in 1731.[4] The London Lead Company leased land at Broseley on the west bank of the River Severn near Ironbridge and opened a smelter the following year. They brought lead to the coalfield by river mainly from Llangynog but also no doubt from Weston and Nether Heath mines in the Marches.[5] The London Lead Company was at this date not a flourishing enterprise, having to sell new shares to pay existing shareholders' dividends. The Marches ventures were not running smoothly and were given up, the smelter in 1736.

The county's large scale lead smelting seems to have remained centred in the Ironbridge Gorge until the late 18th century, taking advantage not only of the river for the supply of ore from the Shropshire and Montgomeryshire mines and the coal but also no doubt also the demand from local industry for the metal and the enterprise culture of east Shropshire at that period. After being used by the Bog Mining Company for nine years until 1748[6] the Broseley smelter seems to have gone out of use. At least two other smelters operated in the gorge in this period, one at Lloyds, near Coalport and one at Bower Yard. One of the smelters, either Bower Yard or Broseley, was dismantled and its equipment sold to Aberystwyth in 1788 (shortly after the beginning of smelting in the Shrewsbury coalfield adjoining the lead mining area). The Coalport smelter seems to have been the last to work; it was relocated in 1810 and had gone by 1849, bequeathing the name 'Smelters Row'[7] to a terrace of cottages.

Both the west Shropshire lead industry and coal mining began to grow sharply in the 1780s, and the first local smelter was built at Malehurst in 1783, beginning nearly 100 years of smelting in and around Pontesbury. The last smelter in the locality was at Snailbeach mine, which survived until the bottom dropped out of the industry in the 1890s. Some Shropshire lead was smelted in north Wales, in the 1780s at Minera and subsequently on Deeside. In 1837 a nearly complete smelter was offered for sale at Maesbury, near Oswestry, no doubt with the Llanymynech production in mind and good transport via the canals. Details of individual smelters are given in the gazetteer and chapter 15.

Industrial scale smelting began in England in the middle of the 16th century using blast furnaces, similar to those used for iron but requiring much lower temperatures. By the mid 17th century attempts were made to increase both the quality of the product and the rate of extraction of metal from the ore, and the outcome was the reverberatory furnace or cupola, in which the ore or metal did not come into contact with the flames. These had been used in bell foundries for centuries but had until then not been used for other purposes. The choice between blast and reverberatory furnaces depended on many factors including the nature and quality of the ores available and the cost of fuel. The reverberatory furnace was more efficient and could successfully smelt finer (in particle size) grades of ore, but it did require coal whereas a blast furnace could smelt using wood or peat. Where coal was available locally, as in Shropshire, the reverberatory furnace became standard though small blast furnaces (as slag hearths) were provided at all smelt-houses for the reprocessing of slags and for certain by product processes. For efficiency and reduction of environmental damage these furnaces were ultimately equipped with long horizontal flues and condensers from which various substances could be collected rather than having them poisoning the area downwind of the chimneys. The flues and chimneys of both the Pontesford and the Snailbeach smelthouses were prominent local landmarks (and the latter still is). Subsequent improvements in lead processing did not impinge on Shropshire as they came too late.

A minor (for Shropshire) but interesting aspect of lead smelting is the production of silver. Certain lead ores contain commercial quantities of silver which have been extracted since at least Roman times. The process they used is called cupellation and works by heating the lead in air where it forms an oxide which is either absorbed by the cupel (a dish made from bone ash) or drawn off as litharge. The process is repeated, each time leaving a greater proportion of silver, until pure metal is produced. The litharge could be sold to the ceramic industry or re-refined to produce a lesser quantity of pure lead. The process was costly and the amount of silver in Shropshire lead ore was not enough (except perhaps at Carreghofa) for the process to be economic. The improvement of the process by Hugh Pattinson in 1829 enabled less rich ores to be used. His process concentrated the silver by taking advantage of the different rates of crystallisation of the molten metals, it thus used a lot less fuel and was claimed to make ores containing 3oz. of silver per ton of lead economic. This figure is that of the best of the Shropshire ores. The first silver recorded for the county was in 1854, but the bulk of Shropshire silver was recorded at Tankerville in the second half of the 1870s and at Roman Gravels in the late 1870s and early 1880s, after the closure of all the smelters except Snailbeach, although it is possible that they did refine silver there in 1881/2.

Transport

This was a limiting factor on the development of many mines and frequently the cause of problems throughout their lives. Four methods of transport were used by the Shropshire mines: roads and tracks, water, tramway or railway and aerial ropeway. The last three had their uses but the first is all-important.

Roads and Tracks

The first reference we have to transport is that of lead for Amesbury Nunnery, Wiltshire, where cart loads of lead are recorded as going to the River Severn for onward transmis-

Fig. 3.11 Early road transport using packhorses here seen passing Bwlch-y-garreg, west of Esgairhir in mid Wales, an engraving from Samuel Smiles' Lives of the Engineers. The arches between panniers held bells to warn other traffic of the packhorses' approach

Fig. 3.12 The earliest mechanical road transport was provided by traction engines. Here Foden and Co.'s engine 'Pride of Yorkshire' is seen hauling two smaller engines and two threshing boxes to Sandbatch LNWR station for display at the Royal Show, (from a Foden Catalogue of 1901). This engine was later registered at 10 tons weight whilst working for Cothercott Co. when it actually weighed 15 tons

sion. In the late 17th century Rowland Nicchols retained the right to use carts for his mining when passing most of his property to his son (see Bog mine entry). The roads in the mining area were sparse until the early 19th century. What roads that existed were often not maintained; when Thomas Poole visited Bog and Snailbeach Mines in 1834 he commented that 'The present spirited lease holders of the Bog, Cross and Ellis of Chester' had improved the road to Pontesbury, but on his next visit in 1836 he described it as being in much worse condition.[8] The 1830s saw a turnpike built through the valley below Shelve from Minsterley to Bishops Castle, which must have improved access at least for the Gravels and Grit mines. In 1860 lead was taken from the Pontesford smelters to Shrewsbury in hefty four-horse wagons which returned with coal, possibly from Hanwood, which was superior to the Pontesbury area's product and

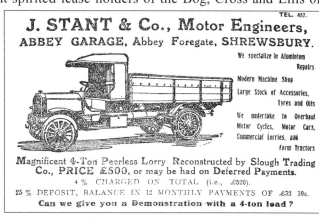

Fig. 3.13 The first major use of motor lorries was sparked by the large quantity of war surplus vehicles after the First World War. the Peerless being a major player. Cothercott certainly used one or more, possibly after refurbishing by Stants

55

Fig. 3.14 Lewis Bros. were a prominent local haulage firm, and several members of the family had been involved in mining at Burgam, Cothercott, Weston and in Perkins Beach. (coll. Ron Davies)

even with transport cost the same at the smelter (15s. per ton).[9] Matters remained static until the arrival of steam road locomotives in the last third of the 19th century. Whilst these could haul substantial loads from the mines to the railway, river or clients they took an immense toll on the roads. The barytes mines (though not the only offenders) fell foul of the local councils in the years up to 1920, often having to make contributions to repair the damage. This problem was not resolved until after the First World War when the highway authorities carried out a major programme of road surfacing, but by this time war surplus lorries, many using pneumatic tyres, had displaced steam and reduced the damage.

Water

There are three uses of water transport in the industry. The prime one is the proximity of the River Severn. This was one of the nation's main transport arteries before the coming of the railways and carried lead ore and lead products from Shropshire and Welsh mines in both directions[10] from the early middle ages onwards. Several of the early smelters were on the banks of the river, for obvious reasons. The lack of deep water channels exacerbated the problems caused by floods, droughts and freezing, and heavy traffic to an extent moved to the turnpikes in the 18th century and by the mid 19th century almost wholly to the railways. Lead traffic on the Upper Severn had ceased by 1862. The 18th century also saw the development of the canal network and whilst this was never all that significant for these metal industries it played some part, notably for products to Birmingham and to the Cheshire and Merseyside chemical industry. The other use of water transport was altogether smaller. The Boat Level referred to elsewhere ran from Bog and other mines to a point near Stiperstones village where the ore was transferred to carts. When the mine was sold due to a bankruptcy in 1830 several boats were included. Despite road improvements in the area, the loading and transhipment problems and the small payload of the boats, they were still being used in 1834.[11]

Rail

Rail transport in some form or another was used in the mines from at least the early 19th century. In 1836 a lease at Bulthy[12] for mining lead and barites (*sic*) refers to existing railways, and a visitor to Snailbeach mine in 1834 refers to several railroads.[13] Most

Fig. 3.15 The Great Western and London North Western joint line to Minsterley played an important part in the later stages of local mining. Minsterely station is here seen around the turn of the 20th century. (Shropshire Archives)

mines of any size had underground tramways and a few had them from out of adits or from the tops of shafts to serve the dressing areas and tips.

Only three lines were developed to connect mines to the national transport system. The Shrewsbury and Welshpool Railway Company (later to be run jointly by the Great Western and London and North Western Railways) set out to tap lead traffic with their branch railway from Shrewsbury to Minsterley (Fig. 3.15). This opened in 1861 and carried substantial amounts of lead, barytes and calcite, to outlive the mining industries, finally closing in 1967. This line was the only one built of a number of schemes to tap mineral traffic and open up the Rea Valley, and proposals to extend it to Bishops Castle were not finally laid to rest until the 1920s. The early 1870s saw much development of mining and a significant influx of capital, one of the schemes emerging from

Fig. 3.16 The Snailbeach railway also used First World War surplus stock, here represented by loco No. 3 built by Baldwin of Philadelphia for the allied trench railways and rebuilt and re-gauged by W.G. Bagnall and Co. of Stafford for sale to Snailbeach. (Shropshire Archives)

this period being the narrow gauge railway from Pontesbury to Snailbeach. Surveying began in 1872 and the Snailbeach District Railways Company was incorporated, the line opening in July 1877. Various later proposals for extensions came to nothing. The line closed in 1959, having been latterly used only by Shropshire County Council for traffic from their Callow Hill quarry. If the Snailbeach Railway was a very minor line, the last of the three lines developed is positively shadowy. Prior to the First World War Cothercott mine had a steep tramway from their principal mining area to the roadside loading dock and later mill site. In 1920, after much heated debate with the County Council over the damage their road locomotives were causing and the delays to their own shipments due to the state of the roads, they decided to connect the mine to the mainline railway at Dorrington some 4 miles away. About a mile of line was built towards Castle Pulverbatch before either money ran out, the receiver stopped the work or the success of petrol lorries rendered the line unnecessary. Its temporary terminus, Outrack, was briefly a transhipment point into farm trailers on a track which gave access to a byroad route to Pontesbury Station.

Air

Nineteenth-century developments in wire rope technology made aerial ropeways feasible. They had obvious advantages over other forms of transport though they required much maintenance and had limited carrying capacity. Two principal lines were built in the mining area, both to Malehurst, from Pontesbury and Minsterley. The first was built by Shropshire Mines Limited over the 5½ miles from Bog mine. It was begun in 1918 using German POW labour and served until the closure of Bog mine in 1925. It had two branches, one from Perkins Beach mine and one from Buxton Quarry, this latter for stone traffic, some if not all of which was discharged where the ropeway crossed the main road just before Malehurst.

The second ropeway was built to connect Huglith mine to Malehurst in about 1922.

Fig. 3.17 Aerial ropeways enabled mechanical transport to be used over terrain unsuitable for railways and various ones served the barytes mines; this one of the same basic type still survives at Claughton in Lancashire at the time of writing. The girder bridge illustrated here is similar to the one over the main road near Malehurst, July 2003. (Author)

4 People

The mines covered by this book and related industries employed a significant proportion of the population of certain parts of the county at certain times. Enterprises ranged in manpower from the Snailbeach company employing 570 (and supporting an estimated 2,170) in 1841[1] at the lead and coal mines (the former at Snailbeach, the latter near Pontesbury), to the odd man or two plundering in Perkins Beach Dingle in the 1930s. Estimating the numbers directly employed in the metal mines is very difficult, but generally it is believed that the total did not ever much exceed 1,000. The 1841 figures quoted above, which come from what would now be called a feasibility study for an alteration to the then quite new Minsterley to Bishops Castle turnpike,[2] indicate that the Bog company employed the same number as Snailbeach in their lead and coal mines (the latter again near Pontesbury) and that Grit employed 160 and that the lead mining part of these enterprises used a total of about 1,100 men plus a few women on the surface. Other mines were working in 1841 but the number employed would not have been great. Quite clearly these figures must be treated with caution as they may well err on the high side.

The importance of the lead and coal mines and ancillary industries at this date and over the following years cannot be denied, however, for even if the figures are inflated, they suggest that 5,200 people worked in or were supported by mining in the district. This figure cannot be compared with the local population as miners travelled well beyond their parishes to work. Slightly earlier, in September 1827, the Grit and Gravels mine company's day-book listed bargains naming at least 160 miners (more if some apparent duplicates were actually different men) many of whose surnames are still to be found locally (a copy is contained in appendix 1, see also Fig. 4.1). Among the sources of information about people are the censuses taken every ten years from 1801, although names are not listed until 1841. A commentary on the 1831 census notes an increase in the population of Worthen parish due to 160 miners being newly employed, although it does not say where they were mining nor from where they had come. This influx was no doubt due to the 'unparalleled Rage for Mineing' in the mid 1820s commented on by John Lawrence, the additional miners probably working at several mines and on the Leigh Level. The census of 1851 indicates that there were at least 335 male lead miners ranging from under 10 years old to over 70; no doubt there were others who sometimes worked in the mines and sometimes farmed (and who preferred to describe themselves as farmers) or laboured. The census also lists several women who worked or formerly worked in mining related jobs. The later censuses up to 1881 give similar figures: 278 in 1861, 342 in

1871 and 362 in 1881; thereafter numbers drop off rapidly. These figures contrast with another estimate of the numbers employed in mining which quote 1,035 in 1882, 794 in 1883 and 300 in 1884.[3] Official statistics collected by the local Inspector of Mines in 1900 record 352 employed in the metalliferous mines, 290 of them underground. The surface figures included two females and 16 boys aged under 18. The two females could well have been two of the Rowsons, the mother and daughters being noted as breaking ore at Snailbeach.[4]

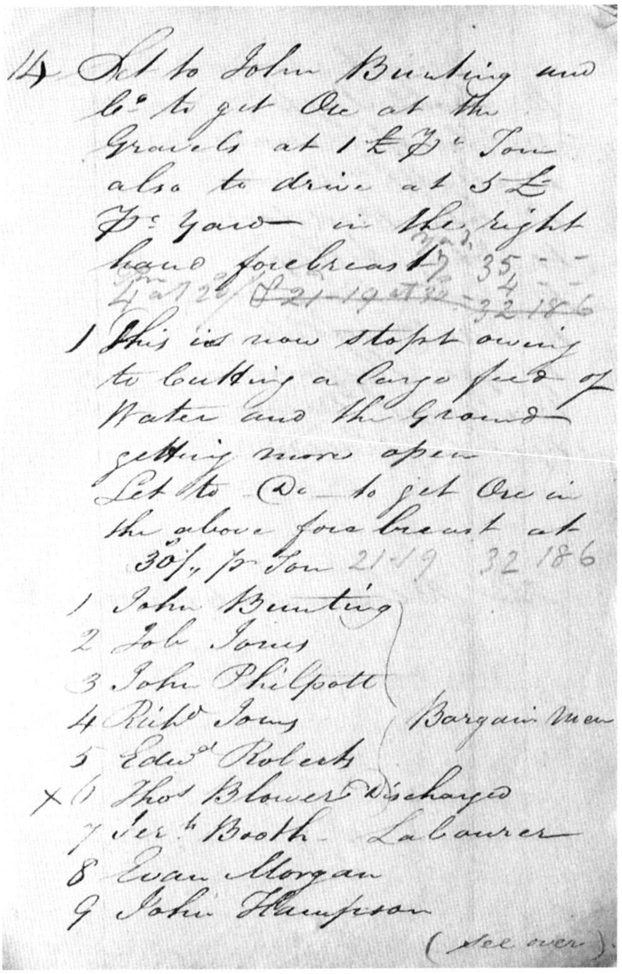
14 Let to John Bunting and Co to get Ore at the Gravels at 1£ p[er] Ton also to drive at 5£ p[er] yard in the right hand forebreast 35 - -
1 This is now stopt owing to cutting a large feed of Water and the Ground getting more open
Let to Do to get Ore in the above forebreast at 30/- p[er] Ton 21 19 32 18 6
1 John Bunting
2 Job Jones
3 John Philpott
4 Richd Jones Bargain Men
5 Edwd Roberts
x 6 Thos Blower Discharged
7 Jer h Booth Labourer
8 Evan Morgan
9 John Hampson
(See over)

Fig. 4.1 Little evidence remains of early 19th-century management but this Bargain Book from the Grit and Gravels company lists all the men employed in that quarter, their functions, the work they were contracted for and their remuneration. (SA 851/297)

Miners as a group were noted for their mobility and whilst clearly many of the men employed were local, many were incomers. The few references we have indicate that Derbyshire provided many experienced miners, including one of the very first names known in Shropshire mining history — that of James 'mynour' in the 1390s at Wenlock Priory's mine. The More family of Linley employed miners from Derbyshire shortly after acquiring the estate in 1653 to search for lead in old mines, and in 1676 gave a lease to a group of Derbyshire gentlemen for what was to become Grit mine. Leases were also granted to Derbyshire men at Snailbeach and Pim Hill during the same period.

The other principal area from which both miners and managers came was Cornwall. When Westcott mine was being developed in the 1860s Cornish miners were recruited. The main imports from Cornwall, however, seem to have been mine captains and managers, the best known of whom was Arthur Waters (see below). Smelters and probably miners came to the area from north Wales and miners from Cardiganshire worked at Bog in 1760. The traffic was not all one way; Shropshire miners moved within the county and as the 19th century progressed, moved to coal mines in Staffordshire, Yorkshire and south Wales. As lead mining finished some miners who lived in the Snailbeach area walked to mid Wales over a Sunday night, worked the week on the dams near Rhayader and walked back on Friday night; this carried on into living memory.

Whilst the miners were known for their mobility, many factors could restrict it. Debt to either management or local traders or both could keep a miner in one place. The occupation of a smallholding made it difficult to move to follow work; money owed on ore bargains, non transferable sickness fund or friendly society contributions all restricted movement, whilst a lack of knowledge of other types of mining could make it difficult to change jobs. Shropshire miners were appreciated in certain quarters, as indicated in a letter to the *Mining Journal* in April 1870, which noted that Shropshire miners 'are not much inferior — if at all to their brethren in Cornwall, and by no means addicted, as is often the case in Wales, to sending threatening anonymous letters to the agents if the pitches are not set to them exactly on their own terms.'

The labour force manager was usually honoured with the title of captain and had assistants as appropriate. The site was overseen by an agent for the mine owners and often an agent for the landowner, the labour force itself being divided into six categories: tutworkers, bargain companies, tributers, craftsmen, dressers and labourers.

The **tutworkers** (from the German word *todwerk* meaning dead work) were the men who dug shafts, drove levels and developed the mine. Sometimes they were paid wages and sometimes they bid for a contract to dig or drive at so much per fathom (six feet).

The **bargain companies** won the ore and were paid by a relatively complex form of piecework called a bargain. An enterprising miner would form a bargain company and either agree a price with the captain or agent or bid against other companies to extract ore from a certain section of the mine for a certain amount per ton. This company would usually consist of at least four men but could be up to a dozen and would include at least one labourer. The price agreed would be based on the two parties' opinion of the difficulty of getting ore at a particular place. At the settlement day the mine would pay the company leader and he would share out the money with the men after he had repaid the mine for items such as candles, gunpowder and tool sharpening (for which the miners would often have to pay the mine at inflated rates).

The system had advantages for both men and owners, though of course more for the latter. The men had independence and a stake in their mine and could, if they judged the ore more accurately than the captain, make a substantial sum of money, whilst the owners had the men tied to the mine and given an incentive to work hard. The men also could and did work quite short hours, so they could spend time on their smallholdings. The system was of course open to manipulation. The owners would encourage bidding between companies to lower prices (and a new company would be willing to work at a loss to get a foothold in a mine), and the men could try and disguise the nature of the work involved; the more difficult they could make it look the higher the price they could get. The system developed due to the impossibility of supervising miners working at several sites in larger mines.

As mechanisation spread in the first half of the 19th century and a concomitant amount of capital was tied up in the increasingly larger mines, the system fell into disuse and the men became waged, so that they had to work the hours the mine wanted rather than whatever they needed to earn enough. This meant that the mine management had to increase supervision and the miners took fewer days off — previously bargain day and the following one (to sober up) would be taken, as would days for Friendly Society Marches. Miners were also much less likely to abandon the mine if agricultural wages rose above mining wages, not that this happened all that often. All this did not, however, completely destroy the final vestiges of the miners' freedom; as late as the 1860s Snailbeach would fine miners for missing a shift but would not dismiss them until they had missed three shifts in any month.

Tributers were paid a proportion of the value of ore they raised. The system was often used in a failing mine, the mine only paying for what was won and the men taking their chance. In small mines or in poor parts of larger mines tributers survived well into the second half of the century.[5]

Craftsmen formed a vital group of workers. Every mine would have a smith, initially to make and maintain tools and later to produce parts for the ever increasing array of machines. Carpenters, joiners and stonemasons were also almost universal and would be employed in numbers when development work was in progress. With the increase in mechanisation engineers also became a necessity. Most craftsmen were waged, although some would work as subcontractors. Later some of the engineers would subcontract to provide fuel and maintenance for their machines.

When the ore was won and brought to the surface it had to be prepared for smelting, a process carried out by **dressers**. For a long time this was work done by women and

Fig. 4.2 No illustrations of mining squatters' turf houses have been found but they would have been very similar to this one built by a navvy during the construction of the Cleobury Mortimer and Ditton Priors Light Railway c.1907. (Shropshire Archives)

children, but with increasing mechanisation and changing attitudes the work was increasingly done by men and boys. The Shropshire metal mines do not appear to have had any tradition of using women and children underground. Boys would work on the surface until their mid teens when they would join their elders in the mines.

Labourers (other than those who were a part of a bargain company) were waged and carried out all manner of work both on and below the surface.

Wages were generally poor, though usually better than agricultural ones. Only the miners working bargains could ever make much. Pay-days and bargain days were often widely spread, sometimes many months apart, and for a long time took place in the local pub, the obvious consequence being worsened by the fact that payment was often in bank notes rather than change and had to be split, usually achieved by buying drinks. Many of the men were regularly in debt, either to local traders or to the mine because they had received 'subsists' (advances of wages) during the periods between pay days. Gradually payment began to be made in the mine office and to be made in coin, Snailbeach were doing this at least by the early 1860s.[6] Up to the early 19th century miners were considered disruptive drunkards, usually with good reason. Matters improved when wages ceased to be paid at the public houses but were transformed beyond recognition when Methodism swept through the area with its stress on temperance. Other nonconformist chapels opened, all with significant support from the miners, a notable number of whom became lay preachers; of the seven men killed in the 1895 disaster at Snailbeach three were such. One early non-conformist chapel was run by Rev. Palmer who formed a Baptist Church at Snailbeach in 1818 which met in 'a blacksmith's shop at Snailbeach Mine' until the chapel at Lord's Hill was built in 1833.

Fig. 4.3 No.4 Snailbeach in May 2005. This is a typical miner's cottage and is one of the very few of a large number of such dwellings to remain in substantially unaltered condition.
(Kelvin Lake, I A Recordings)

Miners' housing was as poor as one would expect. Many squatted and would move onto a piece of common or waste land and erect a dwelling; traditionally smoke had to be coming out of the chimney by nightfall of the first day the land was occupied. The following morning the landlord's agent would arrive and make a fuss about encroachment on the land but then agree a small rent. The miner got a house and some poor land, the landlord got a little rent, the poor land improved by being cultivated and the mine got a settled miner at no cost to themselves.

The smallholdings thus formed are still recognisable

in many parts of the mining area, notably in the Hope valley and on the west flank of the Stiperstones. The smallholding helped to feed the miner and his family and gave him a healthy change of work from that underground. As mines became deeper and miners worked on day rates rather than piece work they could work less on their smallholdings, their overall health decreased and their rate of mortality increased. Over time many of what were initially turf hovels were rebuilt and became moderately reasonable dwellings. At the cessation of mining many were abandoned and the land dropped out of cultivation, whilst others remained occupied and have now been extended and 'improved' to an extent that would amaze their original builders.

Fig. 4.4 Among the miners' cottages that have not been rebuilt beyond recognition are these ruins in a desolate location at Blakemoorgate on top of the Stiperstones, photographed in May 2005. This hostile location is typical of the places in which many miners' families had to live, and the ruins, built as a pair and later converted to a single cottage, represent a substantial number of cottages now long gone.
(Kelvin Lake, I A Recordings)

Some mines could not get or retain sufficient labour by the above means and either assisted their workmen, as one of the John Lawrences did in the 1780s, by giving the men building materials, or built either barracks or cottages. The mines sometimes provided more. Bog, for instance, was the first village in the county to be supplied with electricity, as the mine had its own gas-fired generator.

Historically mining has been neither healthy nor safe. Unlike many coal mines Shropshire's metal mines did not suffer from methane (fire damp) explosions but they had their fair share of risks. The three principal categories were roof or other falls, accidents in the shafts and carelessness, sometimes gross. Shafts proved dangerous to both the miners and the general public, with several deaths being recorded in the local parish registers and in Quarter Sessions records through people slipping into shafts or just not noticing them, possibly when drunk. Miners also fell out of kibbles when being hauled up, slipped on ladders and, in the worst accident in the minefield, were crushed when the rope winding the cage they were travelling in at Snailbeach broke and seven of them fell to their deaths.

Deaths and injury due to carelessness were legion and awesome. Mishandling of explosives was an obvious risk and many deaths and injuries were caused after partial detonation of a charge was not noticed and some gunpowder was left for the next miner to blow himself up with whilst drilling new shot holes. Carelessness with machinery was also common. The mine manager was killed at Bulthy mine in 1885 when greasing a machine whilst it was running; two men died in the same mine in 1921 when overcome by fumes from a petrol engine being used underground for pumping. Petrol was again the cause of a fatality at Ridge Hill mine in 1926 when a miner spilt some on his clothes and set it alight with his candle. The tramways were another common location for accidents, with a number of men being run over or crushed.

If you were not killed in an accident you could survive to suffer from heart or lung complaints. Working in warm(ish) wet mines followed by a long walk home in wet clothes in sub zero temperatures did not do the miners any good, especially considering how hard the work itself was and that the men possibly had to climb several hundred feet of ladders at the end of the shift. Underground ventilation was often poor or non existent, added to which virtually all miners smoked.

If your heart survived that pounding, the dust might well get you. It was always a problem, although worse in some mines than others. A dry dusty mine like Grit led to 'miners' asthma' whereas the damper Snailbeach did not. The introduction of drilling machines during the later part of the 19th century exacerbated the dust problem. The pneumatic drills were known as the widow makers but it took time before the actual cause of death was realised, and dust extractors installed and masks used. It was not until the 1930s that silicosis began to appear on death certificates; prior to that the death had been treated as if it were TB. One of the first miners to have his death certificate so worded was Elijah Parry, who died in 1932 and insisted that his doctor make it clear that his forthcoming death was work-related. The doctor did so (a section of Mr. Parry's lung was exhibited in court) and Mrs. Parry could have received compensation but could not afford to travel to Bristol to make the claim.[8] Matters gradually improved and by the end of mining, dust extraction was provided and used (Fig. 4.5).

Fig. 4.5 Modern dust extraction plant installed by Laporte Ltd at The Sallies mine. (coll. K. Lock)

Fig. 4.6 The miners' social life is here seen in the Snailbeach Band in the early 1900s. (coll. SMT)

The mine companies did not of course provide sick pay but some did run sickness clubs, to which the miners contributed. These were, however, uncommon in the areas of smaller mines, like Shropshire, even in the middle of the 19th century. Snailbeach had an accident and sickness scheme in 1840; the men contributed 8s. per year which rose to 12s. by 1860 with a further 9d. a month for assistance whilst away from work.[9] Schemes were also running at times at Grit and Roman Gravels mines but they only covered sickness and death benefits and not, generally, injuries. This situation was improved by the men's own efforts in running and subscribing to independent Benefit and Friendly Societies. These had begun late in the 18th century and, boosted by appropriate legislation, became important in areas of small mines like Shropshire. Pontesbury for instance had three in the 1790s.

The Friendly Societies formed one of the planks of the men's (and their families') social lives, notably with their annual marches. Bands, football and cricket clubs, the chapel and Sunday school all played their parts at various times in knitting the communities together. At work, although there was much comradeship, there was little group consciousness, due in part to the relative mobility of the labour force, the often short working day underground and the work required on the smallholdings. One effect of this was that was no effective force to improve conditions or wages. Trade unions were less prevalent in metal mines than in coal mines in any case, and were unknown in Shropshire until very late.

Information on individual miners is, needless to say, scanty. Names exist in coroners and court papers, newspaper reports, parish registers and mining papers but they do not tell us much about the miners' lives, work and families.

We have much more information about the more affluent people involved in mining, especially the landowners. Some of the principal players were national figures like the Thynnes of Longleat (the Marquis of Bath), the Earls of Tankerville, the Corbetts of Caus, the Earls of Powis and the Astleys of Patshull. Others were more local; prominent amongst these were the Lloyds of Leaton Knolls (who with the Earls of Tankerville were joint lords of the manor of a large tract of the Stiperstones known as the Joint Lordship), the Hulton-Harrops of Gatten, the Mores of Linley Hall, the Hills of Hawkstone, the Lysters of Rowton, and the Wakemans. All these families and others granted leases for mining on their land at various times. Some of them were also involved as shareholders and at least two in the 20th century ran mines — the Tankervilles at Perkins Beach and the Mores at Grit, in neither case very successfully. The Mores especially took a considerable interest in the industry both as landlords and as shareholders, in at least one case — Crowsnest — not on their own land. The incumbent More in the 1830s provided accommodation and encouragement for Sir Roderick Murchison (knighted in 1846) in his geological quest and in the 1870s, towards the end of Murchison's life, named a path at Roman Gravels mine 'Murchison's Walk' in his honour. In 1898 Sir Jasper More set out to write a history of the mining in the area, some of which was published in *The Advertiser* in the years up to 1903. His successor in 1940 lobbied the government to consider reopening a series of mines, some of which still had some reserves of zinc and barytes.

Fig. 4.7 The 7th Earl of Tankerville in the early 20th century, as depicted in a promotional photograph issued by the Earl during his visit to the area in about 1907

Other well known or quite well known people were involved either as adventurers or as engineers/ agents. Three of the giants of the industrial revolution were involved in small ways. John Wilkinson (1728-1808), a larger than life character who was a major player in the iron industry and had interests in lead mining and smelting in north Wales, sought lead, copper and tin at Cardington and Middletown Hill. He is probably best known for his development of an accurate method of boring iron cylinders for both cannon and steam engines. He was effectively sole supplier of the latter for Bolton and Watt patent engines although the relationship soured when he was found to have supplied not only cylinders to pirate engines, but complete pirate engines.

William Hazeldine (1763-1840), another iron master, was involved both as a speculator and as a consultant and arbitrator. He ran various ironworks in Shropshire and north Wales including Coleham in Shrewsbury where the links for the Menai suspension bridge were made. He also made the ironwork

Fig. 4.8 Sir Roderick Murchison in a very posed studio photograph

for Ditherington mill in Shrewsbury, the world's first iron-framed building. He was a friend of Thomas Telford who described him in a letter as 'the Arch conjuror himself, Merlin Hazeldine'. William Reynolds (1758-1803) was also involved, but only to a small extent; he had a smelter at Coalport and may have sought metals at Shipton near Much Wenlock.

A local family who were involved in lead mining and much besides for generations were the Lawrences. They claimed to have been involved in mining since about 1580, and although independent evidence is now lacking it apparently existed in 1898 when Rose Helen, the last survivor of the family, assisted Sir Jasper More MP with what proved to be an abortive history of Shelve. There were at least four John Lawrences who were involved in mining, and probably others. No information seems forthcoming before the mid 18th century but from then on the family history may be something like:

John Lawrence I d.1769?
John Lawrence II 1729-1811, m. Ann
John Lawrence III 1752-1835, m. Sarah in 1780
John Lawrence IV 1780-post 1857, m. Elizabeth Heighway by 1827

John Lawrence IV was the father of Rose Helen, which would make John Lawrence II, who sold out at Snailbeach *c*.1780, her great-grandfather.

The family were involved at some time or another with all the county's major lead mines. Their fortunes waned in the late 1820s and '30s after John IV was bankrupted in the lawsuits over the Leigh Level. They had also had smelter and coal mining interests, retaining some of the latter at least until the Minsterley branch railway killed the Pontesbury area collieries.

The Lawrences were known outside Shropshire. Bolton and Watt's *Guide to Persons and Firms* includes comments on some of their clients including a John Lawrence (presumably II). It notes that he was a partner in various Shropshire mines including White Grit and Shelvefield Gravels, both of which had Bolton & Watt engines. It also notes that, after the closure of White Grit mine in 1785, Lawrence was in partnership with John Probert in several mines in Cardiganshire. As an engineer he was considered skilled enough to work his engines and diagnose faults, but not to erect them.[10]

Other names of some note in the local industry include Peter Watson, who gave his name to Watson Shaft at Tankerville mine and ran major ventures

Fig. 4.9 Henry Dennis 1825-1906

in south-west England. Heighway Jones was for much of the 19th century a key player and was one of a local dynasty: Richard was a well known portraitist who retired from London to his native Pontesford in the late 18th century; Heighway's uncle, Fred, had a company that ran various mines in the county; other family members were tanners in Pontesford. Heighway's daughter Elizabeth married the last John Lawrence. The family owned land and leased coal mine and smelter sites.

Arthur Waters is another key figure in local mining who managed several mines at various times between the 1860s and 1880s.

The Dennis family came from Cornwall and became well known for their coal mining and clay working interests in the Ruabon area. They effectively controlled both Snailbeach mine and railway in 1870 and masterminded the last phase of investment at the mine.

Another man with a national reputation who lived and invested in the county was John Probert. He was a self-made man, having been a joiner and later a footman to a barrister at Lincoln's Inn. He clearly had both talent and connections as he became the mining agent of the Earl of Powis and had mining interests of his own, principally in mid Wales but including a little in Shropshire. He was to have been appointed by the crown to sort out revenues from various Welsh mines in which the crown received a share of the profit rather than a royalty on the production (and they wondered why none of their mines made a profit!) An outcry from Welsh landowners over his humble origins and his lack of Welshness led to Probert's appointment never being confirmed, the affair becoming known as the Prestatyn Scandal. Instead the crown let subsequent leases on more workable terms. John Probert lived at Copthorne House, now converted into flats and adjoining Royal Shrewsbury Hospital, on Mytton Oak Road, Shrewsbury. He had a substantial private museum and when his sister died in 1827 the collection warranted its own auction; a significant item of local mining history in the museum was one of the Roman pigs of lead now at Linley Hall (see Fig. 1.2).

On the technical side the county has had the benefit of a number of experienced miners and engineers who had made their names in other parts of the country, most notably Stephen Eddy and Arthur Waters. Stephen Eddy came from Skipton in Yorkshire as a very experienced mine agent and took over the management of Snailbeach, where he was assisted by his son J.R. Eddy. Of the many mine captains who came from Cornwall probably the most notable was Arthur Waters, who worked tirelessly at various mines from his arrival in the late 1850s to his early death in 1887. A very competent mine captain, if not always successful, he was best known for making Roman Gravels one of the county's most successful mines in the 1870s. His son, also Arthur, was also a mine agent.

During boom periods some national capital was invested in the county, but by and large Shropshire was fairly self contained in this respect. Three outside companies, however, all multinational giants of their day, deserve mention. The London Lead Company, officially 'The Governor and Company for smelting down lead with pit coal and sea coal' was granted its charter on 4 October 1692 and was one of the relatively few joint stock companies established by Act of Parliament and one of the very few to operate in Shropshire,[11] certainly the only one involved for any length of time. It is frequently known as the Quaker Lead Company though Quaker influence was very little by the time it became involved in Shropshire and Montgomeryshire. They were involved in the county from very early, purchasing lead ore from Shropshire for their smelter at Bristol in 1693 and in 1710 they chose not to acquire a lease at an unnamed local mine.[12] By the early 1720s the company had mines all over the country; this gave them administrative headaches which were exacerbated by poor management and substantial losses in the South Sea Bubble episode. By 1730 attempts were being made to stabilise finances and recover from the South Sea Bubble. Their two local mines, at Weston (later Cliffdale) and Nether Heath were developed in the late 1720s and abandoned in 1735 along with the Broseley smelthouse.

The second concern was even more adventurous. John Taylor and Company worked in a smallish way at Grit and the surrounding area in the 1860s. They were, however, very heavily involved in mining in mid Wales, the west country and, disastrously, Mexico. The chemical giants Laporte are the most recent (and the last so far) large company to involve themselves in the mines covered here. They began operations in 1888 in Luton, Bedfordshire, as hydrogen peroxide manufacturers and were incorporated as B Laporte Ltd. in 1908. They took a controlling interest in Malehurst Barytes Company Ltd. in 1932 and ran most of the county's barytes mines until the major closures following the Second World War. They also ran Malehurst Mill until the mid 1950s, several years after the cessation of barytes production. The company still exists and includes barium chemicals amongst its products.

5 Mines on the western flanks of the Stiperstones I

The Mytton Flags, which contain the overwhelming bulk of the county's lead and zinc ores and a good proportion of its barytes, were commercially accessible in two parallel areas each less than a mile wide and about that distance apart. The western one is centred more or less on the village of Shelve and is about 3 miles long. The eastern one is on the western edge of the Stiperstones and is some seven miles long, stretching from Callow Hill in the north to Rock in the south. This small area contained four of the county's principal lead mines — Snailbeach, Pennerley, Tankerville and Bog — as well as the usual crop of hopefuls.

As with most of the county it is likely that lead was worked in pre-Roman days, although firm evidence is lacking. The Romans were certainly here, and one of the county's famous pigs of lead was found at Snailbeach. Mining took place in the Royal Forest of Stiperstones in the 1220s although this could have been anywhere in the large tract of country. Lead mining took place in medieval times on the Earl of Stafford's land and in the 1550s the estate granted a mining lease to local and outside concerns including in 1552 one to John Clifton in Hogstow Forest, but in no case is the precise location known.[1] Snailbeach, however, seems a possible site. In the early 17th century the Thynnes, later Marquises of Bath, were receiving substantial royalties from a mine in Habberley Office, possibly at Callow Hill.

Lead ore was the prime target and a reasonable amount of zinc and a little silver was produced; the most valuable gangue mineral was barytes though calcite was periodically important in the mines' economies. Barytes production effectively kept this area going from 1900 to the Second World War, though after the 1920s on a steadily decreasing level. Snailbeach has some of the most extensive remains of later 19th-century mining in the country and Tankerville has worthy remains from the same period. The Snailbeach Railway came too late to serve more than its eponymous mine's dying years, although had lead prices risen in the 1890s and reserves been found, planned extensions to the line might have taken it to Bog and round the end of the hills to serve Gatten.

Snailbeach mine[2]

This is a mine for which Shropshire is justly famous. The Romans worked it; in 1827 four ore-bodies were famously and no doubt accurately described as 'rich beyond most things I have been acquainted with in mining',[3] and it also retains a very fine set of buildings. The mine was principally a lead mine, its lead being much prized for use in flint glass and for the production of red lead, which also occurred naturally.[4] This was deemed so pure, due to the absence of copper, that it commanded a 5% premium over all other red lead well into the 19th century. In addition it was the only mine in the county to produce fluorite and one of the few in the world to produce commercial quantities of witherite. Silver was briefly extracted from the lead ore, although it can only have been marginally profitable at best. Zinc ore, calcite and barytes were also produced in quantity. For a time in the early 20th century quartzite was dug, to be crushed and sold for use in the manufacture of refractory bricks.

Evidence of Roman mining consists of the finding in the 1790s of a lead pig near the site and of Roman tools, pottery and candles below ground. Lead mining in the Stiperstones and Hogstow Forests in medieval times is well documented and although Snailbeach is not specifically mentioned it is likely that work was carried out there at least on an occasional basis. Definite references to the mine begin in 1676 when miners from Derbyshire took a lease from the Thynnes; a further lease to the same or other Derbyshire miners was granted in 1686.[5]

Mining no doubt continued at some scale but no further history is known until 1758, when a lease was granted to Thomas Powys for five years,[6] though he appears to have only prospected. A new lease for a further six years was issued and by 1766 the mine was being worked as is evidenced by the series of shafts on a Bath estate map of that date.[7] These shafts were in a field later (after 1838 and before 1864) covered by the 'White Tip'[8] and could possibly have been along the line of a drainage adit, though no evidence has been found to confirm this. An inventory of 1769 (Fig. 5.1) does not mention water handling equipment such as pump rods and pipes, so it is possible that the adit was all that was required at that date.

Little is known of the people involved in this phase of the mine's

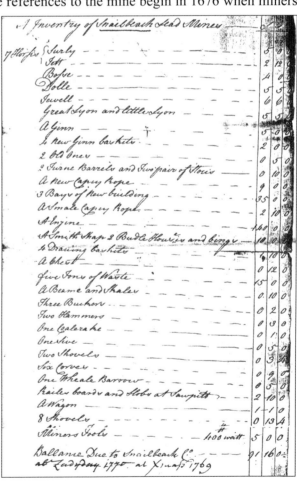

Fig. 5.1 The inventory of 1769 (SA 851/293)

life, but Sir Jasper More's great great grandfather sold a quarter share for £500 before 1780, and an, unfortunately anonymous, father of an uncle of an R.H. Wellings (who corresponded with Lily Chitty the archaeologist) 'gave the enterprise a fair start, sold out to the late company for about 700 pounds'. This gentleman remained in the employ of the mine working the buddles and after their mechanisation worked the tips. Also involved around that time were members of the Lawrence family. One of Rose Lawrence's great great grandfathers worked there until c.1780.[9] The 1769 inventory gives some idea of the then scale of the mine.[10]

The mine had seven horses including 'Surly' and 'Bosse', a gin, probably horse worked, two windlasses and the usual tools and ropes. The most interesting and valuable item was an engine. At £140 it was worth more than half the entire mine. It is not known what manner of engine it was but as it was not valuable enough to have been steam powered it is most likely to have been a waterwheel. No ore is listed as being on site which makes one wonder whether work was at a standstill.[11]

The modern history of the mine began with the formation of a partnership led by Thomas Lovett in about 1781; a T. Lovett, probably the same man, was working the mine in 1779. A lease was signed in 1782 with Lord Weymouth. Lovett's company was not only interested in the lead mine, for by 1784 they had acquired Nag's Head Colliery in Pontesford and built a smelthouse a short distance from there which served until the 1860s. They ran the colliery until 1862 when they sought to surrender their lease; they finally achieved this in 1864. They also ran Malehurst colliery from c.1853 to 1861.

New management shortly before this (see below) instigated a series of improvements in mining, ore treatment and management. Included in these was the development of the Vessons mine, which lay to the east on land owned by the Tankerville estate. It had been run for a few months in 1853 by Fred Jones as the Vessons Mine company. Although the date at which Snailbeach took it over is not known, leases and agreements certainly exist from the late 1850s.

In 1866 the company petitioned for a Bill to dissolve the partnership and form a new company and it was passed by parliament as the Snailbeach Mine Estate Act of 1867. The purpose was to make administration easier, some shares having been split and some being held by trusts, and also to give the concern a proper legal identity as the Snailbeach Mine Company Ltd. At that date the mine was assumed to be worth just over £57,000.[12]

In 1884 the smelter chimney showed signs of collapsing; this may have contributed to the company's liquidation which occurred in 1885 and certainly led to offers to smelt their lead being made by several companies.[13] The Snailbeach Lead Mining Co. Ltd. was formed and ran the mine from 1885.

In 1897 the Vieille Montagne company, a Belgian based multinational zinc mining concern, were said to be looking for good zinc mines in various parts of the UK and Snailbeach mine was suggested to them as a possible investment, but they were not interested.[13] The Snailbeach Lead Mining Company ran the mine until just after lead mining effectively ceased in 1912. In 1900 the Halvans Lime Spar and Concentrating company reworked the tips (Halvans being a Cornish term for such work). In 1912 they took a new lease including underground parts of the mine and sank Black Tom Shaft on the angle below the 40 yard level. They worked the ground above the, by then flooded, 112 yard (adit) level into the 1940s.[15] Edgar C. Gray was involved with the site (as well as some of Shropshire Mines Ltd's enterprises) until about 1929, and for the last three years of this activity Kelly's *Directories* show him as trading as a Spar Gravel Merchant separate from Halvans Co. Kelly's 1929 *Directory* also includes the Snailbeach Trading Co. Spar Gravel Works, but this is almost certainly incorrect as the concern was the Gravel Trading Co. Ltd. The Whitstone Company[16] has entries from 1930 to 1933. By 1929 the Halvans Co. was acquired by Charles Moore and Co. Ltd. of Lymm, chemical manufacturers who were using the barytes from the mine. Joseph Roberts, sometime of the Gravel Trading Co. and proprietor of the Snailbeach Barytes Co., acquired the mine from Moores in 1944, though Moores remained the principal customer for barytes. With the exception of several tons of barytes dug from a specially reopened Perkin's Level as

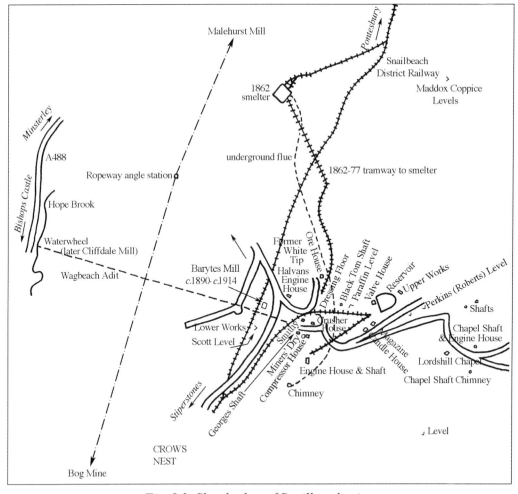

Fig. 5.2 Sketch plan of Snailbeach mine

a nuclear shield for the incident at Windscale Nuclear Power Station in 1957, all underground working had ceased by 1950. The mine remained in official lists as Lordshill mine, a small lead and barytes mine, until 1961.

Joseph Roberts worked the tip for calcite until into the 1980s, this being sold under the trade name of 'Calspar'. Throughout the 20th century roadstone, hardcore and gravel were supplied by various of the going concerns. As at several other sites in the county subsequent prospecting has been carried out. At Snailbeach it was by British Gypsum for barytes in 1979/80 and as with all the other similar cases in the county nothing further happened.

Technical History

The mine was not lavishly equipped in 1769 (see inventory, Fig. 5.1). When Lovett's company took over in 1782 investment began in earnest, this continuing on and off for the following century until by the end of mining it was probably the best equipped mine in the area. There may well have been a rotary steam engine on site in the 1790s which pumped from Old (later George's) Shaft up to the adit level which had been dug the 1,200 yards from Wagbeach from *c*.1782. It served until a waterwheel and rodding was constructed at the outlet of the adit in 1837. This was a 36 foot diameter breast shot wheel powered principally by the Hope Brook which pumped via flat rods and an angle bob in the adit to supplement the steam engine.[17] After the installation of the Lordshill pumping engine, probably in 1848, the waterwheel powered Cliffdale barytes Mill until 1926. The wheel itself was dismantled in 1929.

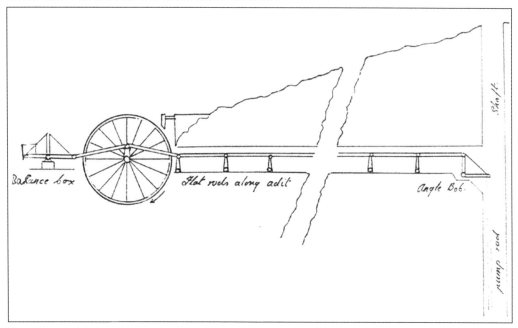

Fig. 5.3 A drawing by the late Malcolm Newton of the flat-rod arrangement by which the Hope Brook pumped water from below adit level a kilometre away

1857 was a key date in the history of the mine. In that year Stephen Eddy of Skipton Yorkshire was appointed as manager with a salary (£100 pa) and a percentage of profits. His son James Ray Eddy handled the day to day management and turned the mine's performance around, reducing manning levels and increasing profits by a factor of ten. This period from the late 1850s saw great changes and massive and successful investment both in the buildings and plant as well as in technical procedures. A French visitor, Monsieur Moissenet, in 1860 noted that waste and costs had been cut by the introduction of 'the Yorkshire method' which seems to have been a combination of working the more easily available ore, and good practice at the dressing floor and smelter. Whilst his visit was principally to the smelthouse his comments were wide ranging and complimentary.

Physical improvements had however begun before Eddy's appointment, under Jonathan Harrison the then mine captain. Day Level and presumably New Engine Shaft at Lordshill had been dug c.1848 (date plaque on Day Level) and a 60 inch[18] beam engine installed for pumping up to adit level replacing the Wagbeach waterwheel with its two-thirds of a mile of mechanically inefficient rodding, the level having been extended to New Engine Shaft prior to 1856.[19] Winding was done by a separate engine of unknown speci-fication which had its own house.

A third later engine on Lordshill powered the railway inclined plane which brought coal and other supplies up to the engines.

The same period of invest-ment saw new powered equipment for ore crushing and dressing, and the replacement of the Pontesford smelthouse with a new one half a mile north of the mine, to which it was initially connected by an internal tramway and later by the Snailbeach Railway.

James Ray Eddy left the company in 187i to be replaced in 1871 as manager by Henry Dennis. Like many in the industry, Dennis was of a Cornish family but by this stage they had very substantial industrial interests around Ruabon, Denbighshire. Dennis oversaw further investment in the mine and the buildings he erected form the core of today's remains. 1872 saw the construction of a new reservoir

Fig. 5.4 The house for the Cornish engine at Lordshill, derelict in 1963. (coll. K. Lock)

Fig. 5.5 From 1871 the mine was run from Henry Dennis' office in High Street, Ruabon

Fig. 5.6 The 1884 chimney for the Cornish engine also served the flue from the smelter and the smaller engines on Lordshill. (Kelvin Lake, I A Recordings)

Fig. 5.7 A recent photograph of the 1872 reservoir (Kelvin Lake, I A Recordings)

(Figs. 5.7 and 5.8). Prior to this reservoir there had been several smaller ones, notably that to serve the engine by Old Shaft and one near Black Tom Shaft. These and the dressing floors were fed partly by streams and partly by water piped from catchments in the surrounding hills (using siphons as necessary), including, for Old Shaft, areas around Chapel Shaft.[20] Maddox Coppice adits also seem to have been used as a water supply as substantial lengths of a 3 inch diameter cast iron socket and spigot pipe

Fig. 5.8 A view c.1910 showing the reservoir and part of the Upper Works. (coll. K. Lock)

survive between there and Snailbeach (see Fig. 5.9). Water for the Lordshill engines may also have been pumped up from dams in Scott Level. Frustrating water problems were common to most mines and Snailbeach was no exception, with too much water underground and not enough for the dressing processes above. The year also saw the erection of a new ore dressing building equipped with four buddles and eight jiggers and the enlarging of Old Shaft (sometimes called Old Engine Shaft and later frequently George('s) Shaft). It was deepened to the 252 yards level and was widened and saw the installation for the first time of cages for the men, this latter saving 1½ hours per man per shift over the ladder-ways used previously. A new engine house dated 1872 was built to house a horizontal twin drum winding engine for this shaft.

Over the next few years the crusher house was reconstructed and the jiggers were mechanised. In 1881 a compressor house was built for two compressors to power drills and winches installed underground (Fig. 5.10).[21] Outside the mine Dennis also promoted and oversaw the construction of the Snailbeach District Railways, which although a separate company was linked inextricably to the mine until 1912 (see chapter

Fig. 5.9 A length of cast iron pipe which appears to run from Maddox Coppice adits to Snailbeach, August 2007. (Author)

15). The mine had had internal tramways for many years and when the railway was built it extended throughout the mine, finally terminating at the top of the inclined plane at the Lordshill engine houses. Unfortunately this period of investment was brought to a rude halt by falling lead prices which led to a loss in 1884. 1885's production, as noted elsewhere, slumped, but output picked up subsequently, though further exploration became less economic, leaving the known areas of ore more or less worked out by the end of pumping in January 1911 following an earlier agreement with Lord Bath.

Fig. 5.10 The restored 1881 compressor house in 2006. (Kelvin Lake, I A Recordings)

To the east of the main mine on Tankerville property (Vessons), Chapel Shaft was sunk or deepened progressively from 1859 in the hope of tapping new reserves, though the ore ran out where it met the Stiperstones Quartzite. Nevertheless the shaft proved important for ventilation and transportation. Its final depth was 342 yards and it was wound by a horizontal engine said locally to be of marine origin.

The mine also had a considerable number of ancillary buildings. Best known is probably the blacksmith's shop but there was also a candle house, a powder magazine (built 1863) and a miners' dry as well as the usual range of workshops, offices and the counting house, many of which are still to be seen, if in some cases rather altered.

The smelthouse closed in 1892 just before a major client, Burr Bros. of Shrewsbury, closed their plant; this was probably not a coincidence. The flue fell into disrepair and was partly demolished after the closure of the smelter, but the chimney remained in use until 1911 for the engine, and still survives.

Fig. 5.11 Upper Works as restored, May 2004. (Author)

From 1911, after the cessation of pumping, only the upper parts of the mine were worked, principally for barytes. The only major work carried out after the First World War, apart from

Fig. 5.12 The entrance to Perkin's Level,
May 2004. (Author)

Fig. 5.13 Underground in Perkin's Level.
(I. Cooper)

reworking the tips, was at the eastern end of the site based on Black Tom Shaft and Perkin's Level, in the 1930s sometimes called Roberts' Level and sometimes Lordshill mine (Figs. 5.11 and 5.12).[22] There were several smaller adits and much shallow working. A small dressing plant, sometimes known as Upper Works, stood near these levels and was used for sorting barytes into the 1950s.

This period was not, however, without its problems including a major rock fall in 1929. That same year, being unwilling to accept piece-work, men were threatening to refuse to work in Paraffin Level, which led to suggestions that the mine might close. This did not happen although Paraffin Level was closed but left in a safe state by February 1930 when barytes was being dug 'from the vein near Black Tom Shaft'.[23] It is clear from surviving correspondence, however, that maintenance was not good either below or above ground, the parish council for instance complaining that the Halvans Company had not fenced the derelict remains of the smelter flue and that cattle were falling into it. At this period barytes was, on one occasion, supplied to Moores via Snailbeach from Edwin Jones and Co. of Perkins Beach mine, but no records have been found to establish whether the sample truck-load was approved.[24]

In 1937 Messrs. Tom Evans and Jack Lewis took a lease on Paraffin Level and worked it on a single shift basis with eight to ten men. This no doubt finished one lunchtime when a roar and a bang announced a major collapse. Fortunately the men were all outside. A lorry-load a day of barytes had been produced.

Black Tom Shaft was an old shaft which had a horse gin at least until 1882 (see large scale OS map). It was reopened in 1912 by the Halvans Company and used by them to work an extended 40 yard level and below for barytes. In 1930 work was taking place to repair Black Tom Shaft and clear and re-timber some of the 40 yard level. This work was finished by September 1930 with the exception of repairs to the head-frame, at the same time as was work caused by a big fall in Perkin's Level three weeks earlier. By this time Black Tom was the only shaft being worked, but for how much longer is not known.[25] The shaft had a winding engine and there was also a horizontal engine. The latter was derelict by 1930 but is said to have been used for a saw-mill rather than the mine. The shaft also had a small dressing plant consisting of a spiral classifier driven by belting from a portable engine or tractor (Fig. 5.14).

The Halvans company used an existing steam crushing engine and engine house on the 'white tip' in 1900 (Fig. 5.15). At George's Shaft in about 1913 the twin drum engine of 1872 was sold and replaced with a smaller single drum engine and the shaft was equipped with new head gear to suit. It was used for winding barytes until the engine was sold for scrap in 1927.[26]

The last stage of the mine's work was a primitive set up consisting of a tractor with a shovel and a fixed screen which operated in the white tip up to the 1980s.

Fig. 5.14 The railway passes through this centre of the photograph of about 1912, going to the head-shunt below the incline to the Lordshill engine house. To the left is the Black Tom area of the mine; the wooden engine house is visible as is the head-frame, though this is lying on the ground awaiting erection. (coll. K. Lock)

Fig. 5.16 (left) Aerial view looking
south over Snailbeach prior to the
reclamation of the white tip, which
dominates the picture. In the top
centre is the chimney which served the
Lordshill engines and the smelter which
is off the lower edge. The Snailbeach
railway entered lower right and ran
along the edge of the tip, leaving
the picture on the middle right and
continuing to a reversing station. The
siding approached the mine between
the line of buildings and the woods and
ran to the locomotive shed just visible
at the top of the tip. The line continued
beyond the left-hand edge of the
photograph for a short length before
returning to the inclined plane to the
engine houses just below the chimney.
Above the locomotive shed the dressing
floor is visible with the compressor
house and chimney above that. (CPAT)

Fig. 5.15 (above) The now demolished ruins of
the Halvans Co engine house on the white tip.
(Shropshire Archives)

Fig. 5.17 The minimal plant used in the last
phase of activity

Underground description

The mine was almost totally worked from a single vein, the Snailbeach Vein, which ran horizontally for about 1,000 yards east/west and from its outcrop 800 feet above sea level down, without fault, thinning or other interruption for 500 or more yards. Some lead workings were carried out on the South Vein though not to any great extent, and some barytes workings on a vein to the north.

Snailbeach was ultimately the deepest mine in the ore-field. Unusually they used yards not fathoms to measure depth and name their levels (showing Staffordshire rather than Cornish practice). The mine was 180 yards deep by 1797 but was described in 1798 as being little worked 'on account of some part of them being under water'.[27] Old Shaft was dug at about this time and the mine was drained at the 112 yards level by the adit to Wagbeach. In 1840 the mine was 360 yards deep, by 1861 it was 440 deep, 462 by 1872 and 492 by 1884. In the late 1880s the landlord was pushing for the mine to be deepened

Fig. 5.18-5.20 (above and opposite) Underground remains in the Forty Yard Level.
(I. Cooper)

85

and possibly for a level to be driven through Callow Hill to Minsterley to drain the mine at a lower level than 112 yards. If the level was intended to drain Snailbeach mine it is not surprising that it was never finished given the amount of digging involved for a relatively small increase in the depth drained by gravity in a mine already much deeper and mechanically drained. The mine was ultimately deepened to 552 yards, partly funded by the royalties being waived for three years from 1896. The final depth was slightly greater than this as winzes went down below that level.

A level known as Scott Level runs under Resting Hill from below the village road. There is no evidence to connect the digging of this with Snailbeach mine but it has been dammed underground and may have been used via a vertical pipe to provide a water source for Snailbeach mine. For more on Scott Level see p.98.

Production
Official returns give production figures for lead ore from 1845 to 1913; these total about 132,000 tons or half the county's output for the period. Snailbeach production was often in excess of 3,000 tons p.a. and until 1881 never less than 2,000. Production plummeted to 254 tons in 1885 when underground mining temporarily stopped, but recovered well though never to previous levels. It remained over 1,000 tons p.a. until 1901 and gradually fell until 1910, the last full year of pumping; thereafter it fell rapidly and terminally, only odd tonnages being noted after 1914. 50 tons were raised in 1920-1 and the last lead was recorded in 1925 though odd tons were almost certainly dug fortuitously from time to time thereafter, for there was sorted galena left at Upper Works near Perkin's Level when work stopped. For the period before official returns start only odd references exist,

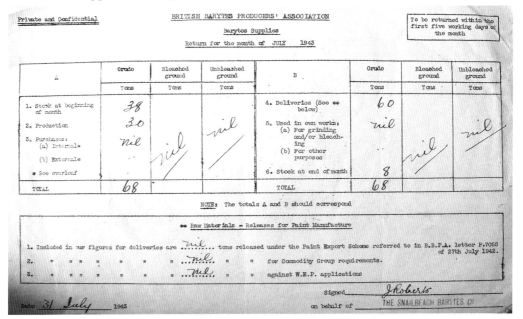

Fig. 5.21 The level of productivity revealed by a return for the British Barytes Producers Association (SA 1950/16-20)

these coming from a number of sources. Royalties were paid on 700 tons of ore between October 1824 and April 1825. 505 tons of lead ore was produced between 1768 & 1772, 108 tons in 1782 and 1,321 tons in 1811. Royalties were $^2/_{15}$th of the annual value of ore until 1822 and stood, I believe, until the lease of the early 1860s. From that time rates varied and were tightly negotiated. Between 1782 and 1820 in excess of £40,000 was paid in royalties, after 1795 never less than £1,000 p.a. with a peak of £3,165 in 1811. 1,400 ounces of silver was recorded in 1882 and 1883.

Barytes was recorded from 1858 (8 tons according to official returns or 30 tons according to M. Moissenet) though serious production did not begin until 1868 when 360 tons was won. Production fluctuated until the end of the century peaking at 1,016 tons in 1876 and bottoming out at 24 tons in 1887. From 1899 output was stepped up and ran at around 3,000 tons until 1906. After a sharp drop it recovered to stand at 3,734 tons at the end of the official returns (1913), completely eclipsing lead from 1910. A total of 42,000 tons was raised between 1861 and 1913. During the First World War production rose to 5,000 tons p.a. Occasional other sources cast a little light on post-war production. Two random quarterly reports under the Mining Industry Act 1920 on production and employ-ment survive; for the last quarter of 1930, 113 tons of barytes and £31 of calcite was dug and 95 pounds of blasting powder was used; there were seven employees. In the first quarter of 1941, as Lordshill mine, 123 tons of barytes was won by five employees.

Returns apparently never sent to the British Barytes Producers Association in 1942 and 1943 record crude barytes at about 40 tons a month with no ground or bleached product being sold. None was made available either for the wartime Paint Export Scheme. Correspondence between Charles Moore & Co Ltd. of Lymm, Cheshire, and the Snailbeach Barytes Company, Lordshill mine, in 1945-6 survives. Moores must have been a major if not the major client for barytes. There are invoices for up to 80 tons a months of jigged, double jigged or crude barytes. Moores were sampling regularly — the quality varied and they often had to complain about contaminants, especially calcium carbonate and silica and, once, witherite. One of the problems seemed to be contamina-tion of the jigger which was used for calcite as well as barytes and not properly cleaned between. Attempts were also made at this time to sell barytes to colliery companies for use in coal washers, but the companies chosen were either not using their washer, as at Lilleshall, or already had adequate supplies, as with Cupola Mining of Sheffield, though the latter did acknowledge that the quality of the product was satisfactory. Production continued from the tips for some years. Although complete records are not available, 8 tons is returned for 1965 for instance and this may not have been the last.

Witherite makes but one entry in the official returns with 2 tons in 1875, but much greater quantities were dug, 941 tons being the estimated total production. It was first noted by Arthur Aikin, a local but nationally prominent geologist, in a paper to the Geological Society in 1811. Spherical deposits of witherite were still being found occa-sionally and sold in the 20th century; in 1922, 20 tons was reported as having recently been sold. In 1932, 50 tons, bagged, was sold to the Commonwealth of Australia and after the war US suppliers were seeking some from Snailbeach although probably without success.[28]

Zinc ore production shows no pattern although it was expected from at least the beginning of the Lovett period as both black-jack and calamine were included in the 1782 lease. Some zinc appears in most years' statistics ranging from 378 tons in 1902 to 10 in 1893, and it overtook lead finally and briefly from 1911 perhaps to 1914 when its production, too, effectively ceased.

Fluorite appears in the returns from 1874 to 1879 (except 1876), increasing over that period from 12 to 512 tons. The last figure includes 'waste', and was presumably worked from the tips and is the last figure quoted. In 1877-79 the mine produced half the nation's fluorite.

Calcite production figures have rarely survived. The Halvans Co. were selling various grades — 'sand', 'gravel', 'double riddled' and 'rockery' — in the early years of the 20th century, though after 1912 they seem to have concentrated on barytes. Some references survive from the 1930s when many of the Gravel Trading Co. clients are known. The material was sorted into 'white' and 'black and white'. Much was used for pebble dashing buildings and gravel for driveways but significant quantities were sold to monumental masons for covering graves, one such locally being the George Phillips Monumental Works, Church Stretton. The material went far and wide with clients noted including the Long Rake Spar Company from Derbyshire, who took best white crystals, and George Young of Croydon.

Figures for quartzite are not available.

Method of working
Until 1873 the men accessed the mine by ladders from Old Shaft. The route which the ore took from the shaft top to the smelthouse via various preparations clearly varied as the mine developed and it is impossible to be precise until quite late in the mine's life. When cages were installed in 1873 vast amounts of time were saved though men still had to make their own way from the 252 yard level to the working parts of the mine on foot. Ore was dug and wound to the appropriate tramming level from whence it travelled to Lordshill Engine Shaft for winding in kibbles. It was wound to the Landing Level (referred to in recent years as the Day Level) some 114 feet below the engine and transferred back into wagons. From here it was trammed to the dressing areas from whence the dressed, crushed, jigged and buddled ore went to the Ore House and on to be smelted, while the waste went to the tips.

Employment
Official returns of employment start in 1877 with 356, a figure slowly sinking to 86 in 1885, recovering to 150 the following year and hovering around that level until the end of the century when terminal decline set in, gently until 1910 then steeply. Figures from other sources add a little. When improvements to the new turnpike road through the Hope Valley to Bishops Castle were being mooted in 1841 the mine was said to employ 500 and a further 70 at its colliery, but this figure could include dependants. In 1870, 130 men were employed, 29 of them on development work. Post First World War figures show that over 30 were employed until 1922, dwindling to single figures by 1925 and ceasing

by 1949. This is not the whole story as the Gravel Trading Company or Lewis and Evans (see Paraffin Level 1937) do not seem to be included, but the decline is still very clear. By the end in the mid 1980s it was almost literally a matter of one man and a dog.

As one would expect in a Shropshire metal mine, few women seem to have been employed. However, Emily Rowson and her daughters, Hannah and Jessie, worked on the surface dressing the ore mined by their menfolk in the early 19th century, this method of working being normal at the time.[29] The 1851 census also lists a handful, but none are recorded in subsequent censuses even though some are remembered as working on the surface up to the time of the First World War.

Fig. 5.22 Minsterley School as built in 1845, photographed in May 2007 by the author. In the gable is the plaque commemorating the munificence of the Marquis of Bath and several gentlemen of the Snailbeach Mining Company
The plaque reads:

THIS EDIFICE WAS ERECTED
A.D.1845
AT THE JOINT EXPENSE OF
THE MOST NOBLE THE MARQUIS OF BATH
AND SEVERAL GENTLEMEN OF THE
SNAILBEACH MINING COMPANY
IN COMPLIANCE WITH THE REQUISITIONS
EXPRESSED IN THE WILL OF THE LATE
JOHN JOHNSON ESQ[R].
OF WORTHING IN THE COUNTY OF SUSSEX:
BY WHOM WAS PROVIDED
AN ENDOWMENT TO ESTABLISH & PERPETUATE
A DAY AND EVERY DAY SCHOOL
FOR THE EDUCATION OF ALL THE POOR CHILDREN
RESIDENT IN THE
TOWNSHIP OF MINSTERLEY

Fig. 5.23 (above left) George's Shaft head frame before 1912, as it was at the time of the 1895 disaster. (coll. K. Lock)
Fig. 5.24 (above) After its 1913 reconstruction with a single wheel and before its collapse. (coll. K. Lock)
Fig. 5.24 (left) As recently re-erected. (Author)
Fig. 5.26 (below) The cage from George's Shaft, similar to that which fell in the disaster of 1895. (I. Cooper)

The presence of the mine led to the growth of the village. There were no houses at Snailbeach in 1766; it grew slowly and achieved its modern size by about 1872. All the cottages belonged to Lord Bath and all were built by squatters, except for one terrace near Lower Works. The censuses confirm this pattern and, assuming that the miners who lived at Snailbeach worked at that mine, give an indication of the extent to which the miners travelled to the mine. In 1851, 11 employees out of a suggested total of 500 lived in the village and made up about half the population. That percentage gradually dropped census by census, to about a third in 1861, 1871 and 1881, and 20 men (13% of the village population) out of 149 working at the mine in 1891. The company were also able to assist in improving local conditions. They (and the Marquis of Bath) contributed to Minsterley National School in 1845 and by 1851 were paying £40 pa towards costs; they expected the miners to contribute 6d. a quarter towards their children's education (Fig. 5.22).

Accidents

Mining has always been a dangerous business and Snailbeach has had its share of accidents. In lead mining the numbers involved even in major incidents were many less than in coal mining accidents, though the repercussions on the local community were no less severe.

Snailbeach was the location of the worst accident in the county's metal mines when a winding rope broke in George's Shaft in 1895 and seven men died (Figs. 5.23 to 5.26). The accident happened at about quarter past six in the morning of 6 March. The engine-man had run his daily test, winding the cages three times up and down the shaft. The night shift were brought out and two cages of the morning shift were safely lowered. The third set of seven men were over halfway down the shaft when the wire rope broke. The 7 foot 6 inch tall cage was reduced to just 18 inches in front of its previous occupants. Death was instantaneous. The rope had been inspected as required and had appeared satisfactory but had been rotting from the inside. The inquest verdict was 'accidental death caused by the breakage of a defective rope'. The inquiry by the Mines Inspector, Mr. Atkinson, whilst censuring the company and their agents, acknowledged that no breach of the regulations in force had been committed.

Ultimately it was concluded that because the cages were left halfway down the shaft between shifts, the same portion of the rope was always in the same place on the winding drum which itself was of a less than optimum diameter. The curve in the rope opened up the fibres, water collected in it, and the rope rotted. Thereafter a careful record of daily rope inspections was kept, but despite this a further breakage occurred in 1897, although fortuitously without injury or loss of life as the cage was empty. A rope found recently during repair work in the miners' dry is reputed to be the one which failed in the 1895 accident.

Transport

The mine's lead ore was sent to various places before the company built their own smelter. Some in the early 1780s went to Minera near Wrexham where Thomas Smith, one of Lovett's partners, had a smelter. Other ore in that period went to John Lawrence's

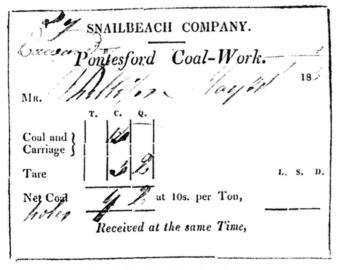

Fig. 5.27 Weighbridge docket

smelter at Malehurst until a dispute took place (what it was about has been forgotten) and some went to Bagillt on Deeside. From 1784 the company's own smelters dealt with their ore and also smelted ore from some of Arthur Waters' mines including Ladywell, Roman Gravels and Tankerville. After closure of their own smelter the Snailbeach company sent the ore to Dennis' facility at Ruabon. The lead smelted at the site was said in 1870[30] to be sent to Bristol, though much went to Burr Brothers' lead works at Kingsland, Shrewsbury, to be converted in to pipes, shot and other goods, and much of the rest went to Walker Parker of Chester and two firms in Birmingham. From 1877 most of the mine's output travelled on the Snailbeach Railway. The use of that line for mine products gradually declined in the 20th century, finally finishing in 1940 (see chapter 15).

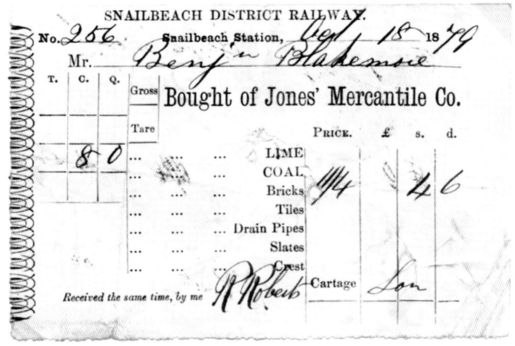

Fig. 5.28 Snailbeach District railway docket for coal

Like most Shropshire barytes, much of that produced at Snailbeach no doubt went to the Merseyside/Cheshire area, to paint manufacturers and chemical producers, though some was supplied between 1862 and 1880 to Peate's at Maesbury Mill near Oswestry, the paints and varnishes made here ending up with a Liverpool paint wholesaler (see p.269). In the 1920s some was also sold to other mining concerns including Wotherton and to Mr. Hulton-Harrop, though he is not known to have been operating any mines at that time. Perhaps he continued supplying customers retained from the earlier years of the century when he ran Gatten and Rhadley mines.

As noted above, calcite went far and wide, until at least 1939 starting its journey from a specially built siding on the Snailbeach District Railway, the Gravel Trading Company being remembered for regularly delaying the trains. The destination of the zinc ore is not recorded but the brass industries at Bristol initially and later Birmingham are the most likely places. Fluorite and quartzite also went to unknown destinations.

Remains

Over recent years Shropshire County Council has acquired most of the site. Stories of contamination abounded and the authority carried out a series of tests which established its extent and as a result have effected a considerable amount of work, notably to stop dust being blown off the white tip. Reclamation, stabilisation and restoration

Fig. 5.29 A 1960s photograph of the hearth and tools in the blacksmith's shop after closure but before dereliction. (Shropshire Archives)

of the tips, underground areas and buildings was undertaken in 1994-5. This saw the re-grading and covering of the white tip, the filling in of the shallower and more unstable parts of some adits and stopes with a mixture of material from the tips and grout, the capping or grilling of shaft tops and the demolition of all but the foundations of the Halvans Engine House on the white tip. This demolition sparked off a protest which led to the restoration of several of the other buildings otherwise threatened with demolition. The site is now a Conservation Area and a good example of industrial preservation. It is open and can be visited at any time even though it is interspersed with private houses, yards and gardens. From time to time the Shropshire Mines Trust and Shropshire Caving and Mining Club open buildings and provide tours both on the surface and below ground. Some mine buildings are in private hands and not visitable, but they feature on the plan both because they can be seen in passing and for the sake of completeness. Car parking and toilets are available by the village hall.

Fig. 5.30 Snailbeach mine's powder magazine showing the double wall arrangement. (Kelvin Lake, I A Recordings)

Fig. 5.31 An aerial view of the Snailbeach site during the stabilisation works in 1994-5. Prominent left centre is the compressor house and chimney, above that the miners' dry and the 1872 George's Shaft engine house. On the other side of the track is the earlier engine house attached to the blacksmith's shop, to the right centre the locomotive shed. In the lower centre of the photograph and in scaffolding, is the crusher house. (CPAT)

6 Mines on the western flanks of the Stiperstones II

Whilst Snailbeach was the great mine, some of its neighbours were at various times comparable players, while others never were.

Hogstow area

As well as the 1522 reference to mining in Hogstow Forest, a subsequent agricultural holding based on Hogstow Hall included several sites at which mining or trials took place and Blackhole, Black Hollies and Black Meadow are all possible mining related names.

The name **Blackhole** first surfaces in a report of a lawsuit 'over alleged destruction and force of arms at a piece called le blacke hole, Mynsterley', in 1603, and again in a conveyance of 1671. The name is likely to derive from the presence of a mine. When the land was sold in 1695 there is a reference[1] which seems likely to be to a mine at an unspecified location at Hogstow and a lease of 1745 mentions mines, but the first certain mention is in a lease of 1806. This lease was for 21 years with a royalty of $^2/_{15}$ths subject to a minimum of £200 in the last 16 years and, significantly, a condition that £3,000 must be spent on the mining. The adventurers were the White Grit Mine Company which included John Probert and R.B. More of Linley Hall together with John Lawrence (II or III?)[2] as agent at a salary of £20 pa. The White Grit Mine Company kept as much as possible in-house: they supplied many of the materials, the White Grit Coal Mine Company provided bricks from Pontesbury for arching the levels and the White Grit Farm Company acted as carriers. Also included in this lease was **Crowsnest** mine. This mine existed prior to 1761 as it was excluded from a lease of that year, but no more is known of this period.

However, from 1806 until 29 May 1813 the history of this mine and Blackhole is crystal clear. An account book titled 'An account of the expenditure in driving the levels at the Crowsnest and Blackhole Mines on F. Lloyd Esq.'s land by the White Grit Mine Company commencing August 23rd 1806' gives a blow by blow account (Fig. 6.2).

Work at Blackhole began on 28 November 1806 when the level mouth was cut, and by the end of the year 67 yards had been dug, extended to 150 yards by the end of the following year. Matters progressed very slowly for the next four years with only 80

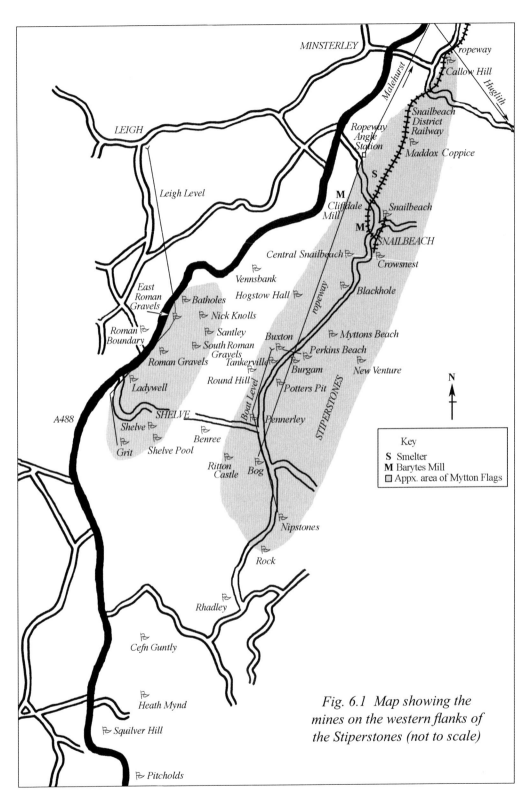

Fig. 6.1 Map showing the mines on the western flanks of the Stiperstones (not to scale)

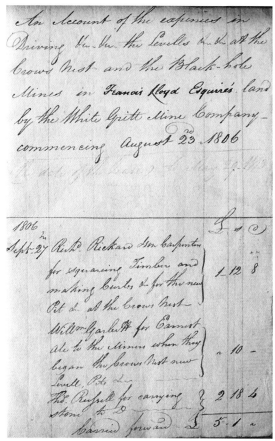

Fig. 6.2 Typical early 19th-century mine accounts from the White Grit Mine Co account book. (SA 103/1/8/175)

yards being dug. There was a final flurry of activity from April 1812 to May 1813 after the cessation of work at Crowsnest, when the last 67 yards were dug and the mine abandoned having gone in 294½ yards. Work had begun a few months earlier at **Crowsnest**, as by 23 September 1806, 26 yards of the adit had been dug and the shaft over it begun. Up to August 1811 most of the company's activity was centred here, with all 593½ yards of the adit being driven more or less continuously. At this date, with a net expenditure of £283 3s. 4d. for each of the nine shareholders, a total a little in excess of the £3,000 required by the lease, the mine was abandoned.

The period of work was punctuated by matters of note. On 7 February 1807 the smithy and the gin were built; on 28 March the shaft, by now 6 yards deep, met the adit; and by 26 December the shaft had reached its maximum depth of 7.5 yards below adit level. In March 1811 five yards was dug in a string (of ore) off the east of the level and repairs were carried out after an inundation. Some if not all of these events, the quarterly bargains and no doubt much else, were greeted with ale, at the company's expense. The account book also details wages and other payments, notable amongst them being the supply of kibbles from a cooper and £13 19s. for a gin horse who was supplied with £5 4s. of grass a half year and periodic strikes of oats. No account is given of ore sales, but these were probably very small and certainly came nowhere near to covering the costs of the enterprise.

The location of either mine is not known though there are two sets of adits in Crowsnest Dingle which are possible sites of the mine, one of which was presumably what was described as a dry level from Crowsnest 'up to Parry's pit on the corner' used as air raid shelter.[3] (It is also possible that that could have been part of the site of the later Central Snailbeach mine.) An undated plan[4] of Hogstow Hall land of *c*.1862 shows 'Crowsnest Level' in the valley bottom. This is part of Central Snailbeach mine which, though very much part of this group of mines, has its own entry below. The location of Blackhole mine is equally uncertain though it is said to be 100 yards west of the road, where there are what could be the sites of long collapsed adits.

Scott Level (Fig. 6.3) heads south-east from Snailbeach village towards Crowsnest for 500 yards before reaching a T-junction, one branch heading south-west for 80 yards and the other north-east for 500. It makes no connection with Snailbeach mine though it is always, though for no apparently good reason, associated with it. Its spoil heaps are marked on a map of 1864. The Scott most involved with mining in the locality was Jonathan Scott who was active at Bog mine by 1760 until at least 1777 and owned a 'hollow' somewhere in the vicinity in which John Lawrence was driving in 1792, which may well be this one. The gated outlet to Scott Level still exists beneath a village house, and the spoil tip and a shaft on the hill behind are still visible.

Fig. 6.3 The gated mouth of Scott Level, with the hard hat of a member of the Shropshire Caving and Mining Club just visible. (Kelvin Lake, I A Recordings)

Other trials were certainly made in the locality at **Hogstow Hall** and **Venus Bank Wood**, both trials believed to have been conducted in the 19th century. The trial at Hogstow was to the south of the Hall. Though the field names Black Leasowes and Black Hollies could indicate mining activity at an earlier date, these are both to the north-west. The Venus Bank trial is a shaft which is marked on the large scale Ordnance Survey map of 1890.

Bog

Lead ore outcropped in various places at and near this mine, which makes it a good candidate for Roman and pre-Roman mining; all that is lacking is any evidence. The 17th century saw mining locally but the common problem of a lack of precise location on old documents raises its head here. In 1642 a lease for the Manors of Ritton and Kinnerton (these seem to have been looked upon as one unit well into the 19th century) was granted to Thomas Nicchols. The first document to mention mining is the Articles of Agreement of 26 June 1684 between Rowland Nicchols (Thomas's son) and his son Orlando. This agreement passed most if not all of Rowland's property, including Ritton (and by impli-cation Kinnerton) to Orlando, but left Rowland with certain incomes and, significantly, a right during his life for him and his servants, to get and cart away lead, coal, ironstone, stone and other ores and minerals from Ritton and Kinnerton. He had to proceed with this within three years and could not cease exploiting it for any period greater than three years or the right reverted to Orlando.[5] The only lead mines in the history of these manors were Bog and Ritton Castle, and Bog is virtually certainly the location.

By 1739 one Mathew Dore or Dove and company were working the mine and had sub-leased the smelthouse built by the London Lead Company at Broseley in 1731/2. The lease was for six years from Lady Day 1740 for the building and slag hearth, and Dores were to build a furnace which they could sell to the London Lead Company or dismantle at the end of the lease. The £15 p.a. rent was paid for at least four years and may have been for all six or even eight, but certainly by 1748 the London Lead Company had surrendered their head lease. John Lawrence II was involved with the mine, as was his father; John II was certainly there by 1760 as he wrote two letters late that year and made a report on the state of the mine at the end of it for Mr. Scott, one of the partners. One of the issues he raised in these was the problem of keeping the mine clear of water, a problem which persisted for the mine's entire life despite substantial investments.

By 1789 Scott and his partners had been superseded by John Weston and Company who installed a steam pumping engine to try and solve the water problem at the 'Good Chance' mine. The mine was said to not be working to any great extent in 1799[6] and by 1802 it was advertised in the *Shrewsbury Chronicle* as being to let for 14 or 21 years. This does not seem to have been achieved until 1809 when a group including John Lawrence III took a 31-year lease. During this lease the mine was further developed and Boat Level was extended from Pennerley, as evidenced by two burials recorded in Worthen Parish register with the note 'The water accumulated in the old pits of the Bog mine bursting into the new level, drowned these two (John Parry and John Morris) and another person' in December 1812. By 1822 the lease had passed to the Reverend Rocke as he assigned it to partners including Lawrence III that year; it was subsequently sold to John Lawrence IV. The company also owned a coal mine at Moorheath near Pontesbury.

Lawrence's tenure was not long, as two years later lawsuits began over the Leigh Level and leases at Grit and Gravels and by 1830 he was bankrupt. Early that year the following appeared in the *Salopian Journal* (also Fig. 6.4):

> To Mining Adventurers are offered the valuable LEASE of the BOG LEAD MINE, steam engine, gins, boats etc the property of Mr. John Lawrence jun. A Bankrupt.

The sale was to be held on 24 February 1830 on site. Included as lot 1 was the lease of 3,000 acres. There was a navigable level for boats that drained at 115 yards, and 2,400 tons of ore remained, free from royalties. There was a 'Capital steam engine 42 inch cylinder' (double power) along with a selection of equipment and fittings including '2 wrought iron boilers and 55 yards of 15 inch pump'. There were also cast iron rails, two railway wagons under ground, three gins, three wood boats and one iron boat.

The mine was sold to Messrs. Cross and Ellis (also frequently referred to as Walker Cross and company or, incorrectly, Walker Parker and Company of Chester, though this major lead industry concern held half the shares) and was run by Captain Clemence, assisted by Isaac Floyd. Lawrence received the following letter (also Fig. 6.5):

Mr Llance Sir
You will have the Goodness to Send For the use of this mine one Caske of Powder I Am yours Isaac Floyd
Bog Mine January 21 1831

It was followed up by Captain Clemence three days later explaining *inter alia* that they were expecting some powder from Chester any day and asking for a loan of a cask. A lease was granted to Cross and Ellis by Henry Lyster of a mine in Ritton and Kinnerton (i.e. Bog) on 5 March 1834. Further leases were granted to Cross and Ellis in 1835 although these were granted by Heighway Jones, one for the mine (or perhaps part of it?) and one for Bog Farm, but reserving the minerals to Heighway Jones. The company at this period also acquired Pennerley, Tankerville and Myttonsbeach mines.

The new company spent £20,000 on the mine and the infrastructure including rebuilding at least part of the road past Snailbeach to the turnpike south of Minsterley. By 1837 water problems closed the mine for six months. In 1838 a new engine was installed but did not save the mine in 1845. The mine and all its plant was put up for sale by order of Chancery and as there were no takers work ceased and the mine flooded. The company lost £78,000. Some

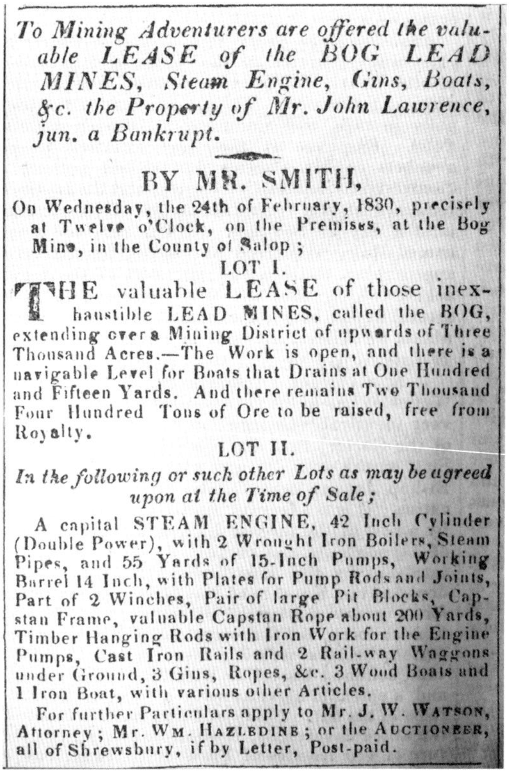

To Mining Adventurers are offered the valuable LEASE of the BOG LEAD MINES, Steam Engine, Gins, Boats, &c. the Property of Mr. John Lawrence, jun. a Bankrupt.

BY MR. SMITH,

On Wednesday, the 24th of February, 1830, precisely at Twelve o'Clock, on the Premises, at the Bog Mine, in the County of Salop;

LOT I.

THE valuable LEASE of those inexhaustible LEAD MINES, called the BOG, extending over a Mining District of upwards of Three Thousand Acres.—The Work is open, and there is a navigable Level for Boats that Drains at One Hundred and Fifteen Yards. And there remains Two Thousand Four Hundred Tons of Ore to be raised, free from Royalty.

LOT II.

In the following or such other Lots as may be agreed upon at the Time of Sale;

A capital STEAM ENGINE, 42 Inch Cylinder (Double Power), with 2 Wrought Iron Boilers, Steam Pipes, and 55 Yards of 15-Inch Pumps, Working Barrel 14 Inch, with Plates for Pump Rods and Joints, Part of 2 Winches, Pair of large Pit Blocks, Capstan Frame, valuable Capstan Rope about 200 Yards, Timber Hanging Rods with Iron Work for the Engine Pumps, Cast Iron Rails and 2 Rail-way Waggons under Ground, 3 Gins, Ropes, &c. 3 Wood Boats and 1 Iron Boat, with various other Articles.

For further Particulars apply to Mr. J. W. WATSON, Attorney; Mr. WM. HAZLEDINE; or the AUCTIONEER, all of Shrewsbury, if by Letter, Post-paid.

Fig. 6.4 Advertisement in the Salopian Journal *for the sale of Bog Mine following John Lawrence's bankruptcy*

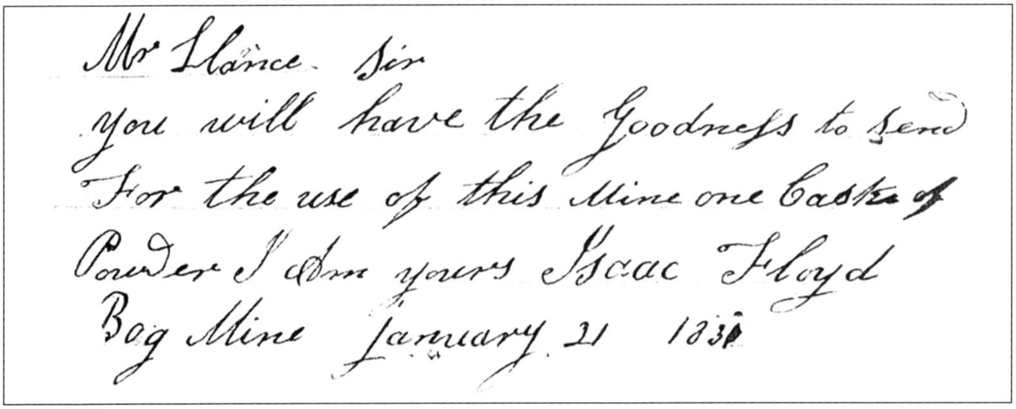

Mr Llance Sir
you will have the Goodness to Send
For the use of this Mine one Caske of
Powder I Am yours Isaac Floyd
Bog Mine January 21 1831

Fig. 6.5 Isaac Floyd's letter to John Lawrence of January 1831 requesting powder. (SA 1118/18)

limited 'private' working took place over the following few years above Boat Level, official returns from 1845 to 1850 showing a generally decreasing output.

The 1850s proved to be a turbulent and unproductive decade for the mine. Leases were granted to Fuller Mckay and others in 1853 and to Jackson Emmerson and others in 1854.[7] Nothing is known of these concerns although those of 1854 were probably involved with the Bog Mining Co. Ltd., who took the lease in 1856 and were wound up before 1859 when Fuller and company reappear as the Bog Lead Mining Co. Ltd. The 1856 company was fraudulent, £24,000 of shareholders' money going mainly into the pockets of one W. Chenall. Total production between 1856 and 1859 amounted to about 50 tons of ore. The return of Fuller and company to the mine was very short-lived, and by the following year it was owned by S. Morris-Ridge, who did a small amount of work the year after that, and then the mine was abandoned again.

In 1864 the mine was purchased for £10,000 cash and £20,000 in £10 shares by the Stiperstones Mining company (alternatively known as the Bog and Pennerley company) from a set of partners[8] and received a lease early in the following year. The Stiperstones Mining company, who had in the past run Batholes and Perkins Beach mines, took over Pennerley, Potter's Pit and Myttonsbeach along with Bog. This began a more or less stable period in the mine's history, even though production returns for the following 20 years show that quantities were not always great. Whilst production continued steadily, ownership did not. In 1865 the company (by either name) was in liquidation though trading carried on until it was reformed as the Stiperstones Mining Company Limited. They used an influx of capital to begin the expensive process of de-watering the mine, but went into liquidation to be replaced by the Bog Mining Company Limited in 1871.

By 1873 both the mine and the new company were completely drained, the mine by another new engine, the *Lady Charlotte*. In addition the company built some iron framed cottages to let to its workforce in 1873.[9] Once again returns were insufficient and the plant was assigned to Edward Corbett who no doubt leased it back in 1874, but this did not save the company and they were liquidated in 1875. The mine flooded again and production fell to a low level. A new Bog Mining Company was formed in 1877 who sold out to Peter Watson who in turn sold the mine to Tankerville Great Consols Limited in 1879/80. This company, who ran other mines including Tankerville, managed a short spurt from 1881 to 1884 when the mine was closed in May and work remained suspended until 1889. In 1890 the landowner Lord Rowton took the mine 'in hand' and the New Bog Mining Company was formed the following year. They lasted until 1897 when they gave way to William Oldfield[10] who, with partners, ran the mine until August 1903. The mine produced a little lead ore and larger amounts of zinc-blende and barytes. The Vieille Montagne company considered acquiring the mine from Oldfield in 1897 but decided that the cost of draining it was too great.

C. Butler took over the mine in 1905, and in the next two years produced a little zinc and less lead. In 1907 Bog Mines Ltd. appeared on the scene and reopened and then closed the mine. Shropshire Lead Mines Ltd. reopened the mine again in 1909,[11] and production of zinc, lead and especially barytes, increased considerably in the years up to the First World War. Substantial investment in new plant in 1914 and further prospecting led to the opening of Ramsden's shaft in 1915 and the digging of the Somme Tunnel in 1916. That year the company was reformed as Shropshire Mines Ltd., having amalgamated with the Wotherton Barytes and Lead Mining Company. Ramsden's Shaft proved successful for a number of years but the Somme Tunnel found nothing.[12] By the post-war years barytes was the only significant product but the quality was not high enough and the mine closed in mid October 1925.

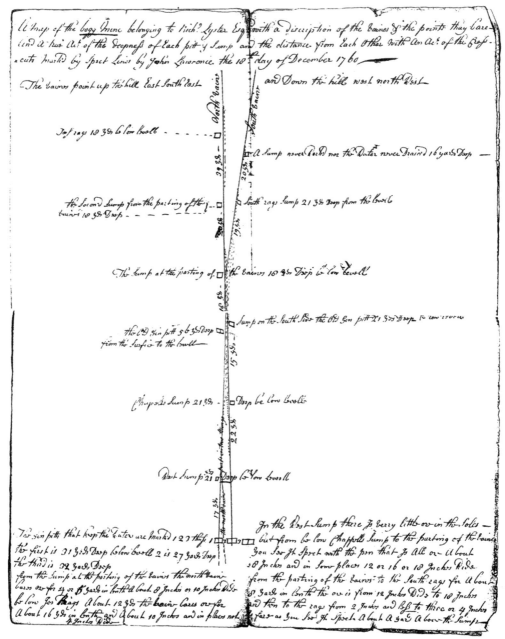

Fig. 6.6 John Lawrence's 1760 plan of Bog mine. (SA 851/286)

This was the end of coherent production although Roundtain Limited[13] tried in 1928 and E. Murgatroyd of Keighley in 1930, with final closure coming in 1932. Jackfield Mines Ltd. examined the mine in the 1960, including removing the cap from Ramsden's Shaft, but nothing came of it. The workmen's hostel near the mine remained in use into the 1940s and the Men's Club into the 1970s, its contents being auctioned in 1975 shortly before the demolition of most of the building.

Bog mine is spread out over the best part of a mile almost to Nipstones mine to the south, a mine always worked by the company working Bog. The principal centre was at The Bog, where most of the winding and pumping was done and where work such as ore preparation was carried out. There were at least three shafts here: Main or Engine, Buntings and Westons. When Shropshire Mines developed the mine around 1914 they dug Ramsden's Shaft about half a mile south of the main complex, and south of that, on the very edge of Nipstones mine, is Swag Shaft, which was inclined. South-east of Ramsden's Shaft are Tews number 1 and 2 shafts. All these latter may date from the Shropshire Mines period.

The mine was worked down to 200 fathoms by 1843 at Engine Shaft which was vertical to the Boat Level at 52 fathoms; then it was inclined and followed the underlie of the vein. Ramsden's Shaft was 390 feet deep to Boat Level.[14] Boat Level was not the mine's first drainage level, for a shallow adit is marked on the Abandonment Plans heading west at a depth of about 48 yards, which must have reached daylight just north of Ritton Castle mine (often part of the same empire as Bog).

Lead was worked from two principal veins which crossed under Buntings Shaft and were met by Engine Shaft. The ore ranged from

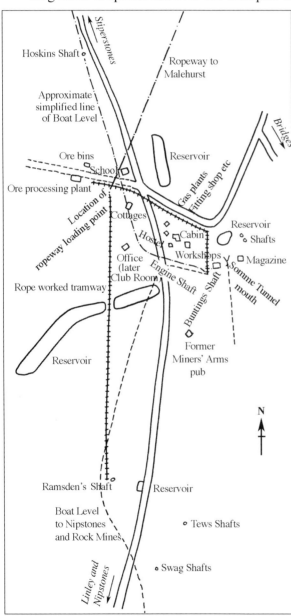

Fig. 6.7 Bog mine

6 inches to 2 feet thick. There were other minor veins. Barytes was principally worked from a further three veins at the south end of the sett.

As has been indicated, at times the mine was very well equipped. By 1760 there were at least three horse gins, various hand winding devices and a 'water engine'. Quite what the nature of this was is unknown. For a true water engine or a bucket and chain system, water would be needed at the surface but would need to empty below it at a drainage adit, which would also be the level to which water from the workings needed to be lifted. Bog always had a lack of water at the surface and much too much below ground, and John Lawrence in his letters notes the problems:

> the water Is verry much increst within thiss three Last days it is verry sharp work to keep it to day I have Sett on the 19yd Gin to draw water and Intend keeping it on in the daytime and the water Ingin in the night for we have not water to work it above 12 hours in 24 ... but am afraid the water will Concur uss for the Winter Except there Comes Some Alteration which we can hardly Expect at thiss time of year for I never Saw any thing Increest So much as the Water has Thiss Last week.[15]

Accident reports are often the only remaining record of a mine's equipment and this is the case here. That in the late 18th century some winding was being done by hand is evidenced by two deaths, one when the turn-tree was loose, allowing the rope to run back down the mine with the victim holding it, and a year later in 1793 when the capstan proved too strong for three men and it unwound giving one a mortal blow. Other accidents are known and were no doubt quite common: deaths from being hit by rock falls in 1778, 'suffocation by damp' in 1781, killed by blasting in 1788 and falling out of a kibble (whilst being wound out of the shaft possibly by the turn-tree) are all recorded and all sadly typical.

A 30 inch Boulton and Watt engine was purchased by Messrs. Scott and Jeffries in 1777 for £800 and did not last long, being sold to a local colliery in 1782. In 1789 a further Boulton and Watt engine, this time a 45 inch one, was ordered by John Watson and company. John Watson does not seem to have been a particularly straight businessman, leaving substantial debts following the failure of a mining enterprise in north Wales that included sufficient debt to Boulton and Watt that they noted on the order for the engine for Bog that 'Penryndu account to be settled'. In 1794 a second-hand 36 inch engine was purchased from Wheal Buston mine in Cornwall, but nothing more is known of it. The 1789 engine was sold to a colliery in Nuneaton in 1797.

Boat Level alone was not enough as most of the productive workings were below it and in 1813 a new engine was being considered for which calculations of capacity were produced.[16] The size of the cylinder is not given but the pump was to have been 14 inches in diameter. In the event a larger engine was ultimately installed, in time to be offered for sale in 1830. This engine, with a 42 inch cylinder was sold along with 55 yards of 15 inch pump; presumably these latter were unused on the surface, they would have only reached halfway down to Boat Level.

By 1803 the mine is noted as being 150 yards deep, thus 50 yards below Boat Level, and as having veins of galena three foot thick and producing zinc-blende.[17] By the time of a visit in 1834 by Thomas Poole the engine is described as a 40 inch, but is no doubt the same one as sold four years earlier. It was made in Cornwall to 'Trevithick and Vivian's plan' and had a two ton bob to offset the weight of the pump rods. Poole refers to a winding engine located next to the pumping engine but does not specify if it was a horse gin, though he would probably had noted its details had it been steam powered.

Four years later this 40/42 inch engine was replaced with or supplemented by a 370 h.p., 70 inch cylinder engine called the 'Queen Victoria' obtained from the Coalbrookdale Company. It was started, amidst much rejoicing, in January 1839 and the mine was 'again in a state of activity', as reported in the *Shrewsbury Chronicle* on 1 February. This engine was sold in about 1845 along with all the rest of the company's assets. The limited mining which took place from then to 1871 probably used no more than windlasses or horse gins to wind from above Boat Level. The next piece of plant known of is another 70 inch 200 h.p. engine named *Charlotte* after Lady Charlotte Lyster, the Lady of the Manor and owner of the mine. This was set up by June 1871 and finally de-watered the mine to the bottom of Engine Shaft at 148 fathoms. She had a 10 foot stroke and a 26 ton beam. By 1875 the engine belonged to Edward Corbett who threatened to seize it, along with all the other plant leased by him, in settlement of the company's mortgage and debts to him. The matter was being prepared for court action,

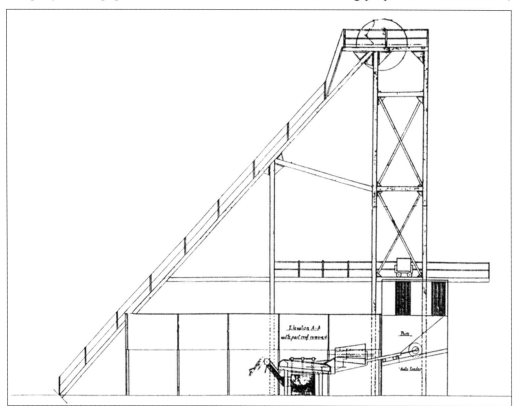

Fig. 6.8 A drawing of the proposed head frame at Ramsden's Shaft; the one constructed was probably very similar. (coll. K. Lock)

2nd Volunteer Battalion,
King's Shropshire Light Infantry.

"C" COMPANY.

BOG MINES PLATOON.

Fig. 6.9 Bog Mines Platoon of the King's Shropshire Light Infantry during the First World War. Not all the men listed on the left were present for this picture. The substantial lance-sergeant towards the right on the front row is the grandfather of Esmond Betton who was brought up at Huglith mine where his father worked, whilst he worked there and at Malehurst.
The corrugated iron building in the background housed the gas plant and the rendered building in front was the miners' barracks. (coll. K. Lock)

Lieut.	A. E. THOMAS.		Pte.	M. JONES.
2/Lieut.	E. C. GRAY.		,,	W. LEWIS.
Sgt.	A. FRANCE.		,,	R. LEWIS.
	F. W. WHITE.		,,	J. LEWIS.
L/Sgt.	G. BETTON.		,,	JAMES LEWIS.
Corpl.	R. H. EVANS.		,,	R. OWEN.
,,	R. TOPHAM.		,,	W. PINCHES.
,,	G. EDWARDS.		,,	T. POTTER.
,,	H. PURSLOW.		,,	J. POTTER.
,,	W. E. BLACKER.		,,	W. PEARCE.
L/Corpl.	H. ROWSON.		,,	R. POTTER.
Pte.	W. BUTLER.		,,	S. PURSLOW.
,,	J. A. BENNETT.		,,	J. C. ROBERTS.
,,	J. CORFIELD.		,,	JOHN ROBERTS.
,,	J. CHIDLEY.		,,	E. SANDLES.
,,	G. DOWNES.		,,	A. SANDLES.
,,	JOHN EVANS.		,,	JAMES SMITH.
,,	T. EVANS.		,,	T. SMITH (1st).
,,	R. H. EVANS (2nd).		,,	T. SMITH (2nd).
,,	J. FRANCE.		,,	T. SMITH (3rd).
,,	J. GROVES.		,,	W. SMITH.
,,	J. GWILLIAM.		,,	W. SWAIN.
,,	F. HALES.		,,	G. THOMAS.
,,	G. HOTCHKISS.		,,	G. TOMLINS.
,,	J. H. HOTCHKISS.		,,	N. WHITTALL.
,,	W. HIGGINS.		,,	J. WATERS.
,,	A. JONES.			

LIVESEY LIMITED, PRINTERS, SHREWSBURY.

106

but no details of this have been found. The engine stayed on site with Tankerville Great Consols.

Judging from recorded production no major plant would have been needed on site after 1884 until the arrival of Shropshire Lead Mines in about 1909, although both a pumping engine and a horizontal winding engine are known to have been at Buntings Shaft in 1897. Shropshire Lead Mines Ltd. invested heavily and turned Bog into a modern mine by 1915. Steam, gas and electric plant was all installed, the main supplier being E. Davies of Atlas Foundry, Shrewsbury. The new plant included a steam engine deep underground near Ramsden's Shaft,[18] which suggests, despite suggestions to the contrary, that the mine was worked below Boat Level. Other equipment included a gas engine, generator, winding engine, headframe, power house, other buildings and the necessary ancillary equipment including at least one 'Wynne's Patent Slimer' (for recovering the finest particles of lead often lost into the local watercourses, with poor results both from a commercial and a pollution point of view).

This was not the end, for in 1918 a ropeway to railway sidings at Malehurst was completed, using German PoW labour. In 1919 a company newsletter stated that there were difficulties with the large engines and the lack of fuel for them. It was hoped to get large supplies of electric power, presumably from the National Grid rather than their own generator which had been in place about five years. In the meantime it was planned to install two 400 h.p. engines with water tube boilers for pumping by August 1920, and a larger steam engine at Buntings Shaft to bale the water out to a low enough level for electric pumps to be installed to drain the entire mine. Unfortunately no later editions of this newsletter have surfaced and it is not known how much if any of this work was done. At some stage money must have run out and the plug was pulled on several projects, quite when is not clear, but judging from work at Leigh Level, which may have stopped by November 1920, some of these developments at Bog may also have been abandoned at about the same time. Despite this, Bog was fairly well equipped, Ramsden's Shaft (named after the managing director) had one, if not the first, electric winder in the county, though it was not successful and was replaced by a steam winder. The mine supplied the locals with power, making The Bog the first village in the county with electricity. Although not recorded, when the mine closed in 1925 some of this plant was almost certainly relocated, with Huglith being a prime candidate. As at so many times in the mine's chequered past any subsequent underground work would have been done with primitive equipment, probably windlasses, and all done above Boat Level.

Unsurprisingly production at the mine fluctuated wildly. John Lawrence IV, speaking in 1853, stated that he got about 100 tons of ore from the mine 30 years before. Thomas Poole, visiting in 1836, was informed that the mine, possibly including Ritton Castle and Pennerley, was producing 240 tons of ore a month, but as this would have been on a par with the highest figures recorded for any mine in the county it must be open to considerable doubt. The landlord had received an average of £770 a year in royalties between 1834 and 1844 which suggest between 300 and 400 tons of ore per annum. In only 14 of the years covered by official statistics did the mine exceed 100 tons of lead ore, production peaking with 625 tons in 1874 and 600 in 1883; at no other time did it achieve more than half of these figures. From a respectable 252 tons in 1913 it fell off by more or less 50% per annum to 15 tons in 1917. The 27 tons recorded in 1918 is the last noted although small quantities were found until final closure. From 1871 zinc ore was mined and production of this also showed fluctuation. Most years saw more than 100 tons produced, with a peak of 685 in 1882. Again production in 1913 was good, at 438 tons, falling off to 165 tons by 1918 and an unspecified amount in 1924. 1,400 ounces of silver were produced in 1882/3 and a further 370 in 1909 and 1912. The last phase of the mine's production, the production of barytes, began in 1891. Between then and 1912 the level fluctuated between 9 and 500 tons, but 1913, when 2,900 tons was dug indicated the future. Production fluctuated during the First World War from 1,988 tons in 1914 to 7,046 in 1916 and 3,260 in 1918, after which production figures gradually fell.

Fig. 6.10 The 'Clubhouse' shortly prior to its demolition. (coll. K. Lock)

Fig. 6.11 The sad remains of the 'Clubhouse' in May 2007,
housing a small display on the history of the mine. (Author)

The employment figures obviously tell the same story as the production figures, though they are unfortunately only available in official returns from 1879, when one man was employed. The 1880s boom saw the employment of around 120 men but then numbers fell off considerably, although most years saw the total in double figures. 100 was again reached in 1913 and that figure was constant until 1918, when it fell off sharply until by the close in 1925, 18 were employed. Roundtain Ltd. never employed more than nine, two-thirds of them above ground. Prior to official returns little is known. An estimate of employment was made when it was proposed in 1841 to build a new turnpike through Shelve. At that date 570 men were said to be employed in Bog mine and the company's colliery. This makes an interesting comparison with Thomas Poole's estimated number in 1834 of 200 underground at the mine.

Transport, as elsewhere, had its problems. Ore was certainly being sent to Ironbridge Gorge by 1739 and this carried on, with at least one change of smelter, presumably until Malehurst smelter was opened on the local coalfield in the 1780s. The ore would have gone overland using either waggons or packhorses to the River Severn at Shrewsbury and from the opening of Malehurst smelter just overland. The opening of Boat Level beyond Pennerley mine in 1812 reduced the road distance by a couple of miles. As noted elsewhere the level was used by boats into the 1830s, when road transport became more important and ultimately replaced the boats; Thomas Poole noted the expensive improvements to the road at his 1834 visit when coal was coming from Asterley Colliery as return loads in the ore waggons.

Rail transport never played a key role at Bog mine though it is said to have a tramway from the mine to a tip[19] and at a later date, probably in the time of Shropshire Lead Mines, there were a series of tramways linking the various parts of the site. Ultimately, the longest was a rope-worked one from Ramsden's Shaft to the ropeway station, the barytes being tipped via chutes into the ropeway buckets. In the early 1870s subscriptions were requested for the construction of the Snailbeach District Railway which it was intended would further reduce the road haulage required from the mine. The failure of the mine in 1873 put paid to Bog's initial involvement with the line. Later ore taken out from and coal supplied to Bog and Tankerville Great Consols' other mines provided a useful amount of the railway's traffic, and the failure of that company coincided with the end of dividend payments by the railway. During the First World War the products were being hauled to Minsterley railway station by traction engines for onward transmission to Hanwood Mill or Warrington. Despite the mine company taking on much of the road maintenance this was clearly not wholly satisfactory as the aerial ropeway was constructed in 1917/8, which went to new sidings at Malehurst, a site later developed by the company for a barytes mill. The barytes (and no doubt odd amounts of lead and zinc ores) travelled down and coal for the gas plant and steam engines came back, or at least the amount left after locals had tipped a few hundredweights out of the buckets. (If you stood in the right place with a stout stick you could tip coal out of a bucket as it went up the ropeway, the prisoners of war who built the line showing the locals how to do it.)

Fig. 6.12 (top) An overall view of the mine site in May 1970 prior to clearance. The 'Men's Club' is visible to the left and the hostel, formerly the barracks, with its distinctive roof, to the right. (G.L. Jones)

Fig. 6.13 (bottom) An aerial view in which the former Bog school is prominent to the bottom right. The ropeway passed behind it and terminated just over the track; the line of the rope-worked tramway from Ramsden's Shaft is the straight line entering the picture towards the upper left. The rump of the 'Men's Club' is visible below this line, as are some of the foundations of the mine workshops and plant below the road. (CPAT)

The remains of the mine are sad, for most was swept away in the 1960s as an environmental improvement. Much of the tips were reused as road-stone, the shafts were filled and the last piece of head gear — a wooden frame at Buntings Shaft — was dismantled. The main site is quite clear. The lower walls of what was latterly The Bog Men's Club stand in part and support a display on the history of the mine. Nearby are the now overgrown reservoir, the track-bed of the tramway from Ramsden's Shaft and the holding down bolts for the ropeway loading point. The gunpowder magazine survives complete and nearby is the Somme Tunnel; this still goes 135 yards into the Stiperstones and is accessible except when the bats need their privacy. Away from the mine itself the one-time Miners Arms public house is now a private house, the village school is an education centre and Ramsden's Shaft is capped in a garden. The other shafts are filled and/or lost in woodland.

Fig. 6.14 The entrance to the Somme Tunnel in July 2007. (Author)

Burgam

This is a minor though interesting mine connected to Boat Level. It may well have been worked earlier but it does not appear in official records until 1866 as a part of the Bog and Pennerley company's outfit along with Ovenpipe (later Tankerville) with Arthur Waters as manager. Clearly even Waters could not find anything worthwhile as it disappears from view by 1869 and shows no further sign of activity until it became part of Tankerville Great Consols empire in 1881. In 1890 it was taken over by Messrs. Poole, Marsh, Job & Toye when it was worked, with Perkins Beach, for barytes. It changed hands to the Shropshire United Mining Co. Ltd. in 1891, to New Bog Mining company in 1894 and was closed the following year having produced a bit of zinc-blende. The mine was the subject of a lease from the Earl of Tankerville and Mr. Lloyd[20] to Shropshire Mines Ltd. on 2 December 1921; whether they worked or sublet it is not known, though the latter seems likely. There were small scale workings for barytes between 1924 and 1943, usually if not entirely by a handful of men at a time. Activity was recorded in 1924, 1930-3 and 1938-43 by various members of the Lewis clan, and finally Jackfield Mines Ltd. worked it from the early 1950s for lead, with Tom Rowson as manager, Norman Evans and casual assistance. When this activity stopped in 1962 it was the last lead mine in the county to close. Its other claim to fame was that an uncommon lead mineral, pyromorphite, was found here. A lead chloro-phosphate, its crystals are bright yellow-green

Fig. 6.15 Burgam mine appeared in the Manchester Guardian *on 7 March 1959 under the headline 'The Philosopher of Burgam Mine', no doubt as an image of an almost disappeared method of mining*

and prismatic, barrel- or needle-shaped in form. It was collected for some years after closure and has all now gone. The mineral rights were auctioned by the Tankerville Estate in 1952, those for this mine being held by Messrs. F.S.H. Tisdall Ltd.

The principal vein worked was the big Spar Vein which also was worked at Perkins Beach; other smaller veins were also exploited. There were at least nine adits on three levels of the hillside with a series of vertical and inclined shafts, none of them substantial, though one shaft went down to Boat Level. In addition trenching and shallow pits were scattered over the hillside between here and Perkins Beach. Equipment was to scale for a small mine. Shropshire United Mining Co. Ltd. had a horse gin which was remembered until quite recently and it is drawn on their abandonment plan; this no doubt was the heyday of major investment. Certainly up to the 1940s a horse sled was used to get ore to the road and by the end the men used candles, hand drilling and wheelbarrows. Output was also to scale. Official returns admit to 40 tons of lead ore prior to 1913, four tons of zinc in the same period and a creditable 2,000 tons of barytes between 1890 and 1894 with a maximum of about 20 men. Later production of barytes is unknown but according to the *Express & Star* of 4 April 1959, 7 cwt of lead ore was dug between 1953 and 1959. Presumably this should have read 7 tons as the value of £450 is given. The locations of many of the adits, shafts and spoil heaps are visible but there are no significant remains.

Buxton/Cross's

Buxton Hill is best known for its quarry but is likely to have been prospected for lead. In 1843 Cross's mine is described as being three-quarters of a mile north of Pennerley and near the top of a high hill, which could have been at Buxton. The other contenders are Potter's Pit, Burgam, Perkins Beach and Tankerville though none of these tie up well. Buxton Hill is at least the right distance north; an adit is remembered locally.[21] Parts of Perkins Beach on the other hand, although further away and to the north-east, do have the necessary high hill and room for the engine, engine shaft and adit referred to at the location later to be called New Venture. At Buxton quarrying has removed some of the possible evidence.

Callow Hill

This mine lies to the north of all the other mines in this chapter and its site is now best known as a quarry, which has destroyed most of the mining remains. It is, however, amongst the earliest mines to appear in written records, as miners were noted prospecting in Habberley Office in 1613 and a mine at Habberley Walk is in a royalty account of the Bath family in 1615 when the figure of £14 5s. 5d. was received — presumably both references to this mine. The sum implies significant output. From the later 18th century until the 1820s the Snailbeach company prospected and mined there, as a condition of their lease of Snailbeach from the Marquis of Bath. One of the key works carried out was the lower adit which was intended to drain Snailbeach mine.

The 1851 Bagshaw's *Directory* notes under the parish of Worthen that Habberley Office Township had lead mines worked by a company of shareholders, without giving names. Given that the southerly shaft is called Powell's Shaft and that J. Powell and Company ran Central Snailbeach mine at a similar period, it is reasonable to suggest they may have run both.[22] In about 1860 the mine was back in the hands of the Snailbeach partners and shortly afterwards a new shaft was being sunk which produced some lead. Some work carried on until about 1874 although an 1869 survey (Liscombe) noted that little work was done. In 1888 the mine briefly enters the realm of official statistics when it was owned by W. & James Yelland & J. Mitchell who became the Callow Hill Mine Company in 1891 and, according to the returns, closed the mine in 1892. However, in 1894 the Geological Association visited a barytes mine in the immediate locality without naming it, and Callow Hill is the only sensible contender.[23]

Although it is not clear who was digging it, some ore was noted as passing up the Snailbeach District Railway to be dressed at Snailbeach mine.[24] In October 1912 and until 1914 William Roberts ran the mine. Three and a half tons of lead ore and one of zinc ore is the total recorded production though given that the Yellands were barytes merchants their tenure presumably looked for but did not find workable barytes or failed to make official returns. It is also clear that quite a quantity of lead was won by the Snailbeach companies over the years though this was probably included in that mines' returns. The maximum number of employees recorded was five in 1912. In the late 1950s an approach was made to the County Council, as landowners, to reopen the mine, but the applicant's name is not noted and permission was refused.[25]

The earliest parts of the mine are an upper adit and three shafts, the westernmost of which connects with the later low level adit which itself connected with a further three shafts. The southernmost of these, at 500 yards west-north-west of Bank Farm, is almost in Eastridge Woods though to what extent this was for working and to what extent to try to drain Snailbeach is moot. Of its equipping little is known, but presumably it had an engine as it had an Engine Shaft which at 360 feet was the deepest at the mine.

The workings at Callow Hill itself are almost entirely quarried away, though old workings have been encountered and the small size of the levels noted as was the presence of wooden tram rails. The low level adit mouth is in thick undergrowth behind Minsterley Fire Station.

Central Snailbeach

This is a classic case of using a 'good' name to 'sell' a dubious mine. The attraction to speculators was not that good ore had been found by prospecting but that, if you extended known veins on a map they could have been expected to pass through the sett you were trying to sell. Unfortunately in practice they did not, money was lost and reputations should have been.

Ore was found here by a private company[26] in the 1850s, quite where or by which company is not clear. The principal recorded history is in the 15 years from 1860 to 1875. J. Powell and Company, who may have been involved at Callow Hill, were recorded as owners in 1860-6 although the Central Snailbeach Mining Co. Ltd. issued a prospectus in 1861 and were incorporated and obtained a lease from the joint landlords, Lloyd and Tankerville in 1862.

A further prospectus was issued in 1864 to raise an additional £30,000 capital above the original £10,000. They ran the mine along with mine(s) on Hill Sett (see Myttonsbeach) until they ran out of money and went into liquidation in 1869. The New Central Snailbeach Mining Co. Ltd. was floated immediately and they saw the mine out. An undated plan[27] of Hogstow Hall land of c.1862 shows 'Crowsnest Level', but although it includes the area developed by the mine, it does not show the shaft or engine house. By 1869 two separate reports confirm that no production was taking place, even though one (Liscombe) notes that a new engine was built the previous year and that an adit was being driven. A series of grants of way-leaves from the Tankerville Estate does nothing to unscramble the history. In 1868 and 1870 way-leaves for the mine were transferred to the New Central Snailbeach Mining Co. Ltd. and in between they were transferred to William Kough of Church Stretton, one-time company secretary.

Fig. 6.16 Central Snailbeach mine in 1864 from a share promotion document showing the first engine house. (coll. K. Lock)

Fig. 6.17 Central Snailbeach in 1963. (Shropshire Archives)

*Fig. 6.18 Aerial photograph of Central Snailbeach showing the mine upper centre.
(CPAT)*

115

The mine was worked from one principal shaft which finally reached 230 yards in depth,[28] and a 640-yard long adit which drained the shaft at 150 feet. There were two other shafts down to that adit and a further adit below the road to the north of the mine. It is not known whether either of the adits up Crowsnest Dingle were part of Central Snailbeach or not. No returns were ever made of production or employment though 126 tons of ore in 1871 and 1872 are noted in a British Geological Survey publication of 1922 (it has become an unlikely 626 in a 1958 publication). If unproductive, the mine was not ill equipped. A pumping and winding engine and house was built in the early 1860s, replaced by new ones of each by 1869; no details are known of either development but the additional depth to be pumped was reason for the change. The prospectus from 1864 survives with photographs, which includes the first of the engine houses.

The remains are fine, if limited and private. The second engine house, with a two tube Lancashire boiler *in situ* and the stump of the chimney, survives, converted into a house clearly visible from the road. The low level adit is collapsed but the one below the road is locatable and was used as an air raid shelter during the war. All the shafts are filled. Parts of the mine were used as storage for Central Stores which had been run by Enoch Parry from the mine house following the closure of the mine. The house had been built for Parry as mine captain and remained occupied (and the stores run) by his descendants until about 1953.[29]

Sundry Stiperstones' Trials

The first edition large scale Ordnance Survey maps show a series of three trial lead levels in the area of the Stiperstones known as The Hollies and several shafts have been dug on the Stiperstones east of Snailbeach mine. That they should exist is unsurprising but nothing specific is known of them.

Also possibly in the vicinity are trials diggings as a result of a one-year permission to search for mines in 'all the land belonging to the Gatton Estate, lying to the North West side of the Quartz rock range on the Stiperstones Hill'. The only land which appears to have been in the Gatton Estate fitting that description is adjoining what is now called Shepherd's Rock at the head of Perkins Beach (around grid reference SJ999373).[30] The trial was worked, as the landowner was concerned a year later at the small number of men employed, but there is no evidence that the standard 21-year lease was requested. Interesting conditions of the consent were that there was to be no 'underground thoroughfare into any other work, except a sough for water, and all the ores to be wound up, washed or buddled, and weighed on the Gatten Estate that are got under it'. The permission was granted to Messrs. Cross Ellis and Co. 'on the same terms as Bog Mining Co had from Mr. Lyster' on 11 August 1836.

The Snailbeach Co. also had at least one trial in the area known as Yew Tree Level. The trial was not successful and there is little left to see.

Maddox Coppice

There was a trial here for lead by Snailbeach mine, to its north-east, of unknown date. It consisted of two adits and quite extensive workings. Both adits are still visible and

Fig. 6.19 The slight remains of the upper adit at Maddox Coppice mine in August 2007. (Author)

the lower one, which was the drainage level, is still used as a water supply. From the surviving cast iron pipe referred to above (see Snailbeach) it seems that, even if this trial was unproductive, it did provide some much need water to Snailbeach.

Myttonsbeach

Confusingly sometimes known as Hill Sett (though only part of it may have been in that sett) and Dingle Sett (though only one of several 'Dingles' in the mining area), this consisted of a number of small workings in Mytton Dingle. By the mid 1830s Walker Cross and company held whatever mine was here along with Pennerley, Bog and Tankerville. Nothing is known of their activity here and the mine, along with all their other assets, was sold about 1844. In the 1850s Horton, Stainsby and Jones worked part of the sett as later did Heighway Jones who sold to Central Snailbeach in 1870. In January 1868, following a take note the previous year the rest of the sett was leased to the Central Snailbeach Mining Co. Ltd., who hoped, vainly, to repair their fortunes. In April 1870 the lease passed to their successors the New Central Snailbeach Mining Co. Ltd. Both concerns worked here with a shaft being sunk and an adit dug. The mine was reported as not working in 1869 (Morton) but was being worked by 1872 and quite possibly for another couple of years until the demise of its proprietors. It is lost to history after this until it was leased to Shropshire Mines Ltd. in 1921, but there is no evidence that they carried out any work. It nearly stole Burgam's crown as the last mine when a local miner tried unsuccessfully to reopen a level in June 1964 aided and no doubt abetted by members of the Shropshire Mining Club (renamed the Shropshire Caving and Mining Club in 1976).

The shaft sunk in 1870 used a horse gin for drainage, but this proved insufficient and a traction engine was used. The shaft reached its final depth of 44 yards the following year. It was drained at 14 yards by an adit. The mine never made official records and can only have produced a little lead ore and possibly some barytes. The scars of the mining are visible in the dingle, two sets of shafts and adits and the matching spoil heaps being visible along with vestigial remains of a building which possibly housed an engine.

Nether Heath

This was probably never the name of a mine but it is the name of a township and is usually grouped with its neighbour Upper Heath.[31] The township certainly contains Pennerley, Tankerville and Roundhill mines, but the activity referred to as being 'Nether Heath' is two different trials or mines carried on by the London Lead Company between 1728 and 1735. In 1729 both sites were being worked under leases from Sir John Astley, one on 'the Common called Nether Heath' and the other 'on the Inclosed land at Nether Heath'. They looked promising. Three good veins had been found in the neighbourhood, possibly at Pennerley, two of which were within half a mile of the London Lead Company's ground and pointed into it. The Nether Heath trials discovered several very large, strong veins of heavy spar 'of which we sent up to London'. They also found 5 or 6 cwt of ore, 'then it proving hard and wet we left it off'. The second site had a 10 yard deep shaft and a level was begun which was or was to be 340 yards long. In 1732 a report to the Assistants (directors) of the company noted a 21-year lease granted in July 1728 from the Astleys and others to Thomas Barker, the company's agent (who also ran his own mines), for all of the commons at Nether Heath except Pennerley. In 1735 the company's then agent, John Morgan, was asked to report on their mines in Montgomeryshire and Shropshire. Referring to 'Neitherheath' he noted he could not inspect the mine because the level was full of water, and thought it not worth continuing, which advice the company took. At the same time they gave up the smelthouse they had built at Benthall.

The precise sites of these two mines are not known, but they were not far from Pennerley, the presence of whose good veins encouraged the London Lead Company. It is reasonably suggested that the site on the common would have been in the vicinity of the later Tankerville mine, and the 'inclosed' site possible near Roundhill.[32] The mine should perhaps be best remembered for having the first reference in the county (perhaps even the country or world) to the extraction of barytes.

Nipstones

To all intents this was a part of Bog mine whose history it exactly parallels, but it was always treated as a separate entity. It touches the southern end of Bog and had access to Boat Level after about 1914. It was developed by the landlord, Lord Rowton (Lyster before his ennoblement) in about 1890 when it first appears in official records. By 1891 it had passed to the New Bog Mining Company who worked it until 1893. It then stood until Messrs. Oldfield, Lewis and Smitham took it on from 1904 to 1911 when it again stood idle. Shropshire Lead Mines Ltd reopened it in 1913 and had closed it again by 1915. In 1922 development was proceeding with hope of finding lead ore[33] though there is no record of any further production unless it is lost in a total figure for Bog mine. It is said to have been an old lead mine hand dug to 30 or 40 yards in depth and worked out,[34] though any other evidence is lacking. Its recorded production is all barytes. In its best years, 1908-10, half a dozen or so men produced nearly 1,000 tons a year, yet in other years the same level of labour force got outputs ranging from less than 100 tons to more than 500. The mine was worked from two adits as well as opencast at its northern end against Bog, and by a shaft over half a mile south. The maximum depth was 88 feet below Boat Level, that is 590 feet below ground level. Barytes was worked only above Boat Level; below that lead or zinc ores were hoped for. There is little left to see.

Pennerley

This is another mine which could well have been working in the 16th and 17th centuries, or even earlier, but for which there is little evidence.[35] The first known record is a lease in 1724 from Sir John Astley of Patshull to a group of partners for 21 years 'of all mines etc on land of leasors called Penally in [the] Lordship of Netherheath'. It gave a right to dig etc. but not to erect a smelthouse. It was considered, somewhat optimistically, to be a lead and copper mine. No doubt a further lease was issued in 1745, with the next extant one 21 years later in 1776. That the mine was working in the early 1750s is evidenced by a Swedish diarist, R.R. Angerstien, who noted that ore from the mine (rendered 'Pannels' by him) was being smelted at the Salop company's smelter in the Ironbridge Gorge. E. & R. Jeffries controlled the mine by 1780 and in 1791[36] took John Lawrence, probably the second, into partnership. His notebook of 1792 confirms that there was a lease in 1776, and records the involvement of both Blakeway who put capital into several mines in the 18th century and Samuel Heighway, forebear of Heighway Jones, who played an important part in its later history. A John Lawrence had previous involvement at a senior level, as a legal bill survives from c.1785 in connection with 'Lawrence v John Fletcher, clerk and others'; the only detail to emerge from the document is that somewhere it involved a lease from Sir John Astley to Lawrence. This ties up with the date when Lawrence is believed to have moved his centre of operations away from Grit mine; however, the White Grit company retained this mine.

The Bog Mine company were working Pennerley in 1809 and constructing Boat Level, in July being granted a lease for the additional land required from the Earl of Tankerville. John Lawrence IV's financial embarrassment (which later led to bankruptcy) in the mid 1820s over the Leigh tunnel affair probably led to the sale of Pennerley which was taken over by Boothman and company from the north-west. They carried out some unsuccessful development work and sold the mine sometime after 1831 to Walker, Cross and company who worked the mine on a similar pattern to Bog for the next few years. The mine was working in 1836 though production was often quite small. It closed shortly thereafter as Murchison in 1839 described it as about to re-open. However, this didn't happen, as the *Mining Journal* in 1843 described it as having been closed for five years. It must have reopened that year as royalties were paid until the following January.

1844 saw the failure of Walker, Cross and the sale of all their mines and plant. There were no takers and Pennerley, like Bog, was allowed to flood to Boat Level. Limited production clearly continued above that level as royalties continued to be paid. The royalty account also reveals that the mine was offered for sale in the *West Briton Advertiser* in May 1845 and that £20 was paid for the roof of the engine house and door frames from Pennerley, which were sold to the Snailbeach company in 1846. The small scale mining of the late 1840s gave way to more formal development with the issue of a one year licence search for minerals probably to Fred Jones (Heighway's uncle), Stainsby and Horton in July 1849. The following month the numbers of partners was raised for a time to five (one disposing of his interests by 1852, another stating in 1864 that 'I gave it up to poor Fred long ago'). A full lease was granted in December 1851 to these partners, who were known as Fred Jones and company. At some stage before 1862 Heighway Jones had bought a share. The company began trading as the Stiperstones Mining company and the mine was extended to include a new shaft (Hoskin's Shaft) and engine halfway towards Bog mine, designed to locate new ore above the Boat Level.

In 1865 the company gained limited liability as the Stiperstones Mining Company Ltd. with a new set of directors and Heighway Jones selling out. Later that year a further set of directors joined, now with Edward Corbett as managing director. After much negotiation, due to the death and bankruptcy of partners, parts of the 1851 lease were surrendered and a new one was issued by the landlords in December 1865. Heighway Jones must have retained some of his holding as he surrendered a part of the 1851 lease in 1870, including Potter's Pits and Pennerley. A year later, in 1871, Corbett's company surrendered the leases for these two mines (at least) to the Pennerley Lead Mining Co. Ltd. The mine closed about 1878 and the company went into liquidation. The failure of Bog mine and the cessation of pumping there had adversely affected Pennerley as did the failure of a client in south Wales leaving unpaid bills. The breaking of a pump rod resulting in a cracked piston in the engine was probably the last straw; by May 1877 the company had just £22 left.

In March 1881 a lease was granted to Watson, York and Shaw, who traded as Tankerville Great Consols Ltd. They concentrated work initially at Pennerley but to little avail. The mine stopped work in 1884 and the company liquidated in 1887. In 1889 the landlords stepped in and by 1890/1 Arthur Waters junior is named as owner. His father had managed the mine in the 1860s and they had jointly managed it from 1881 until Arthur I's death in 1887. Little seems to have been achieved by 1897 when Captain Oldfield took the mine, along with Bog, but did not work it. He offered to sell his take note to the Vieille Montagne Zinc Company, who do not seem to have been interested. W. Edwards tried to work the mine from 1899 to 1901 with little apparent success.

Fig. 6.20 The ore bins at Pennerley in May 2007. (Author)

A sale of the mine's plant (and Tankerville's) took place in 1902, which marked the end of large scale mining. Shropshire Lead Mines Ltd., followed by Shropshire Mines Ltd., owned it from 1910, but eventually just reworked the tips. When the Tankerville Estate mineral rights were sold in 1953 the lime spar (calcite) was leased to D. Tomlins and the road stone to E.E. Hillage. Jackfield Mines Ltd. dug a new shaft in 1956 looking for barytes (the last in the area), which did not lead to a resumption of mining, although William Wooton and Clifford Lewis got their photographs in the *Express & Star* on 5 March 1956 having sunk the 30 foot shaft.[37] It was about 5 feet by 6 feet and timbered, spoil being hauled out in the time honoured fashion using a steel rope and a turn-tree.

The tips were picked over for ore and road stone in the 1960s when further thought was given to new investment, but the thought never became action. The tips were cleared for road stone and the site used as a scrap-yard until well in to the 1970s.

With the exception of the probably unsuccessful Hoskin's Shaft, the mine site was quite compact, though deep; it went down to 130 fathoms below Boat Level at Engine Shaft. Lead was worked principally on Big Ore vein with Red (or Black), Warm Water and Ben Arthur's veins running loosely east / west, each with subdivisions. They were crossed by Rider vein. Barytes was worked from five veins. Three principal shafts were used: Engine, Blands and Gin.

The mine was probably first worked from Gin Shaft, no doubt so named on account of its horse gin. Engine Shaft was sunk in the 1820s and Bland's in the 1850s. At the time that the mine was first recorded, in the lease of 1724, it was drained by a 'Greate Level' from 'Anthony Preece's Beach'. Its location is uncertain but it was probably Boat Level. Some time before 1836 the mine 'struck' lucky when Thomas Blunt[38] notes that it was drained accidentally by an opening being made into a large dry fissure, enabling a rich but otherwise inaccessible part of the mine to be worked. In another sense the mine was (with the nearby Potter's Pit) unique in the county with the scale of its warm water

Fig. 6.21 The only standing building on the main mine site is this building, photographed in May 2007, no doubt an office or store. (Author)

vein. The water temperature was said to reach 140 degrees Fahrenheit and the working conditions in parts of the mine were frequently so hot as to stop work. In 1836 the mine went down to a 180 yard level below Boat Level. The final maximum depth by 1860 was about 1,000 feet below ground level.

Pennerley began life and achieved fame as a lead mine but it also produced substantial quantities of zinc ore, barytes, calcite and 3,000 ounces of silver (in 1882/3). From official returns lead ore production did not exceed 100 tons in a year until 1871. From then until 1884 about 6,500 tons was raised, peaking in 1874 at 940 tons, dipping to 25 tons in 1881 and rising back to 1,140 tons in 1883. The 109 tons in 1884 was the last substantial production, though figures were returned for 1891-5, less than 50 tons in total. Outside the period of official returns figures are few and far between. The royalty account for the Lloyd estate for the period 1747-62 survives and shows production of 1,433 tons of lead ore during those years. The royalty accounts for 1834-44 reveal production rising from c.70 tons to a maximum of 1,000 in 1840, falling back to less than 34 tons in 1844. From then until 1848 smaller amounts were raised by 'miners'. A very little ore will have been raised in the years 1914-21. It is not recorded what was gleaned from the tips or won from the shaft in the years subsequently. The total weight of lead ore produced by the mine was in the region of 10,000 tons.

Four years of reasonable barytes production occurred in 1890-3 with a total of 1,800 tons; thereafter until 1899 an average of 60 tons a year was raised. Judging from what was left in the tips the best of this mineral here was of an extremely high quality. Zinc figures were never high, the 50 tons in 1884 being the peak of production which started in 1872 and petered out with the lead in 1895. At various times these production figures probably include Potter's Pit, Bog and parts of Perkins Beach mines and at other times Pennerley's production may have been included with that of another mine.

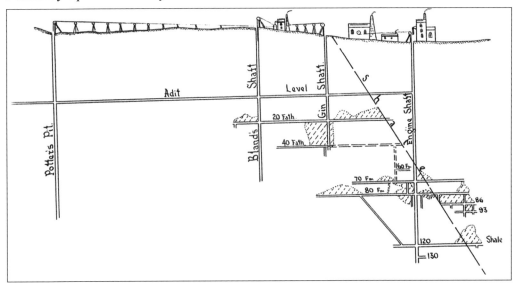

Fig. 6.22 A 1920 sketch section by P. Blight of Pennerley and Potter's Pit mines showing the one time winding arrangement. Adit level is Boat Level. (coll. Author)

As with production statistics so with employment figures. Official returns were made for 1877 to 1884 showing over 100 men each year except in the period 1878-80. Returns were made for a few years in the 1890s, indicating 21 employees in 1890, decreasing to single figures by 1899 and nothing thereafter.

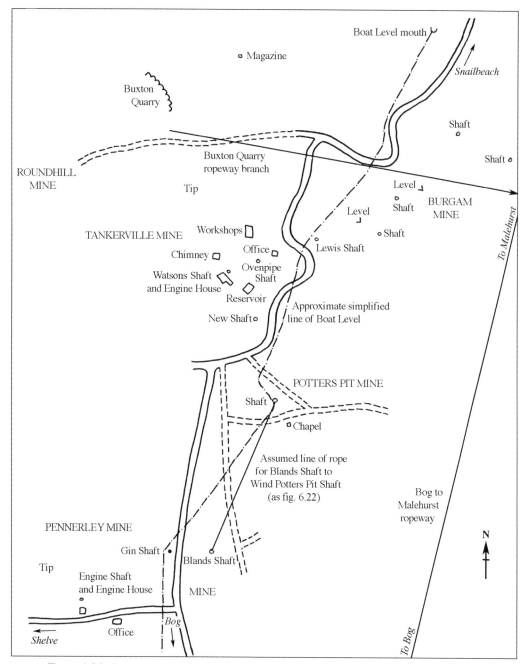

Figs. 6.23 Burgam, Pennerley, Potter's Pit, Roundhill and Tankerville mines

The mine has at times been very well equipped and is known to have had at least ten steam engines of various sorts. No 18th-century engines are recorded but when Engine Shaft was sunk in the 1820s it was supplied with a 24 inch pumping engine, said to have been sold again fairly quickly. By 1831 that shaft had an engine then described as old and too small. The *Mining Journal* reports a 20 inch engine in 1843 though the mine was not then working. Whatever existed by 1844 was sold when Walker Cross failed. Blands Shaft was sunk in the 1850s and provided with a 13 inch engine (12 inch in some sources) which apparently wound this shaft as well as Gin Shaft and, despite a degree of mechanical complexity and frictional loss, Potter's Pit Shaft a quarter of a mile away. About 1860 a 60 inch engine by Harvey's of Hayle in Cornwall was installed to pump Engine Shaft, and by the end of the decade that shaft had three engines. In addition to the pump the mine had a 22 inch horizontal winding engine and a 16 inch horizontal engine to power the saw mill and the capstan, the latter for lifting and lowering pump rods and other items into the shaft. At some stage before a survey of 1890 the mine also acquired a 14 inch engine to drive the compressor for the newly installed drills and a 9 inch one to drive the jiggers. The catalogue for the sale of the mine equipment in 1902 also includes parts of at least one other engine. The 60 inch engine was offered for sale having been

Fig. 6.24 An aerial view of the main mine site at Pennerley. The ore bins (see Fig 6.20) are just below the centre and the remaining building (Fig. 6.21) to the right of centre. The ruinous heaps of the main engine house lie in the trees on the upper left. The remains of a series of (presumably) trial pits are visible top centre. (CPAT)

struck by lightning and collapsing either into or across the shaft, this event probably precipitating the sale. Nothing usable survived that sale, the unsold items including the remains of the Cornish Engine.

The mine had a large dressing floor with an internal tramway system, the 1902 sale including 198 yards of bridge rail and two wagons (as well as underground tramway equipment). In the mine's early days the ore, no doubt to some extent dressed, would have been transported by packhorse or waggon to be smelted, probably somewhere on the River Severn via Shrewsbury, most likely down to the Coalbrookdale area, where it was going by the 1750s, or to Bristol.

With the development of collieries and smelters in the Pontesbury area from about 1780 the ore would have been smelted locally, initially at Malehurst, then Pontesbury then Pontesford until the mid 19th century. Thereafter some of the ore would have gone out on the Minsterley branch line to Deeside. From some unknown date until the mid 1830s the ore would have begun its journey on Boat Level. Otherwise the mine only ever used road transport, for a proposed extension of the Snailbeach Railway failed to materialise as did the later proposal of the Shropshire Minerals Light Railway. Had the mine proved a good source of barytes no doubt Shropshire Mines Ltd. would have served it with a branch of the Bog ropeway.

Time and man have not been kind to the site. Though large it is quite desolate. The collapsed ruins of several building are visible though not easily interpretable. At the time of writing one small, rendered, brick building, possibly an office or store, retained its roof but collapse could not have been far away. A small area of scrub marks the position of Hoskin's Shaft half a mile south. Other very minor pieces of what is probably Pennerley's history are scattered around the surrounding fields in the form of lengths of bridge rail as fence posts.

Perkins Beach mines

This valley behind the Stiperstones Inn has contained a series of mines. At times it has been two setts divided by a fault, **Perkins Beach** and **New Venture** and at times one, though both setts may have been subdivided in certain leases. To add to the confusion, by 1870, when a lease was assigned from Heighway Jones to William Kough it was for Perkins Beach Sett, formerly New Venture Sett. This was repeated in 1906 when a licence to search was given, and in a lease to Shropshire Mines Ltd. in 1921. Perkins Beach mine was also known as Ventnor mine and New Venture as Venture or occasionally Top Ventnor. Ventnor is not to be confused with Wentnor, although whilst the village is some miles away, the parish comes within a short distance and contains Ritton Castle mine (known at times as Wentnor mine but not, contrary to some sources, Ventnor mine). More so than any other sett in the district this has also been the location of a significant number of small or individual ventures, some with the blessing of the landlord, some probably without.

Activity is first recorded in the early 1840s. Perkins Beach is the western, downhill end of the valley and New Venture the uphill end. Unscrambling quite where in the valley any particular mine was is often impossible, and seemingly conflicting information no doubt refers to workings which were within earshot but quite separate. Perkins Beach mine began *circa* 1842 though nothing certain is known of this phase of its existence.[39] It is possible that this mine is the one referred to in the *West Briton and Cornwall Advertiser* for 6 March 1840[40] when a large find of lead ore in the Stiperstones is recorded, the proprietors being Walker Cross and company (also active at Bog and other mines). Perkins Beach and New Venture mines both have a Walker vein (but see Buxton/Cross entry above). By the 1850s it was part of the Horton, Stainsby and Fred Jones Stiperstones empire, being worked in conjunction with Pennerley. By 1860 the mine was independent, worked by Samuel Kough's Perkinsbeach company. This did not last, and by the early 1860s it was again in the Horton empire as part of the Stiperstones company who were by 1862 at least working both Perkins Beach and New Venture Setts, the latter possibly only above deep adit level. Part of the sett was sold to the Ovenpipe Company by 1866[41] and by 1868 some or all was with the redoubtable Heighway Jones. The following year, William Kough (of Central Snailbeach mine) was at New Venture and the Perkins Beach Mining Co. Ltd. at some or all of the rest, the latter reopening their mine by 1871 but being forced to sell up in 1877 by order of the sheriff. The Perkins Beach Lead Mine Ltd. was floated that year, but to what effect is not known as it was in liquidation by the following year but the name was resurrected in 1883. In 1870 the *Mining Journal* carried a brief mention of East Tankerville Sett being ripe for development. This was described as adjacent to the west edge of Tankerville sett and south of Snailbeach, formerly part of Perkins Beach sett.

Some part of the setts were being investigated if not worked in 1881 by Parr and Co. and Perkins' (*sic*) Beach Consols Ltd. was floated that year. The list of those involved changes almost year by year: in 1882 R. Jewell, in 1883 Perkins Beach Mining Company, in 1884 Morris-Ridge at New Venture until 1887 and T.H. Watson at Perkins Beach until 1885 and from 1888 to 1890, and then intermittently until 1911 various combinations of Marsh, Toye, Job and Poole, probably at New Venture. Somewhere in the valley Shropshire United Mining Co. Ltd. (see also Burgam mine) worked in 1891-3 and New Bog Mining Company from 1894-7, this being the end of significant lead mining in the valley.

In 1906 Minsterley Baryta Company reopened Perkins Beach as Ventnor mine supplying their Minsterley Mill, Minsterley Baryta surviving a year or so. The Earl of Tankerville considered reopening the mine as Perkins Beach in 1907, and may have done so. The same year W. Toye and Company restarted New Venture. Wotherton Barytes & Lead Mining Co. Ltd. took a lease in 1912, probably for the whole valley, and they or their successors from 1916, Shropshire Mines Ltd., developed and worked the mines until about 1921, retaining the odd man or two until 1925.

From this period the history fragments, with several men working small, often new mines for small quantities of barytes. E. Jones,[42] another Morris-Ridge and a Lewis are all recorded as being at work here in the years between the two World Wars. Nothing remains on record from after the war but it is possible that small scale mining continued. Certainly at the time of writing there are still men living who remember old men divining or dousing[43] for barytes and themselves working in such 'mines'.

Fig. 6.25 The spoil tip is the area clear of any vegetation at the top of New Venture mine on the col between Perkins Beach and Mytton Dingle with the latter in the centre of this July 2007 photograph. (Perkins Beach lies off the photograph to the left.) (Author)

The principal vein, which the mine shared with Burgam, was the sporadically mineralised Big Spar Vein. Lead was worked down to 270 feet below deep adit level at New Venture and barytes down to deep adit level. Perkins Beach was not worked below its lowest adit level. From the above it will be clear that the layout of workings will be complex, the steep sided valley making it easy for the mines to be worked to quite a depth from adits. New Venture mine was worked from the usual series of adits and shafts, probably half a dozen of each, deep level adit being immediately to the east of the top of the Perkins Beach workings. These consisted of about half a dozen shafts and adits as well as a number of small open workings along the veins. Some of these latter include what are known as Lewis' Explorations[44] and others will have been made by the minor miners referred to above.

Little is known of the equipment installed in the valley, although an engine base survives at New Venture and a 20 inch horizontal engine and two portable engines were included in the 1877 sale of Perkins Beach. Much of the ore left down the valley in carts or later lorries. *Circa* 1918 a branch of the Bog to Minsterley aerial ropeway was constructed from a junction at Beach Hill to serve the mine, terminating at Tabertail close to Perkins Beach mine's deep adit. Powered by a traction engine and reported to have had a 90 foot high pylon in the valley, it rose steeply over the flanks of Beach Hill and this gradient was presumably its undoing. It lasted a very short time; probably the full buckets slid back down the rope to the mine in anything but perfect condition. By

December 1919 it had no doubt gone, as Shropshire Mines announced their intention to build a light railway to connect the mine to the ropeway, presumably in the field behind Stiperstones School, but the proposal never saw the light of day. In the inter-war years a small mine on the steep south side of the valley used a horse called Jack and a car (sledge).

Production from the various mines was never great. No official figures of production or employment were ever returned for New Venture though partial returns were made from 1859 to 1865. No returns were made for Perkins Beach until 1866, and then no production figures until 1870. Returns for lead ore were then made for most years until 1897 with 1871 (200 tons) and 1893 (112 tons) being the only years to exceed 100 tons output, two of the years exceeded 50 tons and output for the rest was very small. Barytes production is first recorded in 1884 and most years thereafter until 1918. Production fluctuated greatly but showed a general increase from the mid 1890s with all but 1904 exceeding 100 tons, peaking in 1911 at 1,084 tons and nearly 3,000 tons during the First World War. Few post-1918 production figures are available though the mine was producing 40 or 50 tons a week in 1921.[45] Employment figures are available for the same years as production. Double figures were reached for a few years in the early to mid 1890s and again in 1906/7, 1911 and 1919/20.

The remains of the mining are very clear to see, especially at the top of the valley at New Venture's dressing floor. Shaft and adit sites, spoil runs and other signs occur throughout the whole valley. No buildings stand though several sets of foundations remain.

Potter's Pit

A small mine which never had a separate existence, it was often worked in conjunction with Pennerley and/or Bog but for a time with Ovenpipe. It got its name from the purity of its ore which was suitable for use in pottery glazes. It has been suggested[46] that the mine was worked in the 18th century, and it appears in records in the late 1850s as part of Horton, Stainsby and (Fred) Jones Stiperstones Mines. Development work was in progress in 1862 under Arthur Waters' management. The mine follows the history of Pennerley quite closely, passing via the Bog and Pennerley company into Heighway Jones' hands by 1868 (though in the official returns it says 'see Ovenpipe'), to Edward Corbett by 1870, Pennerley Mining Company Limited in 1871 and Watson, York and Shaw in 1881, this latter becoming Tankerville Mining Co. Ltd. Licences to search were granted to Arthur Waters jnr in 1890 and to William Edwards in 1899, in each case to little purpose. In 1902 its equipment was sold with that of Pennerley mine. Shropshire Mines Ltd. took a lease in 1921 but appear to have done no work. Like several other sites the tips were worked for road-stone and aggregate into the 1970s.

The mine was worked on Ben Arthur's Vein from a shaft called Old Shaft and Goodest Tuesday Level to a depth of about 630 feet below Boat Level, which drained the mine at about 330 feet below the surface. It shared with Pennerley the hot water vein and associated problems. Official production figures are probably meaningless — 5 tons of lead ore in 1857 and 95 tons in 1867, the rest no doubt being part of other mines' statistics. A report of 1869, however, suggests an output of 60 tons a month. No employment figures exist. The *Mining Journal* reported in 1862 that 'the new engine is working splendidly' but it does not state where the engine was, presumably at Pennerley mine a quarter of a mile away. Pennerley's Bland's Shaft engine is assumed to have pumped Potter's Pit until 1875 when the first of two engines was erected at Potter's Pit itself. Unfortunately little is know of them. The first one of about 1875 was set well away from the shaft and was replaced in about 1880 with an 8 inch and 14 inch compound semi-portable engine nearer the shaft. It cannot have worked for long; it was still there in 1890 but had gone before the 1902 sale. Otherwise the mine was probably ill equipped, everything being done to the ore at Pennerley, Bog or Tankerville. Like Pennerley the site is still very obvious but tells little. The sites of the shaft and adit are recognisable as is a foundation which may have been for an engine.

Ritton Castle

Like a number of other unsuccessful sites this was found by extrapolating known veins from other mines. The geology is not so simple, however. Some lead was found but never as much as various promoters hoped. Assuming that Bog mine had a drainage level before Boat Level was dug in about 1812, the most likely place for that level to have reached daylight was at Ritton Castle, possibly as early as 1760,[47] and no doubt lead veins were found when this was dug. It therefore became part of Bog mine to all intents and purposes. John Lawrence III worked here from about 1820[48] but it was described by Murchison as being abandoned in the early 19th century. It was being worked with Bog, by now in the hands of Walker, Cross and company, when Thomas Poole visited that mine in 1836 as he was taken by Mr. Webb (presumably the agent) to see Ritton Castle 'where they have made 2 levels to intersect the Lady Charlotte vein' which was discovered by accident by a man working in a quarry about 12 months earlier. A company, presumably Fuller and company, was formed in 1852 on what was by then called the West Stiperstones Sett. They were re-structured as the Ritton Castle Mining Co. Ltd. and managed to produce 10 tons of ore in 1856. They were wound up in 1860, following, as the mine frequently did, the fortunes of Bog mine but made worse by its own lack of ore.

In the years prior to this, an engine of unknown size was supplied by Harvey's of Hayle (another source attributes it to Bedford Foundry, it

Fig. 6.26 The remains at Ritton Castle in 1970. They are now much more ruinous and totally engulfed in boscage. (A.P. Wallace)

could be that they supplied it second-hand). To add to the confusion, the *Shrewsbury Chronicle* for 11 May 1860 advertised an auction of mine plant on 14 May to include 'much new machinery and parts of a 60 hp condensing engine by Nicholls and Williams of Tavistock'. Between 1860 and 1865 the mine was called the Wentnor mine and was owned by the Wentnor Mine Co. Ltd. many of whose shareholders had not learnt from their 1850s expense. Work had ceased by 1861. By the mid 1860s the mine looked west rather than its previous east, and was owned by Cooke and Company who worked Ladywell and Grit. Success still inevitably eluded the mine, which was not working in 1869 (Morton). Nevertheless Cookes retained the mine as the West Stiperstones Mining Co. Ltd. in 1870. At this stage there must have been some connection again with Bog mine as Arthur Waters undertook to divert water from that mine to Ritton Castle for the waterwheel (was this underground via the early drainage level?) to power the proposed New Engine Shaft. It seems to have finally ceased operation in 1875 or 1876. History now goes very quiet until 1919 when official closure is recorded in the HMSO Mines Department list of Mines and Quarries. Presumably it was acquired by Shropshire Mines Ltd. with Bog, but there seems to be no reason to suppose that any extraction had been carried out since the mid 1870s.

The mine lay on the western edge of the eastern outcrop of the Mytton Flags and presumably the small quantities of lead ore it produced came from the ends of Bog's veins. It was worked from 5 or more shafts, some opencast and two adits, one of which is reasonably suggested as being the pre Boat Level drainage to Bog mine.[49] The Engine Shaft was 35 fathoms deep in 1859 and was taken down to 53 fathoms within a few months after the installation of the new engine. As mentioned above, it had a pumping engine and a small dressing floor. No returns of either production or employment were made.

The site of some shafts and adits are recognisable and the foundations of the engine house and the stub of its chimney still stood completely engulfed in dense woods at the time of writing. The remains of an earth dam are across the stream and fallen masonry marks the small dressing floor where there was a waterwheel.

Rock

Some way south of Bog mine at the south end of the Stiperstones ridge this mine is unusual in that its story can be told from its very beginning. It was discovered in about 1820 by two men amusing themselves picking moss off rocks and finding galena. They told the proprietors of Bog and Pennerley mines of which one of the redoubtable John Lawrences was manager, and a whim shaft was sunk and good ore found. However, Lawrence could not develop it because of the amount of mining he had in hand elsewhere and miners were scarce. The same source states that in 1853 John Lawrence IV wished the new lessees well when a 'small company' resumed work, clearing out an adit. They decided to divide the mine into 6,000 shares (which could be applied for by application to 'MSM' at the Post Office in Minsterley) and run it on cost book principles, calling the mine South Bog.

In 1854 the adjoining landowners Henry Lyster (on whose land the mine was) and R.B. More agreed to drive a new adit (on Mr. More's land) below the earlier one that

Lawrence had driven in order to develop the mine; how or even if that related to the 'small company' mentioned above is not recorded. This 'small company' had become or had given way to the South Bog Mining & Smelting Co. Ltd. by 1857, and to Fuller and company (also of Bog and Ritton Castle mines) by 1859, although these latter did no work at Rock.[50] In 1864 a prospectus was issued for the Rock House Mine, Shropshire, Ltd. but the company was never registered. At various times the mine was known as South Bog (or Bog South) and Leeds Rock House. If the official returns are taken at face value, in 1867 Bog South mine was owned by Leeds Rock Mining company and Leeds Rock House mine was owned by Marriot and company. By 1868 only one mine, Leeds Rock House appears in the entries, owned by Leeds Rock Mining Company who made returns until 1880.[51] John Gledhill was the owner from 1887 until closure in October 1889. Having then reverted to using the name Rock Mine, returns were again made, anonymously, in 1907 and 1908 and in conjunction with Rhadley mine from 1910 to 13. The tips were reworked during the First World War and Rhadley Mines Ltd. took over in 1920 followed by Shropshire Mines Ltd., who worked the mine in conjunction with Bog until 1925. In the 1930s E. Murgatroyd of Keighley produced some ore apparently by cutting away the pillars. The mine was tried, again without success, in the Second World War.

It was worked from a number of shafts on top of the hill which connected with a series of adits mainly in the valley to the west, where there was a dressing floor. The deepest shaft was at least 220 feet deep The mine always used road transport as far as Bog mine but may have used the ropeway from there in its later years. Lead production was never large although Lawrence took 100 tons in the 1820s and considered that there was still a lot to come. 150 tons was raised in the 1850s and a similar amount from 1869 to 1874, 23 tons in 1879 and 3 in 1888. This mine and Rhadley produced 12 tons of ore in 1907/8. Barytes was noted in 1864 though there is no evidence of extraction until 1887, 700 or so tons being raised by 1889. Little has been raised since. Employment was likewise limited and the available statistics even more so — a maximum of 15 in 1888 with single figures in the previous and following years. Rhadley Mines employed three men in 1921. For several years, however, both production and employment figures were lumped with whichever other mine it was being worked with. Of the equipping of the mine little is known. Lawrence had a whim shaft so must have had a whim. There had been a pumping engine on site when Leeds Rock Mining Company ran the mine because its removal when they left was regretted by John Lawrence shortly afterwards. Several of the shafts are locatable around The Rock, and the adits, reservoir and dressing floor are visible in the valley bottom.

Roundhill

The site is a good contender to be one of the London Lead Company's 1720s Nether Heath mines but the evidence to establish that is lacking. The first documented mention of Roundhill mine is when Thomas Poole visited it in 1836 and was very impressed by the handsome Darby & Co. steam engine with an 18 inch cylinder which worked a large pump to clear a shaft of water. How old the mine was is not known. Little else is known until the days of official returns which confirm that the mine was functioning in 1846. No ownership is given until 1859, when it belonged to Dunsford and company (and was described as part of Stiperstones Mines until 1865) who owned it until 1863, when it passed into the hands of the Bog and Pennerley company who worked it, except briefly in 1867 when it closed. It opened again in conjunction with Ovenpipe in 1868, but possibly only for a short time as it is noted as being closed in 1869 in one survey (Merton), yet as being developed as North Tankerville mine in another (Liscombe). Part of the sett was leased to the proprietors of Tankerville mine for 21 years in 1870 and part, possibly the same part, was transferred from the North Tankerville Mining Company Limited to West Snailbeach Mine Company a few months later. A series of licences and leases were issued on the sett during the rest of the century as follows:[52]

10 August 1875 to Yelland, Boustred and Rogers, license for North Tankerville sett
29 October 1884 to Watson, Robson and Ridge, 21-year lease for Shelfield (part of Roundhill Sett, not to be confused with South Roman Gravels which was at Shelfield). They traded as the North Tankerville Mining Company until 1888
20 August 1885 to Yelland and Boustred, to search North Tankerville sett
24 July 1889 to Morris-Ridge to search North Tankerville Sett
3 September 1892 two-year extension to the above
19 October 1894 to Dawson, Pybus and Miss Richmond, 21-year lease for North Tankerville (and Hope Valley) Sett,
7 July 1898 surrender of the above lease, although official returns list Dawson as owner until 1901 and the mine called New West Snailbeach
14 September 1895 licence to Morris-Ridge to search Round Hill (and Tankerville) Sett
8 July 1898 to William Edwards licence to search North Tankerville (and Hope Valley) sett
17 June 1899 variation of the above

Fig. 6.27 Roundhill mine in the early years of the 20th century, possibly at the time of the Earl of Tankerville's re-opening in 1906. (coll. K. Lock)

In between all the above (in)activity the Round Hill Syndicate Ltd. was floated (1890) and Shropshire United Mines Co. Ltd. held part of the mine from 1891-93 as Roundhill. The part held by Samuel Morris-Ridge from 1889-93 traded as New West Snailbeach Mine. The landlord, the Earl of Tankerville, took the mine in hand in 1905 and reopened it at the beginning of the following year, as much to create work as to make a profit. It was not a success, closing again in 1908.

Shropshire Lead Mines Ltd. added it to their portfolio in 1910 but had not worked it by 1913. The tips were being worked in the First World War but the mine was idle in 1921. By 1923 it had passed, almost inevitably, into the hands of Shropshire Mines Ltd., who worked it above water level for barytes and calcite until 1925, when it closed. The tip was reworked for barytes and calcite in the 1940s.

The earliest development may have been on top of the hill where there were small pits but the 1836 engine was lower down at the main shaft, said to be 390 feet deep. Whether this is the same engine as was described in 1870 in the *Mining Journal* of 9 April as a rotary engine which pumped, wound and worked the crusher is open to doubt. There were several adits including a deep adit for drainage. The only other known engine was erected by the Earl of Tankerville *c.*1905, a tourist guide[53] describing it as a powerful new engine although local information suggests that it was built at Perran Foundry in Cornwall in 1874. Information on other equipment is limited; in 1915 there were two picking grates for washing and selecting the spars and a hand jig for dealing with the smaller stuff.

Lead, silver, calcite and barytes were produced. Figures for lead ore run from 1846 when 11 tons was raised, between 1854 and 1863 the average was about 350 tons per annum with a peak of 490 in 1858. From then on production is recorded in only ten years, just reaching double figures once, supporting the frequently expressed view that the mine was worked out by 1860. Silver was recorded only in 1854, at 100 ounces, though some was produced in 1873 but included in West Tankerville's statistics (see Batholes entry). Barytes was first recorded in 1884 and production occurred in 1897 and again in 1906/7. In 1891 the split in the sett is reflected in the returns with Shropshire United's 10 men producing 13 tons from Roundhill and Morris-Ridge's two men 41 tons from New West Snailbeach. Quantities vary greatly from 12 to 400 tons per annum. Calcite was worked principally from the tips and no production figures are known. In most years single figures of men were employed, the exceptions being 1891 (as above) 1894/5 and 1906/7 with about 20 in each case. The site of the main shaft is occupied by a bungalow and plant yard; there is little to see.

Tankerville

Until 1869 this was known as Ovenpipe mine, on account of the shape of the ore-body. It briefly became a prodigy mine, as Tankerville, producing vast amounts of lead ore for just a few years, at one stage providing 40 tons of ore per cubic fathom as they sunk Watson's Shaft through almost pure galena. This main lode was claimed in its day to be, and may well have been, the richest in the world.

The veins were possibly discovered but not developed during the digging of Boat Level but the mine gets no mention until the 1830s when it was part of Walker, Cross and company's holding with Bog, though they did not develop it. Any ore produced was wound from a small shaft, presumably Ovenpipe Shaft, by a horse gin. Like the rest of Walker Cross' mines it will have been sold about 1844 following the company's failure.

In 1851 it formed part of Horton, Stainsby and (Fred) Jones' Stiperstones Mines. By the middle of the next decade both Arthur Waters and Heighway Jones were involved, effectively developing the mine for the first time and rich finds were being made. In March 1862 Arthur Waters reported that in the last three years the mine had sold £16,000 of ore (probably about 800 tons) without sinking Engine Shaft (now known as Ovenpipe Shaft) one inch. They were then starting to sink it, 'having a rich vein to go down upon'. During the 1860s it was worked with Bog, Perkins Beach and Pennerley.

Tankerville first appears as the mine's name in 1869, worked by the West Tankerville Mining company, and included the Batholes sett to the west. In 1870 additional capital was required for a new shaft (see below) which was beyond the means of Heighway Jones, and a new company, the Tankerville Mining Co. Ltd., was floated by Messrs. Murchison, Geach, Watson, Grundry and Mitchell with a capital of £72,000. They worked the mine extremely successfully until 1875 when, unable to raise more capital from the existing shareholders, they were liquidated and re-floated as the Tankerville Mining Co. Ltd. In 1879 New Shaft was sunk, presumably in the hope, forlorn as it happened, of opening up new veins. In the event the shaft only went down to the adit which connected with Boat Level. In 1881 a new 21-year lease was obtained and the company, further restructured formed the Tankerville Great Consols Co. Ltd.

Fig. 6.28 Tankerville Mining Company Limited, share certificate of 1873

134

This company concentrated its efforts at its Pennerley mine and lost much money de-watering it to find no ore. By this time the rich lode at Tankerville was not quite so rich and the price of lead was falling — terminally as it was to transpire. The mine closed on 2 May 1884 and the company went into liquidation on the 15th. The Earl of Tankerville took the mine 'in hand' in 1889 and in July 1890 granted (with Major Lloyd, his co-landlord) a licence to search to Jeffrey Poole, John Job and others for 12 months, or longer by agreement. The mine was taken on by Shropshire United Mines Limited from 1891-93. Attempts to restart it were made by Morris-Ridge in 1895 and Captain Oldfield in 1898 but to no avail. In 1902 the mine plant was sold at auction along with that of Pennerley. Shropshire Lead Mines Ltd., followed by Shropshire Mines Ltd., tried again and mined some barytes between 1910 and 1923. Calcite was worked from the tips at least in 1924 and 1930 and no doubt for much of the inter-war period. During the Second World War stone from the tips, as at several local mines, was used in runways at various airfields, in Tankerville's case at RAF Tern Hill.

Lead, silver, zinc, calcite, witherite and barytes were all produced. Prior to 1860 returns of production from this mine were included with Stiperstones totals. No production is recorded from then until 1865, though 800 tons is assumed for 1859-63 (see above). 1,250 tons of lead ore, 800 tons of barytes and 36 tons of zinc ore were produced as Ovenpipe mine. Production figures for Tankerville start with 685 tons of lead ore in 1869 and from then until 1879 no year is significantly below 1,000 tons and the best years, 1871 and 1872, are nearly 2,000 tons. The 1872 figure represents over a quarter of Shropshire's and 2.6% of national production. The figure fell steadily from 1880 until at closure in 1884, 100 tons was dug. Single figure tons of lead ore were dug in the odd year after this until 1921. From 1872 to 1883 about 23,000 ounces of silver was produced, peaking in 1875 at 3,948. Zinc ore production was neglected until the early 1880s with a couple of hundred tons dug before closure in 1884. A further 29 tons was won by Shropshire United in the 1890s and odd amounts were dug up until 1921. Barytes production was likewise neglected, none being recorded until 1891 with 380 tons by 1893. Witherite was certainly produced between 1865 and 1868 (10 tons), probably in 1862 when one of the Stiperstones company's mines was noted as having done so, and possibly in other years at around the same time. No production figures were recorded for calcite.

Employment figures are not available until 1877 when 154 worked in the mine, some two-thirds underground. Numbers peaked at 171 in 1879 and fell steadily to 98 at closure. Shropshire United returned a figure of 33 for 1891. The final figures are from the Shropshire Mines period, 8 in 1922 and no less than 26 in 1923.

For the entire life of the mine the men had to use ladders for access though no doubt some kibble riding took place. Ovenpipe mine was worked from a main shaft, Ovenpipe Shaft, which went down to 74 fathoms below Boat Level and possibly from Lewis Shaft which was almost at the junction of Ovenpipe Level and Boat Level. At the 42 fathom level a cross cut found a promising vein. From 1869 an inclined, wholly underground shaft was begun following this new vein diagonally down to the 92 fathom level, but all outgoing ore had to be worked up it, across the cross cut and out via Ovenpipe Shaft. This procedure was both expensive and restricting, the maximum which could be got to the surface being 60 tons a month compared to the 300 tons a month said to be available. The capital raised by the floating of the Tankerville company was used in part to sink a new shaft from the surface to intersect the wholly underground one. Watson's Shaft, was begun in 1871 and was complete and in use by August 1873, ultimately becoming the deepest single shaft in the minefield at over 1,600 feet, nearly 600 of them below sea level.

The veins or lodes here were different from other mines in the county; it is probably best to think of them as like fingers, and their nature meant the mine did not spread far horizontally. It was a very well equipped mine which was expensively re-equipped in 1882, only two years before it closed. The Stiperstones company had a 16 h.p., 16 inch beam engine to pump and wind Ovenpipe Shaft and to power a crusher. The *Mining Journal* for 5 March 1870 carried a report from a visitor to Ovenpipe that the engine raised ore from 6am to 2pm, ran the crusher from 2pm to 5pm and pumped the mine from 5pm to 6am. He also reported that there were workings at 74, 84 and 92 fathoms and that adit level (Boat Level) was at 27 fathoms. The ore raised went to roller crushers which then dropped it onto a rotating screen. Lumps too large for the screen were returned to the rollers, whilst the material which passed through the screen went into a pit containing four jigging machines which settled out the ore from the lighter spoil. It was washed in flat buddles then treated in a finer jig followed by a further buddle, by which time it was ready to leave for smelting.

To help sink the 1869 underground shaft a high pressure Fowler engine was installed on the 74 fathom level with a 1,100 foot high wrought iron flue up Ovenpipe Shaft;

Fig. 6.29 Tankerville mine in the 1870s prior to the construction of Watson's Shaft engine house and chimney. (coll. K. Lock)

this engine had gone by 1874. In 1871 three further engines of 6, 25 and 60 h.p. were acquired, the smaller ones for surface machinery and the larger one probably replacing the 16 h.p. engine at Ovenpipe Shaft. The next engine known was a 32 inch installed on Watson's Shaft in 1873, which pumped and wound that shaft and was known as the 'Big Engine'. It is assumed that this was a horizontal engine, certainly the surviving chimney was built for this engine's boiler. The change in the angle of the shaft to follow the vein below the 52 fathom level caused endless expensive problems. Whilst it had enabled the ore produced during its digging to pay for the shaft it left high friction problems for both pumping and winding. The pump rods and pipes had to change direction and in the case of the rods this involved a complex series of wooden brackets which required constant maintenance and regular replacement. The ore was wound up in kibbles which had to be dragged along deal boards in the angled portion of the shaft, again with serious mainte-nance consequences to say nothing of lost production whilst that maintenance took place; replacement timbers cost £200 a month. Towards the end of the mine's life a machine kibble was installed. This seems to have simplified loading and unloading and no doubt speeded winding, but to what extent it resolved the change of angle issue is not recorded. One positive step which Arthur Waters was able to make was the replacement of the winding chain with wire rope. At Tankerville the saving from the change were dramatic — a halving of the fuel used by the winder due to the lesser weight of the new wire rope. Coal for the boilers came as return loads from the Pontesbury coalfield until the coming of the main line railway when better quality coal came from outside the district. Constant improvements were made to the ore dressing and preparation equipment. This could not however quite make up for one significant problem — water.

The Big Engine proved insufficient to de-water the mine whilst at the surface in dry weather there was insufficient water to supply the dressing machinery. This was to

Fig. 6.30 Tankerville mine from the flank of Round Hill, probably in the mid 1950s with Watson's Shaft engine house and chimney prominent to the right and Ovenpipe's chimney in the centre, now just a stump. (Shropshire Archives)

*Fig. 6.31 Tankerville mine showing the restored ore bins
and Watson's Shaft engine house. (Kelvin Lake, I A Recordings)*

an extent alleviated in 1874 by pumping water back up from Boat Level. Complaints were also made that continuous rain stopped surface work. Too much and too little water were not the only water problems to afflict the mine, for freezing weather would also stop the dressing, freezing the ore in bins and waggons. Some problems were solved by using hot water from the engine's condensers. Water for the dressing floor and boilers was stored in two reservoirs, the upper one by New Shaft and the lower one above the dressing floor. By 1875 the inadequacies of the 32 inch engine were such that, following the restructuring of the company a larger 40 inch Cornish engine by Harvey's of Hayle was installed in a new engine house in 1876 and had cleared the mine of water by the end of the year. The 32 inch was retained for winding and was removed sometime in the 1890s, but the 40 inch survived to be sold in the 1902 sale. By that date little remained. Of the 11 lots, apart from the engine there were two boilers, about 162 feet of 9 inch cast iron pump trees in the shaft above water, a further 1,450 feet of various sizes below, and various mine sundries.

Apart from anything which may have used Boat Level, transport was by road. The existence and reputation of the mine made it a target for the Snailbeach District Railway, but the Tankerville company did not subscribe and insufficient capital was forthcoming for the construction on the railway beyond Crowsnest. The ore during the Walker, Cross period would have gone to John Lawrence's former smelter at Pontesbury. During the Stiperstones' company period it would have gone to their smelter at Pontesford. After the opening of the branch railway to Minsterley in 1861 much of the ore and ultimately all of the ore went further afield.

The remains are second only to Snailbeach in size and, given the smaller scale and duration of the mine, greater in terms of the proportion surviving. It is, like Snailbeach

138

Fig. 6.32 Aerial view of Tankerville mine showing the Watson's Shaft engine house and chimney on the left before restoration. Lower centre is the truncated hipped roof of the former counting house, whilst some of the other buildings are converted mine buildings. Top right are the much churned up tips

mine preserved in the care of the Shropshire Mines Trust. Most visible is the 1876 engine house for Watson's Shaft with its 15 metre-tall octagonal chimney standing on a plinth that ranges from 3 to 4.5 metres high across the slope of the hill. These stand at the top of the grilled shaft which is open for a short distance down. Between the house and the shaft is the Balance Bob tunnel. The bob was a counterweight to the weight of the pump rods in the shaft, initially deigned for use with the 32 inch engine but may have been altered to serve the same purpose for its 40 inch successor. To the side, at the ground floor of the engine house are a row of six stone built ore hoppers. These are the only surviving ones in the county[54] and amongst the few anywhere in the country. At the level of the basement floor of the engine house is the crushing floor onto which the ore bins discharged. A level below this, to enable gravity to assist the process, is the dressing floor now partly under farm buildings. The centre of the site is now a farm which makes it difficult to envisage how the entire site looked. A farm building also blocks access to the remains of Ovenpipe engine house and chimney and to its overgrown shaft head. The upper and lower reservoir sites are visible — the upper is silted up, its dam carrying a green lane, whilst the lower one is rectangular and stone lined and is being prepared for refilling at the time of writing. The Mine Office with a date plaque for 1871[55] stands, much altered as a dwelling, as do various small workshops and part of a terrace of what might have been miners' cottages, some of these are still occupied though much altered.

Ovenpipe Shaft is completely blocked, as is Lewis Shaft, which is in a garden on the east of the road. New Shaft, south of the upper reservoir, is partly open and is flooded; there is a concrete engine base close to it. Foundations of other buildings, including the boiler houses and the 'Big Engine' winding house (which still stood in 1963), no doubt survive below present ground levels as hopefully do machine bases and buddle bases on the dressing floor. Some of the tips remain away from the main site though these are much reduced since the war. Access to the site is not at present regular though the Mines Trust do open it on occasions.

Vessons

Generally considered to be the eastern part of Snailbeach mine, a Vessons Mine company existed and spent money for a few months in 1853. Their cost book from May to October that year survives. It runs to two pages, with the rest of the book being used to make tithe notes. Fred Jones ran the concern which spent £124 during the period and left liabilities of £17, the balance presumably coming from the pockets of the adventurers as no sales are recorded.[56] Clearly the Snailbeach management were convinced of the potential of the mine as they leased the land before the end of the decade.

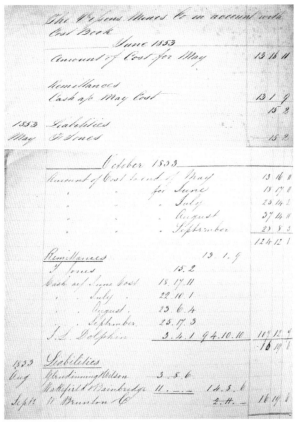

Fig. 6.33 Apparently the entire history of Vessons Mine company is in this page of their account book. (SA 437/17)

140

7   Mines of Shelve and the Hope Valley

These mines are in the shorter of the two outcrops of the lead-bearing Mytton Flags (see Fig. 6.1). Centred more or less on the village of Shelve, it is about 3 miles long and contained two of the county's biggest mine setts — Grit and Gravels — as well as an instructive variety of lesser and optimistic mines. Although there is no firm evidence, Roman Gravels could well have been worked in prehistoric times. Shelve merits a cross reference in Domesday[1] possibly because of the importance of its mines. Certainly a century later and for a century thereafter its mines were providing lead for various of the king's works and for religious buildings including, as tithes, Shrewsbury Abbey (see p.16).

As elsewhere, names give rise to problems. East Roman Gravels was at different times known as Wood, Hope Valley, Upper Batholes, West Tankerville and Minsterley, and on occasion was part of larger concerns some of which traded with one of these names. Shelvefield also gives rise to problems as it was used for different mines at different times both for Roman Gravels and East Roman Gravels, and seems sometimes to have been rendered Shelfield, though that name was used at least for both South Roman Gravels and part of Roundhill Sett. Lead and zinc were the main products of this area, with a little silver and some calcite. Barytes was produced in small quantities for that mineral and was not particularly significant.

Batholes

This is the name both of a sett and of a mine at the north end of that sett, whilst at the southern end of the sett was the often otherwise named East Roman Gravels.[2] The land belonged to the Earls of Tankerville and leases were granted from at least 1785, and possibly before, to John Lawrence (II or possibly III). He is said to have moved his operations from Grit (which ties up with the sale of a pumping engine there), Bog and Pennerley mines to take advantage of the drainage possibilities of adits, not so readily available on those other sites. By 1790 Lawrence was digging Wood Level to drain some of the shafts in Batholes sett (and others), though not Batholes mine itself.

The mine remained in the Lawrence empire until the early 1830s, when, despite his bankruptcy, John Lawrence III was still investing, 'being obliged to fulfil the covenants of his lead mining lease by erecting a fire engine and doing other heavy charges ... or the lease would have been forfeited'. The 'fire engine' was started on 2 June 1831 and he still held the mine in October when he tried to sell it and others to Edmund Buckley for an undisclosed sum with a deposit of £500.[3] The Leigh Level (which was the indirect cause of Lawrence's bankruptcy) set out in 1825 to drain several mines in the area with Batholes being its first objective, but it did not even reach it before the money ran out. The mine was finally drained by this level in about 1920, courtesy of Shropshire Mines Ltd., by which time it was much too late.

The mine's history for the few years after Lawrence's bankruptcy is unknown. It was described by Murchison in 1839 as 'abandoned for some time'[4] but when official returns began in 1847 it was being worked with White Grit, although no owners are given for either. Mr. Ward was paying royalties to Mr. More for Grit from 1844 to 1852, an arrangement that continued until 1850. The production figures for 1851 are separate for each mine, but no owner is named, However, Bagshaw's *Directory* for the year gives Horton, Johnson, Stainsby and Jones as the proprietors, working the mine with their Stiperstones Mines at Perkins Beach and trading as the Stiperstones company. The mine was sold to the Hope Valley Mining company for £4,000 in 1853. During the 1860s the mine was under a succession of owners: Fred Jones & company from 1859-61, Batholes company in 1862-3, whilst in 1864-5 and 1868 it was owned by Heighway Jones and in between it is recorded as part of Ovenpipe mine. 1870 saw a lease granted to four partners, including Peter Watson, under which the sett including Batholes mine was to be called West Tankerville and run with Tankerville mine.

In 1871 Batholes mine itself was sold by the company to the Old Batholes Mining Co. Ltd. for £8,000, which company failed to raise sufficient capital and was bankrupt by 1874. By 1877 the mine was independent again, this time called Old Batholes and run by the Batholes Mining Company. In 1880 it was leased to East Roman Gravels and again became part of the West Tankerville Company's mines, but they were in liquidation the following year. This was the effective end of Batholes mine. 'Take notes' were issued for some part of the Hope Valley, (excluding East Roman Gravels) in the 1880s, possibly for this mine.

Two veins were worked, to the north the Batholes vein and to the south Gate Level vein, most of the productive work being from the former. A series of shafts were sunk, several of which connected to adits at two levels. The vein was worked down to a depth of 192 feet from Gin Ring Shaft to the drainage adit and a further 174 feet below that. Little is known of the workings on Gate Level, although the shaft is said to have been 132 feet deep. There are other shafts and trials along the valley and on the crest of the ridge.

Winding was clearly done at some time at Gin Ring although the location of Lawrence's engine is not known. Little is known of the equipment. The pumping engine of 1831 was built using parts supplied by Ruabon Foundry, whilst parts of the pump were supplied by Burrs of Shrewsbury. It cannot have worked for long and no doubt was moved elsewhere quite quickly. Meaningful production figures are impossible to estimate, but for years when the mine was on its own, it never reached 65 tons of ore in any year with the exception of 1851, and even the 1851 figure is possibly the total for the whole of the Stiperstones Company's production rather than just Batholes. Employment figures are equally elusive; 1877 with two men underground is the only figure in the records.

The ore from the mines went out either by road or for a brief period by tramway (which also served Nick Knolls mine) to East Roman Gravels mine for onward transmission.

There are few surface remains, although the sites of several adits and shafts, including Milne Shaft of the Leigh Level, are visible. The line of the tramway is also discernible.

Benree

If, without the benefit of modern geological knowledge, one were to look at the country between Pennerley and Grit mines, Benree would seem a very good place to dig a mine because it is where good lead veins to the east and to the west appear to converge. Several places in the ore-field had this apparent benefit and were tried accordingly. It is now known that the Ritton Castle syncline is such that in the distance (less than a mile) between the mines at Shelve and those at the Stiperstones the lead bearing Mytton Flags are deeply buried. The 1858 Gravels Mining Company Ltd. prospectus mentions this location, although it does not give any detail other than to stress its proximity to Pennerley and Bog mines and, interestingly, to suggest that when a mine shaft there was dug it could be drained by Boat Level. Following the prospectus in 1859 the landlord, the Reverend T.F. More, granted a lease to John Stanton for 31 years for various setts including Benree. This was assigned by Stanton and Richard Palin to the Roman Gravels Lead Mining Company the following year, although according to the official returns the mine was owned by Richard Palin and company. By March 1867 the Benree part of the lease was surrendered. An 1869 publication (Morton) implies that there was a mine here by informing its readers that it was not working. The lie of the land requires that the mine was worked by a shaft or shafts rather than adits, but of these nothing is known — not even whether they existed. No production or employment figures were made on the official returns.

East Roman Gravels

A mine that often carries other names, it forms the southern part of the Batholes sett and was sometimes worked with that mine. It was probably worked by the Lawrences before its first documentary mention in the 1790s when Wood Level was dug to intersect and drain it down to the 20 fathom level at Wood Shaft. After John Lawrence IV's bankruptcy he managed to hold on to this mine until 1831 when he was trying to sell the remaining years of the lease. At this stage, as again at the end of the century, the sett seems to have been run as two ventures as Lawrence refers in correspondence in October 1831 to leases from the Earl of Tankerville to Shelvefield, Wood (East Roman Gravels) and Batholes (as well as all other mines granted by the Earl elsewhere), all of which were parts of the same sett.

No doubt the mine continued to function but no further evidence has emerged until 1847 when the Batholes Company took it over. They sold Batholes mine itself (see above) in 1853 and went into liquidation two years later. From then until 1866 one of the former partners, Fred Jones, ran the mine in a small way. In 1869 it was not working but was due to reopen under a new company. This duly happened in 1870 when a lease was assigned from individual investors, including Peter Watson, to the West Tankerville Mining Co. Ltd. With much capital and Arthur Waters as captain, the mine was refurbished, drained, and extended to exploit Boundary Vein, with three shafts being sunk, but the rich ground was not found. By 1879 the East Roman Gravels Lead Mining Co. Ltd. had been floated. To raise capital the company followed its predecessor's precedent and sold the Batholes

Fig. 7.1 A postcard from before the First World War of Wood Mine (East Roman Gravels)

Fig. 7.2 A photo taken in April 2004 at the same site as Fig. 7.1 above, but from a different angle. The chimney stump in the background was probably from the ore dressing plant. (Author)

part of the sett. In addition they issued 15% preference shares whose very high return attracted investors, but did not help the ordinary shareholders or the company, which went into liquidation in 1882, only to be resurrected with a further £17,000 capital. Even Arthur Waters could not make the mine pay, and the new company only lasted until 1883 when it was in turn liquidated.

The rest of the 1880s saw further openings and liquidations and little work seems to have been done, although a take note was granted to Parry and Haynes in February 1885. In 1892 the Earl of Tankerville granted a 21-year lease to a new East Roman Gravels Company Ltd., which lease was varied in 1894 and 1896. The following year the mine was acquired by its neighbours at Roman Gravels with which it formed the Hope Valley Mining Co. Ltd., who were registered by the Board of Trade in 1894. Official returns indicate that the sett was split into two at about this time, with Hope Valley Mine owned by William Dawson from 1895 to 1901 (after which no more is heard), and the Hope Valley Mining Company running East Roman Gravels mines. But Skinners *Yearbook* of 1896 states that Dawson's Hope Valley Mining Co. Ltd. acquired East Roman Gravels, formerly owned by Roman Gravels Company.

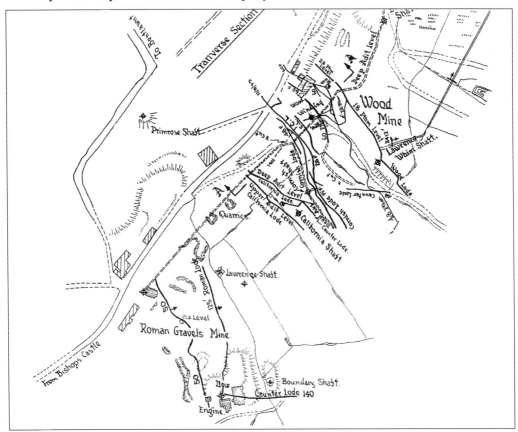

Fig. 7.3 Plan by P. Blight drawn c.1920 of East Roman Gravels mine showing Primrose Shaft at what had been the location of Roman Boundary mine. (SA 328/46-48)

By 1898 the mine was owned by Minsterley Mines Ltd. and it saw a short period of activity with a maximum of 110 men in 1898. By 1900 underground working had finished and only the tips were being worked. It closed in April 1901. Concurrently the Tankerville estate in 1894 granted a lease for at least part of the site to the company running North Tankerville (see Roundhill Mine) and Hope Valley Mines. 1898 saw the assignment of that lease to three new partners in January and its surrender in July, followed a day later by the issue of a tack note to permit a search for minerals to William Edwards. These leases presumably related to part of the sett which was standing, as well as Roundhill. A further tack note was issued to Samuel Atherton in 1905. T. Powell is recorded as employing eight men the following year, although no production figures are given.

The next optimist was Elijah Parry who seems to have employed a small number of men (usually four) between 1907 and 13 and to have produced 6 tons of lead ore and 19 tons of zinc ore. In 1915 it is recorded as the Hope Valley mine and by 1916 as belonging to Shropshire Mines Ltd. when they called it East Roman Gravels and employed three men. The following year, now called Wood mine, it employed 37 men — all above ground. A year later underground working began again, and numbers peaked in 1919 with 46 employed underground and 53 above. At the end of that year the employees were informed in a newsletter by Josslyn Ramsden (son of the managing director) that 'We are now going to connect this mine by telephone with Minsterley, which I hope may be of general benefit in cases of illness in the district. An improved changing room is being erected with a proper ambulance room.'

Fig. 7.4 A view of East Roman Gravels mine in September 1948. (P. Morris)

Numbers fell in 1920 and dwindled to two or less above ground in 1921-24. Unlike its southerly neighbours, no further resurrection seems to have occurred, though activity did not completely cease at the site. When parts of the Tankerville Shropshire estate was sold in the early 1920s, mineral rights in the area were reserved when the surface was sold and leases were issued for the working some of the tips, including East Roman Gravels, for road-stone, whilst Jackfield Mines Ltd. opened up a shaft but to no known effect.[5] When these rights were sold in 1953 various leases were confirmed including one at East Roman Gravels to Messrs. F.S.H. Tisdall Ltd., at a rent of £100 p.a. and 1s. 3d. a ton or 5% of the value of the mineral. This lease ran for 21 years from 1 January 1953.

Basically a lead mine, East Roman Gravels was one of the Shropshire mines which produced a limited amount of silver, some 1,500 ounces between 1881 and 1883; although at 2.3 ounces of silver per ton of lead ore (and the best in Shropshire at that period) it was probably uneconomic to extract. Zinc ore was mined, as was a significant quantity of calcite and some barytes. Known production is about 1,500 tons of lead ore in the early 1880s and 500 in the late 1890s with single figure outputs annually between. The surviving figures from 1854 to 1865 as Hope Valley vary wildly and some probably include some of the company's other mines. Zinc was a bit more regular with between 30 and 300 tons of ore most years from 1863 to 1893 and single figures from 1909 to 1913, a total of some 4,000 tons. Barytes production figures are not available other than 600 tons in 1865 recorded from Hope Valley mine, which may have been or have included this mine. Neither are there any records of outputs from the Shropshire Mines period, when barytes and calcite as well, no doubt, as fortuitous quantities of lead and zinc ores were mined.

Fig. 7.5 A post-war view across the valley to East Roman Gravels mine, the ore dressing plant chimney being visible. (coll. K. Lock)

Employment figures reflect the lead output, with a maximum of 89 in 1882 and 111 in 1898. What figures exist for the 20th century show single figures except for the Shropshire Mines activity in 1918-20, rising from and falling back to about 60 with a peak of over 100 in 1919.

Much mining, especially in the earlier days, was done from adits, the gorge of the Hope Valley making this easy. Three main veins were worked, each running more or less north-west to south-east: Wood, Cornish and California, with some late workings on Boundary vein. This last was near the boundary between the Tankerville estate's East Roman Gravels mine and the More estate's Roman Gravels mine, and is not to be confused with Roman Boundary mine across the valley although that mine's shaft appears as Primrose Shaft on a plan of East Roman Gravels mine *c*.1920 (Fig. 7.3). No connection is shown or described between Primrose Shaft and the rest of the mine. The head gear of this shaft appears in the background of Figure 7.16. Each vein had one or more shafts on it and the site contained at least four shafts to Wood Level. Generally the mine was worked down to the 60 fathom level below adit level, which was 120 feet below ground level at Wood Shaft.

Not a lot is known of the plant at this mine. Lawrence was fitting up a 24 inch rotary engine on the sett by 1831 and there was a 20 inch engine.[6] Engines were built at Wood Shaft (sometimes Wood Winding Shaft) *c*.1850, and at California Shaft, this latter being mid way between two shafts each of which it pumped using flat rods running in what amounted to a ditch. There is photographic evidence of a substantial ore dressing plant between Wood Shaft and the road. A tramway connected the mine with Batholes and Nick Knolls mines to the north, whose ore presumably came here for treatment. The tramway, or a second one, went south towards Roman Gravels but it may not have crossed onto that mine's land and only have served its own mine. As at many mines horse whims (gins) were used, the memory of one being enshrined in the name Lawrence Whim Shaft — unfortunately no-one knows which of two possible shafts it was. Some ore dressing was done on the west side of the main road where no doubt waterwheels powered by the Hope Brook existed.

The remains at the road end of the sett are very visible if not very telling. The tips to the west of the road have been grassed over, but those to the east remain as does the stub of the dressing plant chimney. The site of Wood Shaft is now in a garden. At the top of the site several shaft sites can be made out. The ruins of California Engine house are visible as is the line of 'ditch' for the flat rods to pump its two shafts.

Grit

As with other names Grit (or Gritt) is both the name of a sett and, with various prefixes the name of individual mines, notably **East Grit** and **White Grit**. Ladywell, dealt with elsewhere, was also originally part of this sett. The names have been used indiscriminately in the past and it is often impossible to know what part of the sett a reference is to. In addition to the names already mentioned West Grit, White Grit East and Foxholes are also to be found.

It is at least probable that the Romans worked this for lead, but firm evidence is lacking. Medieval mining took place in the locality in the 12th and 13th centuries but whether at Grit or at (Roman) Gravels is not known. It is more than probable that mining on an 'as necessary' basis carried on through the years until the late 16th or early 17th century when the Lawrence family first made their appearance in the history of mining in the locality. Papers from this period survived at least until 1898 but their whereabouts are not now known, and nor is it certain precisely which mines(s) they dealt with.[7]

The Mores of Linley Hall, who were the landowners throughout the modern history of the mines (and still are, though the surname is now Corfield), acquired the land in 1653 and soon after got miners from Derbyshire to search for lead. This they found by 1655 and mining (re)commenced, but quite how or if this related to the Lawrence activity is not clear. It is probable that a 21-year lease was granted to the Derbyshire men as a similar lease was granted in 1676. This lease included all 'manner of mines pits and veins of lead in More lands in Shelve' except any which occurred in buildings. The following year saw perhaps the most exciting piece of mining history in the area when on 4 April the mine was seized by 10 men armed with swords and guns who departed with four cart loads of ore and 1,000lbs. of lead. This was carried out under the orders of Lord Herbert of Chirbury, better known as a theologian and poet, on the basis that the mine was in the manor of Chirbury of which he was Lord and that therefore he had a right to any minerals. The first assertion was correct but the second was not. Mr. More, as a commoner, had great difficulty in getting a local JP to hear a case against a peer and in the end it was dealt with outside the area, but justice was done and Mr. More got his mine back in 1678. There is no evidence, however, that the ore worked by Herbert during his tenure was returned or compensation paid.[8] A further lease for mining in the parish was issued to another group of miners in 1692. History, or surviving documents now go quiet for a couple of generations.

By the 1760s the Lawrences were involved as part of the White Grit Mine company. In 1783 the partners purchased a pumping engine from Boulton and Watt in Birmingham which was probably located at the site now known as White Grit. The investment was clearly not a success as the engine was sold in 1785, the mine was described as being worked out, and Lawrence turned his attentions to other mines including Gravels and Batholes. The company, however, were still or again in business by 1792 when they bought eight lottery tickets. John Lawrence's memorandum book, which records this, does not relate if the partners won anything.

In 1801 a lease from the Mores was granted to John Lawrence, John Probert and five others. The lease contained various conditions, two of which were that trial was to be made with at least eight men at White Grit and that Wood Level was to reach White Grit mine in three months, i.e. by 25 October. The implication is that White Grit mine was not working in 1801, probably due to water problems. Wood Level ultimately reached Old Grit but never reached what is now known as White Grit. Even so, enough must have been done to enable the lease to run, as evidence survives that mining by the company on the site may have slowed down but did not stop. A chance piece of paper, used as scrap to do some calculations about an engine for Bog mine, lists the 'amount of [unspecified] goods sent from John Onions jnr to the White Grit,' from 1805 to 1811, totalling £809 0s. 9d.[9] A set of accounts from 1814 also survives, and from these it is clear that the White Grit Mine company were at least working Shelve Gravels (aka Gravels, later Roman Gravels). Under the lease of 1801 they had been obliged to drive Wood Level to their White Grit mine so it must be assumed that what is now known as Old Grit was at that date part of White Grit as the valuation of an old engine at the mine was included as part of the accounts prepared by Mr. Hazeldine,[10] who carried out a valuation of their property including sites in Pontesbury and Shrewsbury. Including the capital value of £4,083 and the outstanding sales of £800 the company were solvent as their debts were only £3,645 made up as follows: £800 of principal to Francis Lloyd, J. Probert, Ben Colley and Chas Astley, £114 interest (including nine years back interest to John Probert), £600 to Francis Lloyd which was three years' additional account for Hogstow Farm and Crowsnest Farm and mine, a half year's rent on the colliery at Pontesbury, various property taxes, £90 of sundry bills, £1,888 7s. 7d. to John Lawrence for various matters ('balance due on his account'), a small unspecified sum for property taxes, a small sum to John Brisco for land now given up at Pontesbury and £50 to take down the engine at Pontesbury 'in the event of its being removed'. This latter was either at the smelter or the colliery. No royalties and little rent seems to have been owing. The company were owed nearly £800 by customers.

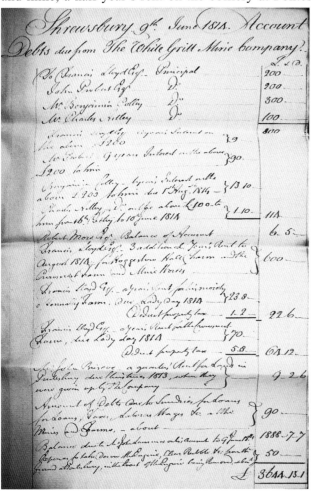

Fig. 7.6 *White Grit Mine Company account of 1814.*
(SA 552/18/8/8/5)

In the early 1820s there was a brief boom. The White Grit company held leases from Mr. More for Grit and Gravels and from the Earl of Tankerville for East Roman Gravels. As these leases became due for renewal both landlords looked into the state of the mines, bearing in mind the apparent failure of Wood Level to get to what is now known as White Grit, and the proposal for a deeper level to drain and explore the ore-field. The reports were not exactly critical but they did suggest that more could and should have been done, especially at Grit. The drainage level called the Leigh Level or Tunnel was promoted locally with capital coming, unusually, from the north-west of England, from the Leigh Tunnel Drainage company, which received leases from each landlord in 1825. As stated elsewhere John Lawrence fought the granting of these leases which his companies had previously held and though he won the case he was bankrupted. Leases for both mines were granted to Lewis and Phillips who were behind the Leigh company and subsequently to the Grit and Gravels company.

In addition to the mines in their title the company worked a large tract of land west of Grit up to the ridge of Stapeley Hill and land around Corndon, Calcot and Priest's Weston (see chapter 8). This company began as a partnership with 35 shareholders including, briefly at least, Mr. More, though he sold out just before the restructuring which occurred in 1829 when there were 64 shareholders. The costs of the Leigh Level lawsuits not only broke Lawrence but damaged the new company, though it managed to keep going until about 1835. A set of accounts of about 1839 list creditors including, significantly, nearly £9,000 to Beck's bank.[11]

In 1839 a new lease was issued to William Jones and four others including Edward Dicken. The royalty was a generous $^{1}/_{10}$th. By 1844 the mine was considered as being run by a Mr. Ward, who paid the royalties until at least 1852.[12] In that year he had also leased the one time White Grit smelthouse at Pontesford from Heighway Jones, a some-time partner in Grit and Gravels mines. The mine was being run with Batholes probably until 1851. The bulk of the 1850s are difficult to fathom — official returns were made for all years but, until 1859, did not name owners. Returns from 1847 to 1855 are made for White Grit. East Grit was worked by Readwin and company from 1850 to 1852.

From 1854 **White Grit East** appears as a separate mine and from 1855 to 1858 partial returns were made as were returns of ownership until 1867. Clearly, however vaguely the returns were completed, two different mines were functioning, White Grit East being a very small concern producing 10 tons of lead ore in 1854 and declaring nothing thereafter. In these returns the names Grit and White Grit have probably been used interchangeably.[13]

From 1859 details of ownership appear in official returns and a little more can be gleaned. At this date there were two mines — White Grit East owned by Richard Palin and Co. and Grit/White Grit owned by Dicken and Co., Dicken being the son-in-law of the Mr. Ward above. By the following year the two are in the hands of Dicken. Separate returns were made for both until 1867 though no production was recorded for White Grit East. In about 1862 the mine(s) was taken over by a major company, John Taylor and Company, who purchased the last three years of Dicken's lease and as the Grit & Stapeley Mines Co. Ltd. issued a prospectus in 1863 in which they refer to a 30-year lease for Grit and a 19-year lease for Stapeley, the sett to the west. Their activities in the county were very small but chapter 2 shows their scale elsewhere in the world as far afield as Mexico. They did not stay for long, however, and in 1865 the mine was advertised for sale as 'the present company has exhausted their insufficient capital'. This seems surprising given the scale of some of Taylor's other operations, but it did follow a few years after the death of John

Taylor senior. It seems that Taylors wished to move from Grit to develop Ladywell but could not negotiate a lease just for that mine so pulled out of the sett altogether.

The mines then passed into the hands of Cooke and Company who probably did not work them, for James Nancarrow described the mine (and Ladywell mine) in 1867 in a printed report for Joseph Cooke as being flooded. The South Salop Mining Company are listed as the owners of both Grit and Ladywell from 1868 having taken over the lease from Cooke and Co. Two reports on the county's mines in 1869 confirm that the mine was not being and had not recently been worked; indeed, it was never to be worked on any scale again. Although a few old men were noted picking over the tips in 1882, all significant action on the sett moved to Ladywell.

The Grit Mining Company tried again from 1897 to 1901 and after reopening the mine in January 1898 produced a small quantity of lead and zinc ores. During the First World War the Wotherton Barytes and Lead Mining Co. Ltd. are reported to have had plans to open up the mine,[14] and if they did not, their successors Shropshire Mines Ltd. certainly did, as they had two men digging a small amount of barytes from the tips in 1921. Not long after, E. Murgatroyd of Keighley used four men to get calcite from the tips. From 1933 to 1935 the Linley Estate had a handful of men, mainly working underground, producing barytes. They ceased in March 1935 and later in the year Murgatroyd tried again. The early 1940s saw a new shaft sunk on Foxhole vein and the tips being picked over for calcite. The More estate wrote to the government that year pointing out that several mines on their land including Grit could be reopened, but this was a forlorn hope and, in the case of Grit, would have been a costly failure.

Fig. 7.7 The remains of the circular powder house at White Grit. (Kelvin Lake, I A Recordings)

152

The geology of Grit is probably as complex as its history. It is on the Mytton Flags in which, crossing the sett, are significant lead veins which also contain smaller amounts of zinc ore, barytes, witherite and manganese, these latter being worked to a very limited extent, some being raised before 1869 (Morton). On a plan which was probably with the Nancarrow report of 1867 (see above) 17 veins are named, mainly running east-west but one or two, including the New Briton vein, running north-south. Two key places in the mine are not surprisingly where various of these intersect, the first being the junction of the Squilver and Rider veins at the White Grit engine house, and the second the junction of Foxhole, Rider, and New Briton veins at the Old Grit engine house.

It is unclear which is the earliest part of the mine, but is possibly the part of East Grit which lies over Engine Vein just south of Old Grit. Wood Level travelled along New Briton Vein as far as Old Grit. The development of what is now known as White Grit occurred in the early 1780s, the shaft being 10 yards deep in January 1783 when the partners ordered a 30 inch engine from Bolton and Watt with the intention of sinking the shaft to 60 yards. This phase was not successful and the engine was stopped in 1784 and sold to a mine at Wanlockhead in Scotland the following year. A further stage of development here in about 1840 may have been sparked by the construction of a turnpike from Minsterley to Bishops Castle, which not only improved transport, but probably reduced water problems by draining Hyssington Marsh. Excluding what was to become Ladywell mine there were at least 25 shafts on the sett, working usually taking place at a number of places simultaneously. The sett was frequently the recipient of large influxes of capital even if it did not always repay them, the *Mining Journal* reporting that £50,000 had been spent up till 1841. Steam pumping engines were erected at Old Grit, East Grit and White Grit, and ancillary buildings tended to surround them, principally at White Grit where there were an office, smithy and carpenter's shop in addition to a house and a cottage.

The mines were well equipped at various times but equipment came and went, and was also spread over a large area. Work took place mainly from shafts though several had day levels. The 25 shafts were concentrated around White Grit and East/Old Grit and on the Rider, Squilver, Foxhole and New Briton veins. Engines were erected at three shafts from 1783 onwards, although it is not clear which shafts had which engines. Old Grit engine drove two other shafts — Flat Rod and Angle Rod (or Footway), the latter being some 500 metres from its engine working via angle rods which must have been both inefficient and expensive to maintain. Several of the shafts were 60 fathoms deep with the deepest, New Engine Shaft at East Grit and White Grit Main Shaft, being 100 fathoms. Working were generally stoped between these levels, many from crosscuts between shafts.

At times the mine was a sizeable employer but few figures survive. The earliest record is the Grit and Gravels mine Bargain Book for Michaelmas 1827. At the time of that 'snapshot' 160 men and boys were on the books of the two mines and Lee (Leigh) Level. They were in 32 (bargain) companies who were generally paid either by the ton of ore dug (20s. to 100s. depending on the difficulty) or by the yard (15s. to £9) if driving headings or sinking shafts. A company would typically have a leader and perhaps five others though some were much larger, one even including 19 labourers. It is clear from the Bargain Book that men were moved from site to site and that jobs were stopped because things were not going well — 'This is now stopt owing to cutting a large feed of water' in one case. On these occasions some men were discharged and some sent to

Fig. 7.8 A view up a series of workings at Grit mine with White Grit engine house in the right foreground. Just visible half way up the hill and to the left of the engine house is the ruin of the powder house (see Fig. 7.7). (Kelvin Lake, I A Recordings)

Fig. 7.9 Aerial view of Old Grit with the engine house ruin and two filled shafts forming a triangle. (CPAT)

other companies. Of the 160, about 100 were at Grit, a dozen on the Leigh Level and the rest at Gravels.

In 1841, when consideration was being given to an alteration to the turnpike, a survey of population and employment was carried out. At that stage Grit and Gravels are said to have employed 130. By the time of the next available figures, the official returns for 1898 to 1901, Grit was employing between 22 and 38. Records for the 20th century show a maximum of four in 1935.

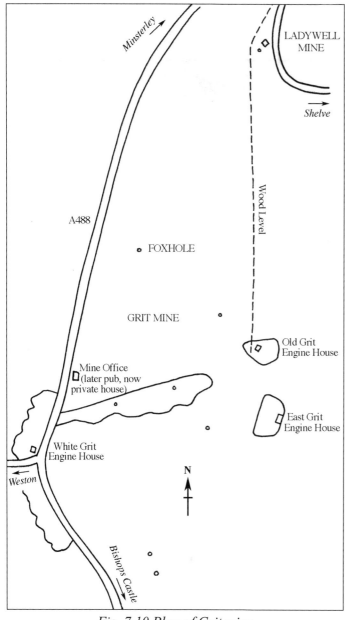

Fig. 7.10 Plan of Grit mine

Production figures are no easier to come by. Odd references occur. For instance, a memorandum book survives from the late 1820s which notes 'Ore weighed from 24th Oct to 31st Dec 1829, Gravels 65 tons 10cwt, Grit 181-8, total 246-18'. The two mines were producing between 300 and 700 tons a year between 1835 and 1845, and official figures show about 2,500 tons of ore in total between 1845 and 1858 with another 300 at the end of the century, plus 12 tons of zinc ore. Not only is this nothing like the whole story but the figures for most of the time include Roman Gravels as well. In the late 17th century, at the time of the seizure of the mine by Lord Herbert's men, smelting must have been taking place on site, and both ore and metal were removed. In the 1780s and '90s some of the company's ore went to Minera for smelting.[15] After the late 1780s ore would have gone to Lawrence's smelter at Malehurst. At some date

Fig. 7.11 Aerial view of East Grit with the engine house ruin upper centre. It is possible that some of the farm building have mining origins. (CPAT)

Fig. 7.12 East Grit engine house in July 1968. (A. Roberts)

Fig. 7.13 The ruins of East Grit engine house in July 2007. (Author)

Fig. 7.14 The remains of Old Grit engine house photographed in July 2007. (Author)

— and certainly by 1814 — the company leased their own smelter at Pontesbury which saw them out. In 1857 some ore was purchased by William Lefeaux of Penyclun mine in mid Wales to be smelted there.[16]

Grit sett has the best set of engine house remains in the county; counting Ladywell (covered in the next entry) there are the substantial remains of four (Figs. 7.8 to 7.14). White Grit engine house dates from 1783 and was extended and heightened in about 1840 to house a new engine. Lying to the east are houses at East and Old Grit, the latter of unknown provenance. East Grit house is impressive and was built by John Taylor and Company c.1862. At Rider Shaft, on the eponymous vein halfway between White and Old, is the vestigial remnant of a horse gin ring.

Uphill from the White Grit engine house, on the other side of the main road, are the ruins of a magazine that must date from after the Explosives Act of 1875. It consists of two circular walls one inside the other, and would originally have had a lightweight roof, so that if the explosives 'went up' the roof would blow off and the walls protect anything at ground level. Some of the houses, cottages and offices survive, the latter now a private house, but for some 70 years several of them formed the More Arms public house. All across the sett the ground is littered with the remains of shafts, some of which are open at least part way down.

Half a mile north-east of Old Grit is an adit known as **Shelve Trial**, dug at some unknown date, no doubt when searching for lead.

Ladywell

For a long time considered as part of Grit sett, veins here were discovered during the driving of Wood Level in the late 18th century. Those holding leases for Grit or Grit and Gravels were able to exploit Ladywell — as Lewis and Phillips did in the late 1820s — at Ladywell Shaft (later to be called Flat Rod Shaft) on the vein of the same name and further west on New Briton vein. These may have been the surface workings noted by Murchison in the 1830s. Later there was interest in developing the mine to the extent that at least two parties, John Taylor and Company in the early 1860s and Cooke and Company later in the decade, wished to pull out of Grit in favour of Ladywell. Taylors were refused but South Salop Mining Co. Ltd., as Cooke and Company had become, succeeded. This company, formed in 1867, was succeeded in 1872 by the Ladywell Mining Co. Ltd., which folded in 1884. 1885 and 1886 saw South Roman Gravels Mining Co. Ltd. owning and running Ladywell and the following three years still owning but not running it. Ladywell Mine Co. Ltd. had a last fling in 1899-1900. Someone made money, but it was not the shareholders.

The South Salop company sold the lease to Ladywell for £17,000 out of the latter's capital of £30,000, but all this was lost as was £8,000 of preference share investment made to enable the search for ore to be continued in 1876. The *Shrewsbury Chronicle* for 10 April 1885 reported the special general meeting of Ladywell Mining Co. Ltd., under liquidation proceedings. It includes discussion of a lawsuit between the company and the promoters, principally Dr. Brookes and to a lesser extent Arthur Waters, the other three promoters being dead. The report in the paper

Fig. 7.11 Ladywell engine house in May 2007. (Author)

Fig. 7.12 Aerial view of Ladywell engine house. (CPAT)

unfortunately does not give sufficient background or detail of the case to piece together the whole story, but the basic issue was that Dr. Brookes had misled the shareholders as to the potential of the mine, that the lessors had foreclosed, that the engine and boiler were mortgaged although in good order, and that the mine was flooded. A five-man committee was established to settle an out of court offer by Waters for his part. The outcome is not known but it was neither mining nor profit. Eddowes' *Salopian Journal* of 8 April 1885 reports that the mine was then let to Mr. Watson of Yorkshire, but no more is heard of this. As at Grit, in 1940 the Mores tried to persuade the government to reopen Ladywell, but to no avail.

The mine seems to have worked at least intermittently from 1862 to 1880 although no production figures were returned until 1875, a total of 800 tons of ore being recorded prior to closure; a little zinc ore was dug but no record of the amount survives. No more than 43 people were ever employed, and the numbers fell to 14 in 1880, 8 in 1881 and 3 in 1899/00.

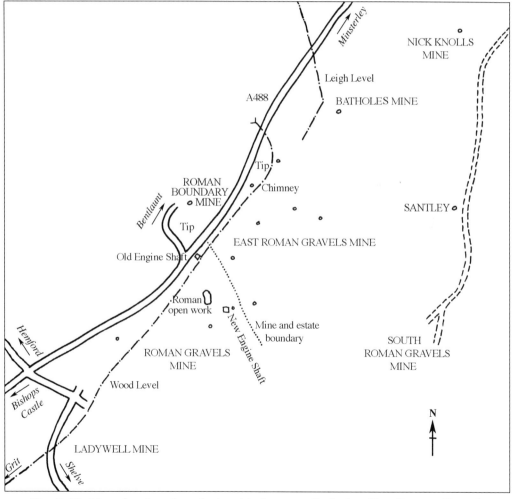

Fig. 7.13 Map showing the relationship between Batholes, East Roman Gravels, Ladywell, Nick Knolls, Roman Gravels and South Roman Gravels mines

When the mine was equipped expense was not spared, as shown when a 40 inch Sandycroft Foundry engine was purchased in 1875 to pump and wind, and a fine engine house built for it. The adjoining dressing floor was equipped with a horizontal engine to power the crusher and other plant including impeller buddles. The mine was worked from a series of shafts on eight veins and almost met Grit to the south and Roman Gravels to the north. It was worked to 32 fathoms below Wood Level, 66 fathoms below the surface.

The ruins of the fine engine house, now stabilised, form the principal reminder of this mine though in various plantations open and filled shafts exist.

From a comment in the official return for 1872 the mine was then known as North Central.

Nick Knolls

Batholes mine is on the western slopes of the hill called Nick Knolls and the mine of that name is a little to the north on the eastern slope. It was neither as early or as successful as its neighbour, being just off the edge of the principal mineralised area. There was a plan of 1844 extant in 1922 which indicated an adit on Nick Knolls vein, but of this nothing further is known. When the North Tankerville company were developing their Roundhill mine in the late 1860s they also obtained a lease from the Tankervilles for Nick Knolls which they worked for a few years for a little lead and barytes. The mine was probably closed by 1876 and definitely by 1883, although at some earlier stage it had been connected via Batholes to East Roman Gravel's mine by a tramway. The mine was reopened in 1915 following prospecting in the previous four years[17] for barytes, but only worked briefly. It became part of Shropshire Mines Ltd. by 1922 by which time it had closed, being flooded after the cessation of pumping on the Hope Valley Sett, presumably upon the abandonment of the Leigh Level project. The mine was connected underground to either Batholes or East Roman Gravels mines though whether by man or nature is not known. Local information collected by the SCMC held that the mine had been worked until 1956, presumably intermittently and on a very *ad hoc* basis.

300 tons of barytes was produced between 1872 and 1876 and an unknown amount more after 1915, probably by the Wotherton Company. Employment statistics are even less illuminating, but show that five men were employed underground in 1915.

Two veins — Big and Nick Knolls — were worked from two shafts, the deepest to 300 feet, and later from adits. In addition to lead ore and barytes a little calcite was raised. Nothing is known of the equipping of this mine though there was an engine house so there was or was intended to be an engine, but nothing now remains except disturbed ground.

North Roman Gravels

A North Roman Gravels Lead Mining Co. Ltd. was registered in 1875 and a North Roman Gravels Ltd. in 1887. No doubt the mine, if it ever functioned, was north of its near namesake, but how far north is anyone's guess. The western slopes of the Hope Valley are one obvious location, as is a site at Bentlawnt, known as Upper and Lower Lawnt, which was purchased by Wotherton Barytes and Lead Mining Co. Ltd. and conveyed at their liquidation to Shropshire Mines Ltd. during the First World War but never mined.

Roman (Gravels) Boundary

This was a site selected on the principle that veins go in straight lines and obvious directions. It was thought it should have tapped the same veins as its neighbours on the other side of the main road at Roman and East Roman Gravels, but there was a fault between, and nothing commercial was found. The first reference to the mine is that it was to be reopened as part of the West Tankerville Mines in 1869. That it did reopen is, sadly evidenced by a fatality in 1874, when Lewis Evans fell down the shaft. In 1881 the Roman Gravels Boundary Mining Company Ltd. was formed and again reopened the mine, but it only lasted until 1882 when G. Schofield Underwood became the owner for two years followed in 1885 by Alt S. Underwood. From 1886-9 James Yelland and William Boustred appear in the official returns as owners although the New Roman Gravels Boundary Mining Co. Ltd. was registered in 1886. The mine had appointed a receiver by October 1883 and it is recorded as suspended from 1884. In 1885 it was in liquidation and the miners did not receive what was owing to them. Official returns continued being made until 1889, in which year one of the owners, William Boustred was himself bankrupt, in part due to this mine. One undated plan of the sett[18] shows it split into Roman Gravels Boundary and Roman Boundary setts though there is no evidence of any separate workings. A dozen or so men were employed at a maximum but no returns of any production were made.

An undated plan and section of the mine of c.1870, which is a proposal rather than a survey, suggests that the shaft was to be sunk in the valley floor just west of the main road. The plan optimistically shows all the Roman Gravels veins crossing the sett. There was known to be a shaft up the hill on the road to Bentlawnt, and possibly a lower one which may never have been constructed. Little else is known. Further mystery surrounds this mine as it appears on a plan of East Roman Gravels mine as Primrose Shaft but is not shown as having any other connection (see plan). A head-frame on the shaft is also clearly visible behind the bridge shown in Figure 7.16 of Roman Gravels mine c.1890 which is, presumably, the by then disused gear of Yelland and Boustred's enterprise. There must have been an engine, probably portable, as the receiver paid a driver for a week in February 1883.

Roman Gravels

This was called Gravels or Shelvefield Gravels mine until c.1858[19] when romanticism was exploited to sell mine shares and the 'Roman' was added. It seems certain that this mine was indeed worked by the Romans, as Roman pottery, wooden spades and candles were found in the 1870s 50 feet below the surface.[20] Some sources say that a Roman lead pig was found in the bottom of the open workings though this does not tie up with any of the survivors (see chapter 1). The large open workings are certainly early and could well be Roman, and some parts of the underground workings, now destroyed, had the

Fig. 7.14 The pre-industrial opencast lead workings at Roman Gravels mine said to be of Roman date. (coll. K. Lock)

appearance of Roman work in that they were as narrow as possible and followed the vein, however twisty its route.

Mines were being worked in the locality in the 12th and 13th centuries although nothing is known of the workings. They were no doubt on similar lines to those of the Romans, but they could have been here or at Grit. In the late 18th century John Lawrence (II?) was working the mine by 1784 when his company purchased a 24 inch Bolton and Watt pumping engine. He worked here until about 1820 when he had doubts about the mine's viability. A 31-year lease for this and Grit mine was given to a group of local men in March 1825 on condition that the Leigh Level was dug to both mines within 15 years. This lease was sold to 35 partners known as the Grit and Gravels Mining company with two local men — Lewis and Philips — taking the lead. Much of the capital came from the north-west of the country, the first time that outside investment had been significant. The law suits over the Leigh Level took their toll on the Grit and Gravels company as well as on Lawrence.

The company was reformed in 1829 with 64 shareholders, but by 1835 work on the Leigh Level and probably at the mines had stopped. A further new company, using the same name, was formed in 1839 with a more generous royalty of $1/10$th rather than the previous $1/8$th. That company was wound up in 1848 with considerable animosity and without any notice. The engines and tools were sold and the miners laid off without their wages. So precipitate was the cessation that the pumps were allowed to be lost under water because pumping was stopped too soon. 'Such a disgraceful record it is hoped

Fig. 7.15 An engraving taken from a photograph of Roman Gravels mine showing the workings said to be Roman. This must be the earliest surviving record of a photograph of a Shropshire lead mine. It is taken from The Intellectual Observer *volume 1, p.295. The journal was published from 1862 to 1868 but individual issues are not dated*

could not find a parallel in all Great Britain.'[21] In the mid 1850s the company working Pennerley and other mines to the east investigated de-watering and restarting the mine but were unwilling or unable to raise the necessary capital.

The next move was in 1858 when the Gravels Lead Mining Co. Ltd. (noted as being registered under the Joint Stock Companies Act 1856) issued a prospectus wanting to raise £25,000 and having the promise of a lease for 31 years upon the formation of the company. The prospectus gives a lot of detail of the mine and includes a glowing reference from Captain Richards and an equally glowing report from the current lessee (both seem unusually to have been no more than the truth). The lease was granted in January 1859 but the company does not seem to have been registered in its intended name as the lease was assigned to the Roman Gravels Lead Mining Co. Ltd. a year later. Official reports give the owners as Richard Palin and Company, Palin being one of the principal promoters of the mine. Of the £25,000, £15,000 went to the former lessee John Stanton to buy the lease, and the balance was hoped to be in excess of that needed to get the mine working efficiently.

The venture was well capitalised and successful and carried on until 1867 when the lease was surrendered (at which period the mine or part of it was named on official returns as Sawpit mine). In 1871 the mine was sold to the Roman Gravels Mining Co. Ltd. for £70,000 of that company's authorised capital of £90,000. The balance of the investment

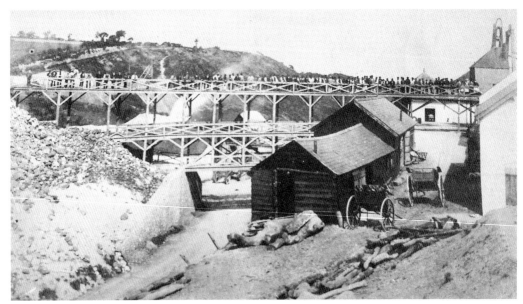

Fig. 7.16 The three level bridge across the main road (now A488) at Roman Gravels mine linking the mine site with the dressing floor etc., c.1890. A head-frame at what appears to be either Roman Boundary mine or Primrose Shaft of East Roman Gravels mine (depending on when one became the other) is visible in the background. (coll. K. Lock)

was used to sink New Engine Shaft and install an engine. Initially it was proposed to wind from this shaft and pump from Old Engine Shaft, but the amount of water found led to a rethink and a pumping engine was acquired (see below) and Old Engine Shaft used for winding. Despite falling ore prices the mine continued to be successful because Arthur Waters had prepared it well and a lot of good ground was ready for working. A year after his death in 1887, his son, also Arthur, was at the helm and the company was again reformed as the Roman Gravels Co. Ltd. to enable fresh cash to be raised to continue exploration. However, insufficient ore was found and the company was liquidated, only to be relaunched under the same name, in 1891 but with no more success. This saw the end of one of the most successful of Shropshire's mines. It was well funded, equipped and managed and had good ground, and was probably the only mine in the county in the 19th century to sell more value of ore than its authorised capital.

By 1894 the Hope Valley Mining Co. Ltd. was formed, and held Roman Gravels and its northern neighbour East Roman Gravels. The new company was not successful as the mine was effectively worked out, and only a small production of lead and zinc was recorded for 1894 and 1895 with none thereafter. The mine was maintained until 1900 when pumping ceased. It was reopened about 1909 when small quantities of lead and zinc ores were produced by unspecified owners. By 1923 it was owned by Shropshire Mines Ltd. though possibly not being worked. In 1924 Hillages employed quite a number of men working the tips for calcite. As at Grit and Ladywell, in 1940 the Mores tried to persuade the government to reopen this mine, but to no avail.

The mine was worked from at least six shafts on five principal veins which ran generally west-north-west to east-south-east. The principal and earliest worked was Roman vein. Prior to 1870 mining was also carried out from Boundary Shaft which, unlike the rest of the mine, was on the Tankerville Estate.[22] The sett divided itself into three distinct areas, low ground to the west of the main road, a 'ledge' above the east of the road with Old Engine Shaft and an area on top of the hill which was developed later; between the last two were the three early opencast workings. The low area was occupied by the dressing floors, crusher house and mill, access being via a three level bridge from the principal workings, with power provided by three waterwheels on the Hope Brook which passed under the site in a culvert. This area was probably not developed until the 1860s — it was certainly not in use in 1834 when the new turnpike road to Bishops Castle was built — but it was in existence by 1872.

The earliest 'modern' workings were on the east of and above the road where Old Engine Shaft and its engine house, ore bins, Day Level adit and the offices were sited. This was the location of one of Lawrence's engines of 1784 and 1788. No one knows where the other was, though there may have been another now forgotten shaft. One of these shafts had an adit, now also lost, to the Hope Brook, which was superseded by Wood Level around 1790. A 14-inch blowing engine, again from Bolton and Watt, was delivered in 1790 implying a blast furnace (a blacksmith's would at this date have used

Fig. 7.17 A pre-1918 view across the valley to Roman Gravels mine with the tips in the foreground, the site of the possible Roman opencast mines to the right centre, and the New Engine Shaft engine house on the skyline. (G.T. Atkinson)

bellows) which given the context would have been a slag hearth in a smelthouse. This suggests that Lawrence had a smelter here and the one at Malehurst at the same time.[23]

How long the Lawrence engines stayed is not known but a new engine house was built sometime before the 1858 take-over. The nature of the engine it housed is not known but whatever it was it was presumably the one sold quickly after the cessation of work in the late 1840s. The Palin investments of *c.*1860 saw the installation of a 45 inch pumping engine in an existing engine house at Old Engine Shaft along with a 15 inch winding engine. New Engine Shaft at the top of the site was developed in the 1870s, its 60 inch pumping engine being delivered from Harvey's of Hayle in Cornwall in 1875. This shaft was pumped up to Wood Level and wound up to Day Level 216 feet below the collar of the shaft. This level came out by Old Engine Shaft and gave direct access to the three level bridge and across to the dressing floor. This engine stopped in 1900, any further workings would have been above Wood Level. Compressed air rock drills were introduced by Arthur Waters probably in the early 1880s and a compressor house built near the Old Engine. The mine had surface (and no doubt underground) tramways which ran from the Day Level to the crusher house and elsewhere on the site.

The mine was worked to a depth of 100 feet by the Romans (or 40 fathoms or 100 yards according to some sources, though these seem unlikely) and a maximum of 155

Fig. 7.18 An aerial view of Roman Gravels. The scars around the 'Roman' open workings are visible in the woods on the left, whilst the site of Old Engine Shaft and the main mine buildings are parallel to the road below and New Engine Shaft is at the lower edge of the clearing, upper centre. (CPAT)

fathoms below Wood Level at New Engine Shaft later. Wood Level passed Old Engine Shaft 246 feet below ground level.

Production figures of lead ore for Lawrence's period are quoted as 20,000 tons.[24] When being worked in the 1830s and 1840s with Grit the total output is given as around 700 tons of ore per annum with, in a no doubt typical quarter (September to December 1829), three-quarters of this being from Grit. From 1859 to 1870 lead ore production steadily increased to almost 1,000 tons per annum and took off thereafter with a slight reduction in the late 1870s as prices fell, peaking at 3,100 tons in 1883. By the end of the decade prices had fallen again and production was back below 1,000 tons and it was down to double figures by the end in 1895. In total the mine produced 50,000 tons of lead ore. Zinc ore, the amount of which increased in depth as lead reduced, was never comparable being generally under 100 tons a years with random surges peaking at 290 tons in 1877, giving about 3,000 tons overall. Silver was obtained from the lead ore but the quantity per ton was so small that it could not have been economic. 1851 saw 1,162 ounces then nothing until 1877; then over the next six years some 28,000 ounces were produced. In 1883 the mine produced over 2% of the nation's silver output as well as 6% of the nation's lead ore. A small amount of barytes was also produced, possibly from a shaft well away from the rest, a quarter of a mile south-east of New Engine Shaft. 13 tons of lead ore and 26 of zinc between 1909 and 1912 were probably recovered from the tips. A vein of feldspar was encountered but not worked.

The numbers employed, as usual, follow the same basic pattern as the production figures. The earliest figures are from the memorandum book of 1827 (described under Grit mine, see page 155) listing 'bargains' for the two mines (see Appendix 1). Nothing further is known until 1877, when there were 252 workers with 60% underground, rising to 321 in 1883, falling to 196 in 1891 and four by 1894. If there was not a smelter on site during the Lawrence period the ore would have gone to Malehurst or later to Pontesbury. For some of its history lead was smelted on site. It is not now known when, though clearly the 1790s are a possibility.[25] Smelting on site was finished at the latest by 1863 when a trade directory noted that ore was shipped to Shrewsbury for transport to a smelter on the River Dee. The zinc will always have gone out as ore, probably to either Bristol or Birmingham. Most if not all of the silver will have been extracted on the banks of the Dee. Transport would have been difficult especially prior to the construction of the new turnpike from Minsterley to Bishops Castle in 1834/5. This passed between two parts of the mine's site and would have eased both the transport of coal in and lead or ore out.

The mine structures have suffered in the national interest. The three level bridge was demolished as explosives practice during the First World War and the engine houses by artillery practice in the Second. Despite this there are worthwhile remains though they do not stand far above ground. The Roman open workings are visible in woodland and New Engine Shaft and its engine house foundations are visible from a footpath. At road level the dressing floor and associated area to the west has been reclaimed. The retaining walls which were such a feature have been lowered. The Old Engine area is accessible but getting overgrown, the engine house ruins are clear but the rest is a bit confusing.

Other shafts are visible in woodland and in the case of Spring Vein Shaft the 'ditch' which housed the flat rods which pumped it is still visible.

The geologist Sir Roderick Murchison was and still should be remembered at the mine. In 1870 the British Association held a meeting at Liverpool which the then elderly Sir Roderick attended. During that meeting the path from the road to Old Engine Level and on to the top of the mine was named 'Murchison Walk'. It seems very appropriate in view of the length of time which Murchison spent in the county, often as the guest of the Mores at Linley Hall, whilst he devised his reading of the rocks and named the Silurian System. It is a shame that his 'walk' has, for the moment, been almost forgotten.

Santley

This was probably only a trial on the hill above the eponymous farm which was the home of Samuel Naylor (or Nealor), one of a prominent family of mining agents and managers. The land was leased from the Tankerville Estate and what work was done was carried out by John Lawrence (probably IV). Certainly he held a lease in 1831 as he offered it for sale, apparently unsuccessfully to Edmund Buckley of Manchester. The site reveals nothing except that there is a little disturbed ground where there were two shafts.

Shelve

Being the name of a parish and a village this is a confusing name for a mine. The parish includes Benree, Ladywell, Grit and Roman Gravels mines. The earliest reference is a passing one in More family papers to Shelve Pit Field in 1598. Leases which just specify the parish date from the late 17th century at least and gave permission to mine in any undeveloped area, including the edges of the village itself. The confusion does not stop here as the locality was synonymous with mining and its name was used with abandon — there are mines called Shelve Gravels, Shelvefield, Shelvefield Gravels, Shelve Pool, Shelfield and Shelve Trial as well as a mine actually in Shelve.

The most likely early contender for a mine which could reasonably be called Shelve is a site referred to in a lease from the Mores to Francis Lloyd, John Probert, John Lawrence III and five others at $1/6$th royalty. The conditions of the lease include driving a level from the top of the valley near the dwelling house occupied by John Lawrence II in order to prove the Shelve vein 'lately discovered formerly worked and given up by Sir Thomas Bonsall & company'. Of Bonsall's activity nothing is known, but the level required was driven from Shelfield and is now referred to as the Shelve Deep Level. The lease covered all the mines in the parish but clearly distinguishes between White Grit, Gravels and Shelve, the latter being the only one of the three mines worked by Bonsall.

The 1858 Gravels Mining Co. Ltd. prospectus included this mine. It does not give much detail as the mine was not being worked, but it does tell us that the level had been dug. It was hoped that work underground at Roman Gravels would break through into and drain Shelve mine. But this did not happen, although the shaft from which Romans Gravels' small amount of barytes was gained is almost in Shelve. The mine was mentioned again but still as not working in 1869 (Morton). There is no further history until between the wars when More Shaft was sunk as a trial, no doubt unsuccessfully. The mine presents one other problem, in that the site described here as the location of the main shaft is described elsewhere as the site of More Shaft worked c.1885/6 by the South Roman Gravels Company and also as the location of More Shaft between the wars. The shaft is marked on the 1881 OS map, but there is doubt as to where the shaft dug at the mine in the 1930s was located.

The mine centred on a site a few hundred yards east-north-east of Shelve church with a shallow level north of the church and the deep level near Shelfield. There were a series of shafts between the shallow level and the main shaft. Nothing is known of the mine's equipping, depth, employment or production.

Little remains. The spoil heap of the main shaft is visible in a garden and the other shafts are represented by disturbed ground. Water still issues from the mouth of the deep level but by now it looks almost like a spring although in the 1960s a stone arch was still visible, now presumably buried in the soil and undergrowth. The site of an air shaft up the hill on the other side of the track is visible as a rubbish-filled depression.

Shelve Pool

Shelve Pool is an artificial pool constructed as a fish pool by the Mores shortly after they acquired the Linley Estate in the 1650s, and near its west bank the Shelve Pool Mining Company set out to make their fortunes, and failed. Even Arthur Waters when manager could find no lead, trying for two years from about 1872 before giving up. Between 1882 and 1886 the shaft is said to have been sunk 'to 78 feet, apparently on a vein but no serious mining was done'. In 1898 the Thornthwaite Mining Company took the site and opened the mine in February 1899, looking for barytes with very limited success and closing it again in 1901, having indicated on the official returns that they were exploring. As at several of their other mines the Mores tried to persuade the government to reopen this mine in 1940, describing it as 'practically unworked as yet'.

As there was probably no production no detailed official returns were made although 12 men were employed in 1899 and 1900, eight of them underground. One shaft 78 feet deep and two adits were dug by the pool; these are now blocked and in thick woodland. To the north of the pool there was an adit dating from the barytes period which is now not visible.

South Roman Gravels

This mine lies in More land just south of Shelfield Farm and is sometimes known as Shelfield mine. Matters are confused by the fact that the Mores of Linley owned and leased a Shelfield sett as did the Earls of Tankerville, the latter associated with Roundhill mine on the eastern side of the same valley. Following the success of Roman Gravels in the 1860s interest was aroused in other possible sites including this one where the veins at Roman Gravels and Tankerville were assumed to continue. The name first appears in 1869 when a report of the county's mines (Liscombe) notes that not much had been done. In 1870 leases from both landlords were granted to Edward Geach for land at Nether

Heath, which location includes both sides of the valley. Geach assigned those leases to Edwin Crawshay who in turn assigned them to the South Roman Gravels Mining Co. Ltd., but the dates of these transactions are not clear. Roman Gravels Mining Company appears in the official returns as the owners in 1870 followed by the limited company of that name a year later. Following the liquidation of their predecessors the South Roman Gravels Mining Co. Ltd. appear in the returns for 1877. Activity at the mine was suspended the following year. George Green then appears in official returns as owning the mine, yet from 1883 to 1889 it is back to being owned by the South Roman Gravels Mining Co. Ltd. despite the registration of the New South Roman Gravels Mining Co. Ltd. in 1887. In 1885 exploration was taking place, unsuccessfully, as work was again suspended in 1889. According to the *Mining Journal* the company worked More Shaft at Shelve mine during this period. Shropshire Mines Limited are the next occupants, probably by the end of the First World War and certainly by 1923. They were succeeded by Walter Hillage until 1928 and from 1936 to 1940 by E. Hillage.

The mine was worked for lead, barytes and calcite from three shafts on the line of the adit from Engine Shaft into the valley bottom at 72 feet deep; Engine Shaft goes down another 30 fathoms. Witherite was also found here, though not in commercial quantities. The total production recorded is 11 tons of lead and nearly 60 tons of barytes. Employment figures are lavish for the level of production, decreasing from 20 in 1877 to four in 1882/3 and rising back to 14 in 1886, always with the majority underground. Having a shaft known as Engine Shaft implies a steam pumping engine, but beyond that nothing is known of the mine's equipment.

The remains are as visible as they are small, a spoil heap by the track with slight remains of the engine house foundations.

8   Mines to the west of the A488

(except bits of Grit and the west side of Hope Valley)

This chapter includes mines which may have been Roman, some optimistic small lead mines and a number of more or less successful barytes mines, some of which began life looking for lead. Several are either in Wales or cross the border, the ones in Wales usually being worked in conjunction with one of the nearby English ones, and are geologically related.

The mines can be sub-divided into three groups. To the north lie the (mostly) lead and later barytes mines of Bromlow, Meadowtown, Pentirvin, Rorrington, Ridge Hill and Wotherton as well as the outer end of the Leigh Level. The south end around Corndon Hill is mostly a Welsh peninsular projecting into Shropshire. It contains only three very small named mines — Cwmdwla, Roundtain and Todleth Hill, if one assumes Old Churchstoke and Roundtain to be one and the same. The third group or middle portion, loosely describable as Stapeley Hill to Priest's Weston, has a much more complex history. Weston mine, later often known as Cliffdale, began as a lead mine and ended up as a barytes one. The area was dug and squabbled over during what John Lawrence IV described as 'the unparalleled Rage for Mineing' from about 1824 to 1830. Also in the vicinity were Stapeley and Middleton mines, the latter not to be confused with Middletown a few miles north in the Breidden Hills.

Stone axe making is recorded in Hyssington, these axes being found at several local potential pre-Roman mining sites. The Romans are also believed to have at least smelted lead near Churchstoke. The entire area was prospected in the 19th century.

Bromlow

This is a small lead mine which produced some ore from the mid 18th century. John Lawrence I or possibly II was running the mine on behalf of Henry Bowdler by 1749, when ore was already being raised. Partial accounts survive which make it clear that at least one shaft and one adit existed and were being extended in 1749/50. Lawrence may have had a stake in the mine as the £49 19s. 10d. he received between July 1749 and July 1750 was described by him as 'for payment of workmen's wages and other incidental expenses relating to the digging for ore on Bromlow Common and for which I am to be accounted ... being for the threefourths of the expenses of working Bolemere (*sic*) for ore due from Mr. Richard Ireland and Mr. Bowdler'.

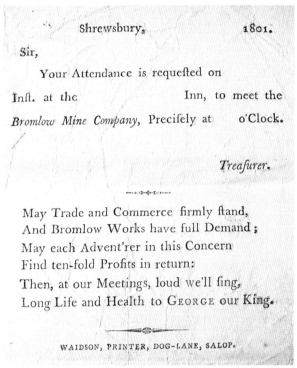

Shrewsbury, 1801.

Sir,

Your Attendance is requested on

Inst. at the   Inn, to meet the

Bromlow Mine Company, Precisely at   o'Clock.

Treasurer.

May Trade and Commerce firmly stand,
And Bromlow Works have full Demand;
May each Advent'rer in this Concern
Find ten-fold Profits in return;
Then, at our Meetings, loud we'll sing,
Long Life and Health to GEORGE our King.

WAIDSON, PRINTER, DOG-LANE, SALOP.

Fig. 8.1 A pro forma notice for calling meetings, Bromlow. (SA851/278)

By 1801 the Bromlow and Meadowtown Mine company were running the mine as a cost book company, the partners' contributions to the running costs being one guinea each on three occasions in January and February 1801. Whether these payments were towards the expenses of the mine or as royalties to Mr. Mucklestone, the landowner, or a proportion of each is not clear. Four partners are named, including William Hazeldine. The survival of an unused pro forma notice of a meeting (Fig. 8.2) gives an insight into the almost pre-industrial nature of the business world at that date, with its six lines of doggerel. The mine seems to have ceased working about 1815 to judge from the first official records which state in 1860 that the mine ceased about 45 years earlier.

In 1859 Wood and Company owned the mine and 1863 saw the issue of the Bromlow Mining Co. Ltd.'s prospectus, which covered Rorrington mine as well as Bromlow. This company may not have succeeded in raising its capital as Peake and Company are recorded as the owners from 1862-6, Mr. Peake having been negotiating for a lease from the Rev. Mucklestone from as early as 1859. Success did not follow them either as no more is heard of the mine, although the editions of Kelly's *Directory* for 1863 and for 1870 note that lead had been discovered. Unsurprisingly little is known of the features or equipment of the mine. No returns were ever made of production or employment and the only known remnant is an adit at stream level which has insufficient headroom to be other than for drainage.

Calcot

In 1826 two companies were working at Calcot. Weston Hill Mining company had opened up old workings and driven a level in the Dingle and they complained to the landlords, the Powis Estate, that the Grit and Gravels company had sunk a shaft above them in Calcot Bank. The estate found in favour of the Weston Hill company, agreeing that the boundary between the holdings ran east from the top of Calcot through Corndon to The Marsh.

In June 1839 the estate granted John Frank a one year take note at $^1/_{10}$th royalty for the 'commons and wastes from Calcot Dingle to Old Churchstoke & Park, Hurdley called Round Bank, Llanfawr Hill, Cwm Dyla, Roundtown Bank and Brightier Bank'. This included this mine but no more is heard of Frank's activities.

Calcot is best known as a small barytes mine just in Wales worked as part of Weston mine by the Cliffdale Barytes Co. Ltd. and opened in 1914. It suffered from water problems and was almost certainly uneconomic. It was closed in 1919 even though it was expected that the barytes present would be worked by driving a crosscut from the then new Powis Shaft at Weston mine, though this does not appear to have happened. Calcot was worked from two levels on opposite sides of the valley and an inclined shaft.

The Bromlow Mining Company, Limited.

CAPITAL £30,000, IN 30,000 SHARES OF £1 EACH,

10s. payable on Application, the remaining 10s. on Allotment.

REGISTERED UNDER THE JOINT STOCK COMPANIES' ACT, WITH LIMITED LIABILITY.

DIRECTORS.

J. N. BROWNE, Esq., UNION CLUB, LONDON.
R. GILLMAN, Esq., 28, BUCKLERSBURY, LONDON.
H. J. HOLMES, Esq., DERBY.
F. H. SALVIN, Esq., KILLINGBECK HALL, NEAR LEEDS.

With power to add to their number.

BANKERS.

MESSRS. ROBARTS, LUBBOCK & Co., LONDON.
MESSRS. ROCKE, EYTON & Co., OLD BANK, SHREWSBURY.

SOLICITOR.

JOHN BROUGHALL, Esq., SHREWSBURY.

SECRETARY.

MR. J. LOCKWOOD (*pro tem*).

REGISTERED OFFICES—5, BARGE YARD, BUCKLERSBURY, LONDON.

THE BROMLOW MANOR LEAD MINE comprises about two thousand acres of land; is held under Lease for twenty-one years, subject to a royalty of 1/14th. It adjoins the Gravels Mines on the north, and contains the whole of the lodes of that sett at present worked, and is three and a half miles to the west of the justly celebrated Snailbeach Mine, containing its main lode. The Grit's lodes also pass into it. Both the Gravels and Grit's Mines are well-known productive Lead Mines, and the Snailbeach has for many years made, and continues to make,

Fig. 8.2 Just over half a century after the form of notice in Fig. 8.1, much needed Acts of Parliament had brought in the modern world. (SA 851/279)

The ore was apparently graded on site before being sent to Cliffdale Mill at Wagbeach.

There is little to see except spoil in the area of the shaft and levels and the remains of the foundations of a small building of unknown purpose.

Churchstoke

John Frank (see Calcot entry above) may have been responsible in 1839 for the barytes trial which is known to have existed before 1869 when a mine under the name of Old Churchstoke was reported as not working (Morton). In 1883 and 84 a part of Weston mine was for some reason referred to, for the purposes of an official return, as Churchstoke. The precise location of the mine is not certain though it was probably what was later called Roundtain mine, but it was certainly in Wales. Roman lead smelting activity is believed to have taken place near Churchstoke which raises the possibility that the Romans also sought and possibly found small quantities of ore.

Cwmdyla (or Cwmdulla or Cwmdwla)

Like Calcot to its north, this mine lay just in Wales and was effectively a part of Weston mine, though it is more than likely to have been prospected from the early 18th century until about 1830. It was owned and worked for barytes by the various Cliffdale companies from 1895 to 1913. Work was suspended from 1898 to 1902 and again from 1905 to 1910. No records exist of production and the maximum recorded employment is two workers. No remains are known.

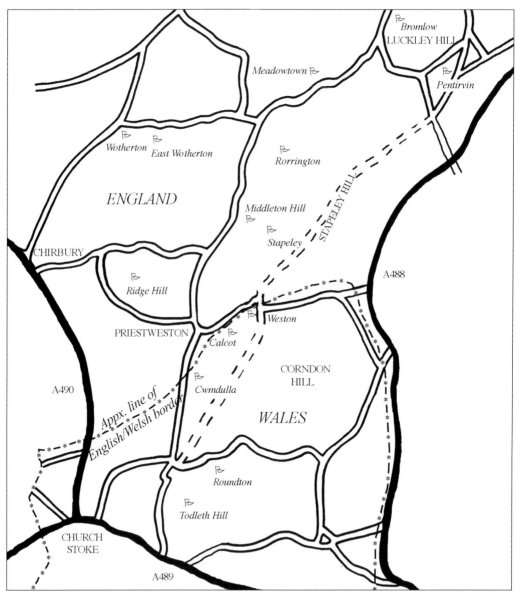

Fig. 8.3 Map showing the location of the mines mentioned in this chapter

Meadowtown

In a way this small mine was a microcosm of the county's mines. It was being run for lead by John Lawrence III in the 18th century and ended up as a barytes mine. The first reference to the mine comes in 1792 when Lawrence noted in his memorandum book: '3rd November 1792, Henry Fox and Company have agreed to drive the level at Meadowtown 10 yds'. From 1793 to 1798 John Gibbons was a principal shareholder here, his account books making reference to the mine in 1793 and 1798. He held most of a half share in 1793, Lawrence no doubt holding the other half, and a profit of £347 2s. 8d. was divided in 1798. In 1801 the mine was being run jointly with Bromlow by the Bromlow and Meadowtown Mine company. A partial account has survived for December 1824 to December 1825 when Messrs. Lewis and Phillips (see Grit) recorded 60 yards of a level driven and 7 yards of a shaft sunk. Official returns provide the next glimpse: by 1859 the mine belonged to John Harrison but had closed a year earlier. The mine is mentioned in directories for 1861 and 1863, although according to official returns it was closed. The final information is that in 1869 it was a closed barytes mine (Morton) or in 1870 a lead mine.[1] Neither production nor employment figures exist, nor does any real knowledge of the layout, equipment or working of the mine. There is not much to see, simply an adit used as a water supply and a spoil run.

Middleton (Mucklewick and Hyssington)

Little is known of the mining here. There may have been one or more mines, but possibly all were little more than trials. Unspecified mines were left to the Reverend Samuel Stokes in 1820 by his cousin William Calcot. These may well have included the mine whose account survives in Powis Estate papers as the 'abstract of Middletown Mine acct 1819-24'. It was unsigned and sent from Hawkstone on 16 April 1826, and lists advances of c.£7,000 and production of c.£2,200.[2] The locations of the mines were not specified but Kinton Hall, Middleton Hill, Heaply Marsh and Mucklewick are all mentioned. In 1826 the Weston Hill Mining Company were trying to do a deal with Mrs. Calcot and Mr. and Mrs. Sutton; again the location of the mine(s) is not given but Mrs. Calcot could be Williams' widow. Matters become clearer with a lease of June 1830 from Joseph and Mrs. Sutton and John and Rev. James Calcot Hayes Stokes for lead mines to Richard, Thomas and John Lewis (all farmers from north Shropshire and Wrexham) on land at Middleton in Chirbury Parish as well as land at Mucklewick (south of Shelve and then in Hyssington parish). In 1848 Stokes died and left mines in Chirbury and Hyssington to his children, from which they were expected to receive £500 in royalties. Certainly mining took place on Middleton Hill, but whether any was done at any of the other Calcot/Stokes properties is not clear. In 1850, when an allotment of land was offered for sale on Mucklewick Hill, 'mines and minerals lying under the allotment' were referred to. The mine makes one more brief appearance, sufficient to clear doubts as to its existence, when official returns were made for Middleton Hill, Montgomeryshire, in 1885-6 as owned by the Cliffdale Barytes Company with William Boustred as their agent. This, whatever the returns may say, is not a reference to Middletown Hill, Bulthy (which unlike Middleton

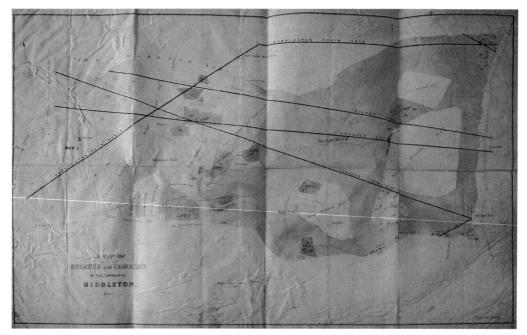

Fig. 8.4 A map of the estates and commons at Middleton of 1850 indicating many mining sites, most of which cannot now be clearly identified. (SA 708/6)

Hill, Chirbury is actually in Montgomeryshire, not Shropshire) as that mine was being actively worked in 1885-6 by the Bulthy Lead Mining and Barytes Works Company. The returns give no details and no more is heard of the mine. No precise location can be given and one can only guess at which bits of disturbed ground may have been this mine.

Pentirvin

This mine is known only by virtue of its tip and an adit which flows with water. No documentary evidence has surfaced to fill in the picture. It has generally been assumed that it was a mid 19th century lead mine and that it was a failure.

Ridge Hill

This was a short lived but fairly productive barytes mine several miles west of the main ore-field. A lease for the land was given by the Powis Estate to W.S. Sneade in 1915 but no action seems to have taken place until 1918 when Sneade and others took a 42-year lease for 420 acres. Before 1920 it had passed into the hands of H. Blackwell and J.H. Cumpsty who that year formed the Ridge Hill Barytes Mines Limited to acquire 'certain mining properties in Ridge Hill, Churburry, Salop'.[3] The company was based in Liverpool and had a capital of £20,000. Ridge Hill had been quarried in several places and presumably some barytes veins had been noted, otherwise it would have seemed an odd place to try. The acreage covered by the lease and the plural 'mines' in the company name suggest that much more was hoped for than actually happened. The mine closed in 1927 and was purchased

176

by Malehurst Barytes Company Ltd. and reopened in 1930, briefly. It closed in 1931, effectively worked out. Production was often small, as little as 35 tons a year, the total output believed to have been about 3,000 tons. Employment declined from a peak of 27 in 1923.

It was worked from two shafts, the first being inclined and starting 20 yards inside the main adit. In 1924 a new shaft had been dug down to 177 feet

Fig. 8.5 The surviving building from Ridge Hill mine (photographed in May 2008) is a First World War army hut, partially re-clad and somewhat altered, in use as a workshop near Churchstoke. May 2008. (Author)

by August, to be subsequently deepened by a further 60 to 90 feet. Various cross-cuts located ore bodies.

For such a limited mine it had a bad safety record with two fatalities. In 1922 a roof fall killed a miner and in 1924 a miner spilt the petrol for his blowlamp on his clothes which then caught fire, with disastrous consequences.

Fig. 8.6 A view over Ridge Hill mine site in May 2007 with the (vertical) shaft centre left, the winder base in front of that and other machine bases scattered around (the vertical steel beams are said to be of agricultural origin). The main adit went in below and to the left of the photo and the adit in Fig. 8.7 further to the left again. (Author)

177

Consent was given for tramways in two directions to public highways, one west to Whittery Wood and one south to Hagley, but only the latter was built and ran to a road loading point. In the early days of the mine the ore went to Cliffdale Mill at Wagbeach, possibly after some sorting at the mine. It will have gone to Malehurst Mill from 1930, although the former owners carried on purchasing the final output. Barytes out and coal and oil in were delivered from Montgomery station by steam lorry or traction engine and trailer, the latter especially doing the roads no good; in 1925 the company entered an agreement with Chirbury RDC to maintain the 'Whittre' Chirbury to Churchstoke road.

The mine had an office remembered as a 'hen house', and a larger First World War surplus building housing plant. There was a steam winder and electricity was generated by a Blackstone oil engine. The men were wound up and down in the kibble (much to the mine manager's 10-year-old daughter's horror).

Fig. 8.7 A typical exploratory adit, this one went a few yards in looking for the vein at Ridge Hill mine, May 2007. (Author)

The sites of the main adit, the vertical shaft and a smaller adit are visible as are several concrete machine bases and two steel uprights said to be part of an oil engine installation, though whether for the mine or for later agricultural use is not clear. Also surviving, near Churchstoke, are the plant building, a cast iron winch, a saw bench and rails and wheel-sets from the mine.[4]

Rorrington

Quite how much land the London Lead Company held in this area is not now known but they certainly held Rorrington but gave it up in 1735 without having mined it. Documentary evidence first appears from 1770 in the form of a report on the mine on the behalf of the Powis Estate bailiff Hugh Jones with an attached testimony by Joseph Brown 'aged (as he believes) about 76' regarding his working the part of the London Lead Co.'s lease from the Herberts of Chirbury about 35 years before. The London Lead Co. did not intend to work the land and he entered into an agreement with Thomas Barker, the company's agent, as a result of which a small amount of ore was raised. Hugh

Jones' report of 1770 is primarily concerned with the right of Francis Plowden and a few others to work the mine and quotes that in 1767 'some writings' were given to a Mr. Baldwyn concerning a right to work it, but he does not appear to have done so. Francis Plowden's activity must have been sporadic as the adit had to be dug out to enable Jones to inspect the works.

By the 1790s the White Grit company held the mine with John Lawrence III running it, although nothing is known of the level of activity.[5] It is inevitable that the mine was tried or worked during the booming 1820s and in 1825 M. Briscoe of Wrexham enquired of the estate if a lease was available, only to be informed that it was Mr. Jones of Maesmawr's land, although in the Lordship of Chirbury. Whether Mr. Jones mined or let the mining, the 1,000 acres of Rorrington Manor was advertised for sale in the *Shrewsbury Chronicle* for 9 March 1827, including a lead mine suitable for development. The Wakeman family bought the land and a lease for the mine was granted in 1830 to Leeke and Adlington.

Sir Roderick Murchison visited the mine during his geological researches in the late 1830s, noting that trials had taken place, that there was no lead but that barytes and witherite were present. Barytes was clearly developed as by 1843 the tithe map marks a 'spar work' on the site. The 'spar work' is shown on various maps of the early 1850s but no detailed information is available until 1853 when the Rorrington company took it over. They are said to have had one good find of lead ore, but were wound up in 1856. A John Taylor was manager in 1854 when a miner was charged with stealing tools, but it is not known if this was the John Taylor of John Taylor and Company, the company that worked the nearby Stapeley and Grit Setts a few years later.

At some stage the mine was worked in two parts by different companies as there is a reference in an estate paper in 1933 that there had been an unsuccessful mine at The White House. This split must have occurred in or around 1859. March 1858 saw a licence to dig for lead and other metals under land in Chirbury for one year from 25 March 1858, to be followed 'if the adventurers desire' by a 21-year lease for a mine that became known as West Snailbeach. The adventurers, as the West Snailbeach Mining Co. Ltd., included Samuel Morris-Ridge and Thomas Orchard. The lease was requested but was still unsigned four years later as a result of a dispute within the mining company. However, official returns for 1859, when the 21-year lease would have commenced, have J.D. Brunton & Co. as the owners. On 25 March that year a further lease was granted to Leeke and Adlington to be followed in February 1862 by a lease to partners including Brunton and Fitzgerald, and subsequently to Robert Gillman and partners in the September. Despite this, official returns quote Fitzgerald and company as the owners from 1860-5 with the mine not working in or after 1863, the year in which Gillman and his colleagues formed the Bromlow Mining Co. Ltd.,[6] their prospectus giving the impression that Rorrington was the sett they were to acquire. Previous adventurers were said to have spent at least £30,000 on the mine which would therefore need little additional capital. Whether they raised their capital is not known, although there is no evidence that they did. The royalty agreed here was very unusual for a metal mine: $1/12$th for the first 500 tons of lead ore p.a., $1/15$th for 500 to 1,000 tons and $1/18$th thereafter.

The split is still apparent later with Booth and Company as owners from 1867 to 1875 followed by the Rorrington Mining Company in 1878 as owners of Rorrington mine, whilst in 1870 a lease was granted to Geach and partners for West Snailbeach. Reports of 1869 do not list it as two mines, but do manage two descriptions, one describing it as a closed barytes mine (Morton) and the other (Liscombe) as not very profitable, although the difference may be due to out of date information in one of the sources. Just to add to the complexity, part of the mine was apparently called Roman Gravels West (which was definitely in the parish of Chirbury), for which the owners are recorded from 1873-5, including Morris-Ridge and Arthur Waters and from 1879-84, E. Bunny, C. Saxilby & S. Darwin. The mine of that name only worked in 1879-80 and 1884. After that, no activity is recorded until 1889 when four years of barytes extraction occurred.

The last period of activity occurred following the granting of a licence on 10 June 1918 from Sir Offley Wakeman to Shropshire Mines Ltd. to search for minerals on 500 acres of the estate, this phase lasting until July 1920. Throughout the inter-war years prospecting was carried out but to little effect, the estate noting that 'for 70 years prospectors have explored the old workings and found nothing significant'.

The principal mine is spread over a hillside with shafts and dressing floor at the top and several adits in the valley bottom. The secondary mine was by what are now the ruins of The White House on the other side of the valley. As will have been gathered from its history the mine was not wholly successful, production figures being notably lacking. From the point of view of the official statistics, 1850-2 is the high water mark for Rorrington mine with just over 80 tons of lead ore produced per year, thereafter only 1854, 1855, 1858 and 1864 have entries with a total of almost 55 tons. West Snailbeach returned no production and Roman Gravels West 6 tons of lead ore and 100 tons of barytes in 1879-80 and 1 ton of lead ore in 1884. An unspecified company whose returns are not recorded produced 347 tons of barytes between 1889 and 1893 and Shropshire Mines 16 tons in 1919/20.[7] There is no record of any production of witherite (or of fluorite or barytocalcite), all of which are found here and in few other places in the county.

Even fewer employment figures are available, the occasional entries are all in single figures except for 1919/20 when ten workers were employed. As is often the case with the less successful mines, little is known of the equipment which must have existed. Steam pumping engines were ordered and due to be delivered in 1858 to West Snailbeach and again around 1863 to the Bromlow company but nothing is known of their details or fate, though the latter was (or was to have been) supplied by Thornewill and Warham of Burton-upon-Trent for £600 to include delivery and erection of the pumping and winding engine, boiler, pumping winding and crushing apparatus. How much if any of this arrived is a moot point, but the same prospectus gives some information of what existed — the results of the £30,000 spent by the previous adventurers.

The engine shaft was 75 fathoms deep, the deeper of the two shafts. It was cased and divided and furnished with ladders, pumps and pitwork. There were also all the buildings required for carrying out large scale operations — engine and boiler houses, counting house, smith and woodworking shops, powder magazine and storehouse. The presence of an engine house suggests that the 1858 engine may have been delivered but had certainly gone. Transport was always by road.

The remains are generally in thick private woodland, although the engine shaft and some ruins can be seen from a public footpath. Another public footpath runs in the valley from which the sites of several adits can be seen. The ruins of The White House adjoins this path but there are no visible remains of this mine.

Half a mile or so north is **Rorrington Hill** which was certainly worked for a few tons of barytes as a 1933 report by a Major Kerr to the Wakeman estate said 'This has been pretty well pig rooted by fossickers extracting a few tons of barytes from the outcrops.'

Roundtain

About a mile into Wales, Roundtain may well be the same mine as Churchstoke but the names were used in different periods. Mining was clearly in progress in the vicinity by the late 18th century as Wm. Oldfield and Walter Waring asked the Powis Estate for a lease at Rownton Hill and adjoining wastes in the parish of Churchstoke, Montgomeryshire with royalty the same as the present lease at Rownton Hill. Whether that lease was to Oldfield and Waring is not known, and nothing else is known of these activities.[8] This area was clearly scoured in the 1820s and there are uninformative references in accounts in the More of Linley papers to mining in 1827, presumably for lead and equally presumably unsuccessful. In 1839 John Frank took a one year take note (see Calcot). In 1873 the proprietors of Weston (Cliffdale) mine sought a lease to work the area including Roundtain; this lease and a further one of 1890 exist as drafts though what was signed or worked is not clear. No royalty payments were made but the dead-rent of £25 per annum was paid in full for 1898-9 and in part or at a lesser rate in 1900-2 when the lease was cancelled. Matters in the late 1890s are, however, complicated as Minsterley Barytes Mining and Milling Co. declare themselves on their headed notepaper to be the 'owners of the Great Roundtrain Mine', Old Churchstoke. In April 1897 Mr. Balmain of the above concern noted that Pugh and Gittens seem to have been working barytes at Roundtain without the landowner's (Mr. Owen) knowledge or consent, though his tenant was said both to know and to have received payment for damage! By June of that year they were driving a new level in to the bottom of the sump, the intention being to clean out the old level and construct a 'drum and rails down the face of the hill to the washing place'.[9] This company's successors, Minsterley Baryta Co. Ltd., were active (milling at their plant in Minsterley) until 1907 but it is not known how long either of them worked at Roundtain. The mine was worked briefly in 1920 when signs of earlier mining were encountered. E. Murgatroyd of Keighley who was working at the Bog (possibly as Roundtain Ltd, but see note 13, chapter 6) also worked this mine around 1928 when George Evans recalls driving lorry loads of barytes from the mine to Montgomery Station.[10] No figures for production or employment survive nor any details of the mine except that there was one shaft and a few small adits. Calcite and barytes were produced. A spoil run and an adit mouth are the only visible signs.

Stapeley Hill

This is not the name of a mine but has been used for the areas not covered elsewhere in this chapter under Weston, Middleton or Rorrington. As in those areas, extensive prospecting and trial mining took place, not least in the 1820s. Not a vast amount can have been found. The area was seen as a westward extension of Grit sett and the same veins were assumed, incorrectly, to pass across it. In 1851 the Weston Hill Mining company (see Weston mine below) made enquiries about a lease at Aldress and Aldress Dingle, but there is no evidence that any actual mining took place. For a brief period in the 1860s there was a mine called Stapeley owned initially by Dicken and Company and subsequently run by John Taylor & Sons, in each case as part of Grit mine. This Taylor involvement comes to notice with the issue in 1863 of a prospectus for the Grit and Stapeley Mines Co. Ltd. which extols the expected virtues of the sett and includes reference to the railway being available from Minsterley. At that date John Taylor & Sons held the lease for Grit and Henry Darvil for Stapeley. The entire mine functioned from 1863 to 1866, Grit was offered for sale in 1865 and Stapeley was given up the following year.

Production figures which exist cover both mines and offer no clue as to what if anything may have been won at Stapeley. The mine was worked from several adits and shafts, the sites of some of which can be found if looked for carefully.

Todleth

Little more than a trial can have taken place here but slight remains have been noted. These may be from the activities of John Frank (see Calcot) whose take note certainly included this site. Though no documentary evidence has come to light it is virtually certain that prospecting took place at least in the 1820s.

Weston/Cliffdale

Lead was mined to a limited extent on and off from at least 1728 to the 1850s when barytes became the main product. The operators from 1857 were the Cliffdale Barytes Company and the mine effectively took their name and is remembered as such although it officially remained Weston. In its final days the mine had shafts in England, Wales and straddling the border — at Bowers Shaft and with workings crossing the border below ground.

The known early mining was principally in Wales but prospecting at least took place in Shropshire. The London Lead Co. took a lease from Hugh Jones (or in some sources Mrs. Jones, his wife or more probably widow) in 1728 to mine near Priest's Weston. Parts were subcontracted to Joseph Brown and William Johnson, who also worked lead leased to the company at Rorrington.[11] It was not a success and as part of their internal financial restructuring the London Lead Co. pulled out of all their Shropshire and Marches activities in 1735. This was not, however, the only mine at Weston as that company noted in one of their reports that a very likely vein was discovered at the top of a hill 100 yards from their boundary and pointing towards it. Presumably it was this that caused the company's regret that 'the partners [probably Moore, Roe and Blackmoor] have got the

Fig. 8.8 An undated photograph of Weston mine first published in 1919 in a textbook (with the caption 'Cloud banner on Cordon near the barytes mine'). (G.T. Atkinson)

lease on the common'. This was not all, for Thomas Barker, the London Lead Company's agent until 1733, also ran mines on his own account and by 1735, when the company were considering pulling out, he is reported to have had an adjoining mine, which he could possibly have acquired from the above partners.

The mine(s) appears to have lain fallow until July 1751 when Mr. O'Connor from the 'Governors and Company of Mine Adventurers of England' visited the site with a view to the company taking the mine. A limited amount of work was done. Three shafts were sunk on the Sun vein, and 16 tons of ore were found in 48 hours but then it ran out. The company were clearly not willing to provide the substantial capital required and took no further action. The mid 1820s boom saw a lot of activity at what was then known as Weston Hill and between there and Grit mine. A formal attempt was made between the Powis Estate and the Linley Estate to enable the Grit and Weston Hill setts to be worked together, though this does not seem to have actually come about. (For the workings between Weston Hill and Grit see under Stapeley.)

The Weston Hill Mining company sought permission to begin trials on that site in March 1826 but were delayed by another, unnamed company who had some rights. It is probable that this other company were the Grit and Gravels company, also at the time called the Leigh or Lee company on account of their involvement with the drainage scheme of that name, or just The Grit or just The Gravels company. All these names appear in Powis correspondence of the period[12] as workings adjoining Weston Hill sett which went up to the Shrewsbury Road (replaced in 1836 by the turnpike along the valley and now an undefined path along the ridge of Stapeley Hill from Mitchel's Fold to Hemford), with the land to the east of it promised to Grit. This led to later problems as the Weston Hill company believed that Grit would benefit if they drained land on their part of the sett. As a result the estate were requested to provide a plan showing the division between the two companies (see also below and Calcot).

By September an 18-month take note had been signed at ^{1}/10th royalty with a 21-year lease at ^{1}/8th available to the Weston Hill company, if wanted for 'that part of the wastes and commons in Priestweston and Churchstoke called Weston Hill, Pidgeon House Bank, Calcot Bank bounded on the east by a road from Corndon into Middleton township called the Shrewsbury Road'. In November the Weston Hill company took over some land formerly let to Grit, which led to the boundary dispute noted at Calcot. By the end of 1828 Weston Hill had taken even more land from the estate, unfortunately unspecified but probably the land which Grit had leased but not been working 'about Cordon' and which the estate wished to lease to others. This is borne out in November 1828 when, having had water problems with a shaft at the summit of the hill by Shrewsbury Road, the Weston Hill company suggested that a drainage level could go right through the hill. Whether the lease was ever taken up is not known but if it was it was not in effect for long as some Weston Hill shareholders refused to pay their contributions and working was suspended. The mine may have been closed in 1843, for the tithe map of that dates marks only old levels, but it does mark a 'lead works' without specifying that it was closed.

At some stage Walker, Cross and company (see Bog) presumably held a lease as in June 1848 Mr. Walker wrote to the estate giving up all claims on behalf of Mr. Cross, whose lease was assigned a few months later. This may have been a separate concern from Bog as that mine was sold by order in chancery in 1845. However a level called Cross Level was still in use in 1852 as samples of spar with very high silver content were found by Mr. Readwin. The nature of the spar was never established, however, nor was any more found.[13]

In 1851 a Mr. Urwick of Churchstoke enquired about a lease on Weston Hill, but the outcome is not known. The next lessee was Mr. Eddleston with a company from Liverpool, who took over the lease and iron rails at valuation and agreed to extend the level by 100 yds or so as a trial. Eddlestons were still owners when official returns started asking for the ownership of mines in 1859. They were replaced by Richard Croft & Co. a year later when the mine had ceased to be a poor lead mine and become a successful barytes one instead. Richard Croft with partners Reeve and Boustred had formed the Cliffdale Barytes Company in 1857 and taken on what was to become known as Cliffdale Mill at Wagbeach in 1858.[14] They ran the mine until 1926 or 1927 with breaks in production between 1867 and 1871 and 1876 and 1880. Over the extended period it was run under various different names — Cliffdale Barytes Co., Cliffdale Mining Co. and Cliffdale Barytes Co. Ltd., this latter being registered in 1905 but not appearing in official returns until 1913. Personnel changed over the years. Richard Croft died and was replaced by his son William Reeve Croft, and William Boustred was declared bankrupt in 1889, one of the reasons cited being the loss of his appointment at the mine when he sold his shares the previous year. The Powis Estate took the mine in hand by 1934 and ran it briefly, and subsequently it was run by a Mr. Lewis.[15] It finally closed in 1936.[16]

The London Lead Co. trials involved trenching and a short adit, the adjoining 'partners'' mine had a 10 yard deep shaft. The 1751 exploration carried out trenching and sank three shafts and the activities of the 1820s left shafts and adits liberally scattered, as witnessed on older maps. The barytes mine was a bigger prospect altogether. Four principal shafts were sunk: Powis, Bowers, Weston and Sump, the deepest (Weston) going down 75 fathoms. Bowers and Powis did not connect with each other or with any other part of the mine. The mine was drained at 35 fathoms by a level into Cwm Dingle.

No lead production figures have survived but there is no reason to assume them to have amounted to much. Barytes figures exist from 1860 with the gaps mentioned above until the end of the returns in 1913. Though showing the usual massive variations it generally increased as the years went on, getting over the 500 ton per year mark in 1865 and being nearly 1,500 in 1913, giving a total of about 36,000 tons. Interestingly, they made their returns as being in Shropshire until 1885 and as in Montgomeryshire thereafter. A further 14,000 tons were produced in the First World War.[17] Small quantities of calcite were produced late in the mine's life. Employment figures reflect the production — none are available until 1881 when five were employed, numbers then generally rise, peaking at 26 in 1911 and remaining thereabouts until the end.

Little is known of the methods of working or the equipment used, though obviously pumping and winding engines must have existed and concrete bases survive. A compressor and appropriate drills were in process of installation in 1915.[18]

Lead ore during the London Lead Company's tenure probably went to the company's Gadlys smelter at Bagyllt, Flintshire, until the opening of their smelter at Benthall in 1731. In the 1750s the ore went to Pool Quay smelthouse. After hand picking and washing on site, the barytes was carted to the company mill at Wagbeach using traction engines from the 1870s until about 1920 when steam wagons took over.

Little remains to be seen. The location of Weston Shaft is clear, being on private land on the corner of the track (the one-time Shrewsbury Road) to Mitchel's Fold stone circle. Other shaft and adit sites are visible but all the shafts are infilled. One small building, which was for a time an engine house at the mine,[19] survived until the autumn of 2007, relocated to the east edge of Minsterley. The adit and sites of filled shafts and open workings which remain in **Cwm Dingle** were part of this mine under at least some of its incarnations.

Wotherton

Three different mines functioned here between the late 18th century and 1920. Up until 1865 there was a mine east of the road which was to become Wotherton No. 1, from 1866-74 run by M. Maginnis. One part was then run by various owners until it became East Wotherton from 1882 until closure in 1890. The part that had been retained in 1875 (by Mrs. Maginnis) ran as Wotherton mine until 1881. Finally there was Wotherton No. 2 from 1865-1920 to the west of the road, a much more productive enterprise. Regrettably some documents do not make it clear which bit of the mine they are dealing with, which offers scope for confusion. Issues are further confused because the Powis Estate owned the mineral rights and the Wakemans the land, so leases had to be obtained from both.

Crest Wood east of the mine was prospected for lead and barytes at unknown dates, where there were several sets of workings including one shaft (shown on the 1881 Ordnance Survey map), but little can have been found.

Fig. 8.9 A very fine late 19th-century photograph of Wotherton mine demonstrating the problems mines faced if they only had road transport. (coll. K. Lock)

East Wotherton/Wotherton/Wotherton Number 1

Like so many mines this one first comes to light in the late 18th century in the hands of John Lawrence (II?) who was presumably mining lead. There would not have been a great deal of it to find, but Lawrence was certainly working there in 1793[20] and a descendant[21] knew of a share transfer between two of the Lawrence brothers of 1799 indicating not only that they were working it but also that they valued it to some extent. Robert Townson, an eminent geologist, visited the mine in 1798[22] and noted the presence of heavy spar and that the mine was formerly a lead mine, indicating that by that date barytes was being mined.

History then falls silent until 1829 when 'Jas Whitney,[23] Chymist of Shrewsbury' negotiated for a three-year (the surviving draft is altered in pencil to one year) take note at Wotherton Graig (later East Wotherton), to pay royalties of ⅛th on ore and ¹/₁₂th 'clays earths spars and other fossils', a 19-year lease being available if wanted. It is not known if he accepted the offer. Four years later a Mr. Maginnis worked the mine. Royalties accounts for several years up to the mid 1850s have survived and indicate that the mine was probably worked continuously. An M. Maginnis was owner of part of the mine, known as Wotherton No. 1, from 1866-74 when part carried on in other hands and a Mrs. M. Maginnis ran Wotherton (unspecified), which made returns in Shropshire (correctly) and Montgomeryshire (incorrectly) from 1875-81. During this period of Maginnis involvement the history of the other part of the mine started. Two mines made returns from 1865 to 1874, three from 1875 to 1881, and two from 1882 to 1890, and one from then onwards. M. Maginnis ran Wotherton No. 1 until 1874 when after a year's break (when its production was recorded jointly with Wotherton No. 2) a mine called

186

Wotherton No. 1 had W.T. Parker recorded as its owner. Mrs M. Maginnis, presumably a widow, made returns as Wotherton each year until 1881; she may have moved mines or more likely only worked a part of the previous Wotherton Number 1. She must have actually run a mine because she quotes an agent's name, Robert Williams, the same agent as had worked for 'M. Maginnis' at the then Number 1 mine. In 1878, anomalously, in addition to numbers 1 and 2 mines, two returns were made for Wotherton, one being submitted as being in Montgomeryshire. The entry under Shropshire, presumably for Mrs. Maginnis' mine, recorded a surprising 325 tons of very low grade copper ore (about 60% of all that material recorded for the county between 1845 and 1913) which produced 4 tons of metal.

After Mrs. Maginnis's time Wotherton No. 1 passed through various hands, including the landlord's in the early 1880s, until it ended up with William Boustred (75%) and George Young (25%) in 1882 and was renamed East Wotherton from then until it arrived in chancery (to resolve the partnership with Young) on Boustred's bankruptcy in 1889. In 1885, for just the one year, it was in the hands of the East Wotherton Mining Company. Alfred Stevens acquired the mine from the wreckage of the bankruptcy in 1890 and ran it for a year, before considering assigning the lease to Major Patshull. As only a draft survives it is open to doubt if this change of ownership actually happened.

Wotherton No. 1 was worked from two shafts and an adit as well as opencast. The Maginnis mine(s) may well have always been opencast, and certainly were in the late 1830s when Sir Roderick Murchison visited. Apart from the anomalous copper the only contemporary production records are for barytes. Maginnis paid royalties on 82 tons in the second half of 1834 and 287 in the first half of 1837. By the 1850s figures had risen to around 1,000 tons per annum. A report to the landlords in 1933 states that from 1850-55 270 tons of lead ore was won with a further 2 tons in 1858 and 10 in 1864.

Fig. 8.10 Wotherton Mine c.1909. (coll. K. Lock)

187

Fig. 8.11 Wotherton mine c.1909. (coll. K. Lock)

The Maginnises do not seem to have made complete official returns as none of this is declared. When the mine was functioning as Wotherton No. 1/East it produced in excess of 500 tons per annum most years from 1874 to 1887. In 1888 the mine's production was returned with the same proprietors as Cefn Gunthly mine, whilst 1889 and 1890 saw much reduced production. As usual employment figures parallel production figures. No figures are available under Maginnis ownership; thereafter No. 1/East had single figures except for 1885-8 when they rose to a maximum of 15.

In the Maginnis period at least up to 1853 the ore went out by canal boat — in 1834 by Goolden of Union Wharf at Welshpool, in 1835 in Lord Clive's Boat, in 1851-53 via the Shropshire Union Railway and Canal Company (i.e. Welshpool) and in 1855 via Pool Quay. Shipments via Welshpool (i.e. on the canal) would probably have been heading for the Warrington or Liverpool area, both of which contained paint manufacturers. Any shipments from Pool Quay could have been on the canal and for the same destination but as Welshpool was nearer they were probably heading for the River Severn which had wharves there (until the cessation of river traffic in 1862). The use of the river requires a destination south or east, perhaps Shrewsbury. As nothing is known of the location of barytes mills at this period this one clue suggests that milling on the river in Shrewsbury may have carried on after the expiry of the 1838 lease at Abbey Mill, though probably not at that particular mill in 1855 as it is believed to have closed in 1851. There is little to see at East Wotherton.

Wotherton Number 2

From 1865 returns were made for Wotherton No. 2, from 1866-71 in the name of Goodlass[24] and Company. If anything can be taken as read, this mine passed via James Yelland in 1872 into the hands of a succession of similarly named companies: Wotherton Mining Co. in 1873-6, Wotherton Barytes Mining Co. in 1877-9 and Wotherton Barytes & Lead Mining Co. Ltd. from 1880 onwards until the end of the official returns. It made a loss for its first two years, after which profits followed though obviously not enough as the company went into liquidation in 1887 and was re-floated the following February under the same name but with greater capital of £10,000 plus debentures and £1,000 mortgage. A new shaft was sunk and more ore was mined.

From 1891 they were the only company working a mine at Wotherton and may have mined the former East Wotherton site as well. Production fell off with depth and due to this fall in quantity, a fall in quality and the perpetual problems with water the mine was economically worked out by 1911, when the last production figures were returned. The mine was, almost inevitably, tried by Shropshire Mines Ltd. in 1919 and closed for the last time in 1920. Approaches were made to the Wakeman estate in the 1930s but no action resulted, though the mine was surveyed down to Shallow Adit, Arch Level and Deep Level Adits (all wholly underground) and it was suggested that if 'number 1 shaft was put into shape and equipped with a wooden hand windlass for hoisting with wheelbarrows used underground, four to six men might be employed fossicking'. They ultimately decided not to proceed. The Wotherton Barytes and Lead Mining Co. Ltd. worked other mines and, by acquiring Shropshire Barytes Co. acquired Hanwood Mill in 1890 to process their product. They remained in business there after the closure of Wotherton mine, amalgamating with Shropshire Lead Mines Ltd. in 1916 to form Shropshire Mines Ltd.

Fig. 8.11 The engine house and office at Wotherton mine, now a dwelling, photographed in June 2004. Note the cut-out for the flywheel. (Author)

Wotherton No. 2 was to the west of the road where there were three shafts down to maximum depth of 850 feet and opencast workings. The only production records are for barytes, and despite the name of the company from 1883-1913 there are no records of lead production. With a few hiccoughs it probably averaged 3,000 tons a year for the period that records are available (1873-1911) with a maximum of 6,100 tons in 1901, a total of 128,000 tons being raised. 16 tons was raised in 1919-20. The barytes from here was reported as being the purest in England. Towards the end of the mine's life some calcite was raised and some obtained from the tips.

As usual employment figures parallel production figures. No. 2 ran with an average of about 30 employees rising to a maximum of 62 in 1909. The mine had an engine at Old Engine Shaft from which it pumped, and it wound New Engine Shaft using pulleys. The floating of the Wotherton Barytes and Lead Co. Ltd. in 1880 heralded an investment programme, including a new shaft completed in 1893 at a cost of £3,394, (and £116 for a weighing machine and boiler). A new engine was erected but the cost is not given. At some stage there was a mill on site, possibly until the company acquired Hanwood Mill in 1890. The output always travelled by road, latterly to the company's mill. They ran a fleet of steam tractors and traction engines for this purpose and problems with road damage were constant. Several former mine buildings at Wotherton Number 2 mine have been converted into dwellings, the most notable being the engine house with its unusual cut-out for the flywheel which is visible from the road (Fig. 8.11).

9   Lead Mines south of the Stiperstones

Most of these are in a group of small mines of which much was expected; that is, they were holes in the ground into which money could be poured. The majority were in the parish of More and all to the west of the Pontesford Linley Fault (see p.15). Many were on land owned by the Mores of Linley.

Mining activity is recorded in Linley parish in the late 17th century, a lease of 4 September 1696 being recorded between Rich. More and Edward Lewis and John Lewis of mines, pits and veins of lead, copper and tin ore, for 21 years, at a $^{1}/_{9}$th royalty, and under which they could set up mills.[1] There is no specific location for the mines, anywhere in the manors of More and Linley in the parish of More being included. The next known lease is from 1714. Again it was for 21 years, but this time the royalty was £4 a ton 'for mines, pits, groves and veins of copper, lead or tin ore in the manors of Shelve & township of Moreswood'.[2] The mention of the township of Moreswood indicates that the mine was either Pitcholds or, more likely Squilver Hill.

Two mines, Reilth and Whitcliffe, do not fit better in any other chapter and are therefore included here. For a map of the mines included in this chapter see Figure 6.1.

Cefn Gunthly

This mine deserves to be well known if only for the instructive variety of spellings it engendered; 12 known ones are cross-referenced in the gazetteer and it is not difficult to guess that other variants existed. The most interesting is from a scrap of an account which records the activity of the 'Cefnagunthley Brites Mine Co' from 1863. The use of the word 'brites' for barytes is also interesting as the substance was called that (or britus) locally until it lost any relevance with the end of mining.

In this book Cefn Gunthly has been used to denote workings on top of and on the east of the hill of that name and those to the south-west by Pultheley Farm, though these latter were sometimes known as Pultheley mine. Mines on the adjoining Heath Mynd are referred to under that name, but at various times all of those have been called Cefn Gunthly, and the mine which came to be called Cefn Gunthly was known as Rhadley prior to the development of the mine now known by that name.

Originally worked for lead and optimistically mined for copper and tin from the middle of the 19th century onwards only barytes was ever won.

In 1827 a lease of the sett was negotiated between Mr. More and a group of partners including Messrs. Boothman and Buckley which was intended to run for 30 years from 24 June 1828; but the miners wanted additional land at Rhadley included, which was not agreeable to Mr. More, and the lease was never signed. The managing partner, Richard Briscoe, was allowed onto the property whilst the details of the lease were still being discussed and began work but without much profit. The mine was worked sluggishly and inefficiently until *c.*1842, latterly by Briscoe alone. Had the lease been in force there would have been a condition that the landlord could re-enter the mine if it was not worked for two calendar months in any year, but there was no lease. Mr. More wished to get Briscoe off the site together with his cabins, tools, timber and ore, so that the mine could be let to others. His solicitor, W. How of Shrewsbury, wrote numerous letters to Briscoe and the other partners and for five years received a continuous stream of excuses, almost all from Briscoe. Legal opinion was that More should serve a demand for possession on each of the partners, who by virtue of the lack of a lease were tenants at will. Whether the matter went to law or how it was resolved is not known, but there is no record that the mine was let again until 1857.

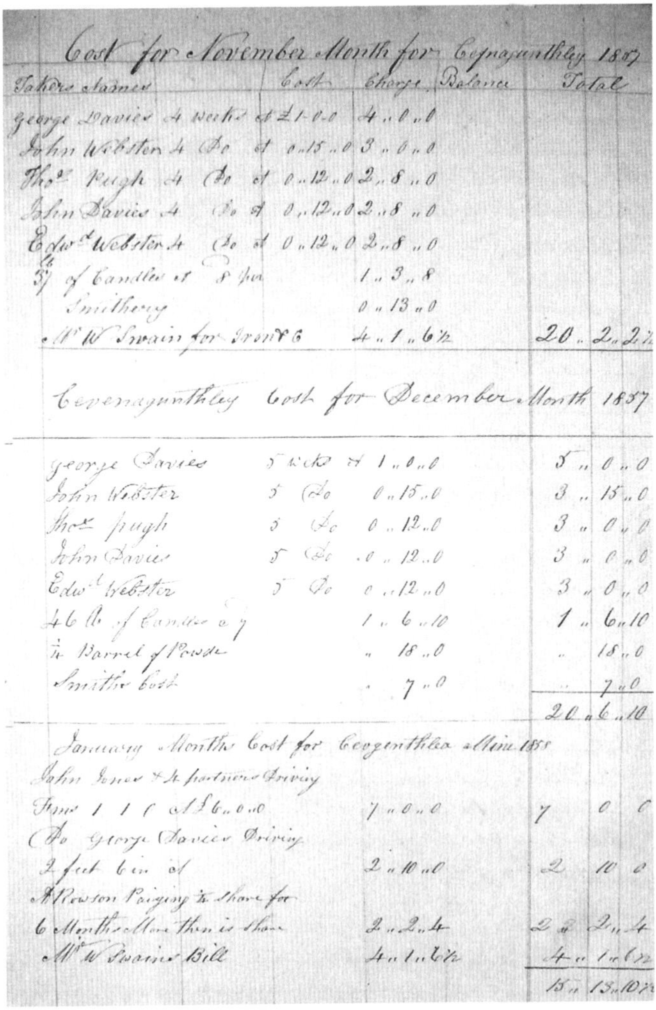
Cost for November Month for Cefnagunthley 1857
Takers Names | Cost | Charge | Balance | Total
George Davies 4 weeks at £1-0-0 4..0..0
John Webster 4 Do at 0..15..0 3..0..0
Thos Pugh 4 Do at 0..12..0 2..8..0
John Davies 4 Do at 0..12..0 2..8..0
Edwd Webster 4 Do at 0..12..0 2..8..0
37 of Candles at 8 per 1..3..8
Smithery 0..13..0
Mr W Swain for Iron &c 4..1..6½ 20..2..2½
Cevenagunthley Cost for December Month 1857
George Davies 5 wks at 1..0..0 5..0..0
John Webster 5 Do 0..15..0 3..15..0
Thos Pugh 5 Do 0..12..0 3..0..0
John Davies 5 Do 0..12..0 3..0..0
Edwd Webster 5 Do 0..12..0 3..0..0
46 lb of Candles @ 7 1..6..10 1..6..10
¼ Barrel of Powder 18..0 18..0
Smiths cost 7..0 7..0
20..6..10
January Month Cost for Cevgenthlea Mine 1858
John Jones & his partners Driving
Fms 1 1 1 at £6..0..0 7..0..0 7 0 0
Do George Davies Driving
2 feet 6 in at 2..10..0 2 10 0
A Rowson Paying his Share for
6 Months Mon then is share 2..2..4 2 2 4
Mr W Swains Bill 4..1..6½ 4..1..6½
15..13..10½

Fig. 9.1 A good example of a cost book from Cefn Gunthly complete with interesting spellings of the name. (SA 2652/1)

Official returns did not catch up until 1859, by which time Arthur Rowson and company were running the mine and did so until 1864. In that year Cefnagunthley Brites Mine company appear, probably the same concern but put on a slightly more formal basis. The cost book which survives gives an insight into the development and running of a small mine (and uses three different spellings of the mine's name). The book lists payments, mostly for labour, but all sorts of sundries appear including wheelbarrows and wheels, 'ruff' and fine powder, lots of candles, poles, tobacco and outside work, for instance by smiths. From its beginning in July 1857 until May 1861 the book only covers these payments, but from then it includes the contributions made by the shareholders who paid these costs on a monthly basis and ultimately hoped to share the profits on a similar basis. The shareholders held 'ounce' shares — 'Captain' Arthur Rowson held 3.5 ounces, two others two ounces each and another 16 half or quarter ounce shares — and they had to pay between 7 shillings and £1 per ounce per month during the currency of the book. Notes of a meeting in May 1860 are included at which several shareholders dropped out, there having been no profits to date. The remainder agreed that Rowson and John Thomas should see the landlord, Rev. More, and negotiate a take note and a lease, for they had clearly been working for three years without such. The result of those negotiations are revealed the following July when £2 is paid to Mr. Whittall, Rev. More's agent, for a take note. After this date entries become few, only eight up to the end of the book in August 1864. The productivity of the mine clearly did not improve, as is testified by there only being two royalty payments totalling less that £2 10s. between them. Little evidence of the working is included but it does mention driving westerly and shallow, middle and deep adit levels, including clearing out a sump on the shallow level, the three levels presumably being those at the north end of the hill.

The mine is recorded in two publications in about 1869 as not working (Morton and Liscombe). Cefn-y-Guntla Mine Ltd. was floated in 1872 but to what effect is not known, and the mine may have lain fallow until it was acquired to be worked for barytes in 1887 by William Boustred, who like many others both had a hand in several local mines and went bankrupt in the process. In his case this latter event happened in late 1889 when in the statement of his interests it is noted that his failure was due to speculation in mining and loss of appointment in the Cliffdale Barytes Company. He also had interests in East Wotherton mine which, according to the official returns, was being worked in conjunction with Cefn Gunthly. His methods are perhaps revealed by the following comment: 'There are no books of account, the bankrupt stating he has never kept any.' The only production and employment figures available for the mine are from this period, when about 1,100 tons of barytes was produced by a maximum of six men in the three years, and some of this was from East Wotherton mine. By 1899 the mine was standing, and had been owned (but not worked) by Edmund Wardman from 1893. The mine does not warrant a mention in the British Geological Survey's volumes on barytes mines in 1915, 1916 or 1922. For the last stage of the mine's history as for the first its fortunes were to be linked with Rhadley. Skinner's *Mining Year Book* for 1921 shows its being owned by Rhadley Mines Ltd., which had been formed in 1919 to acquire leases on this mine and Rhadley from leaseholders who do not appear to have worked either mine. No more is heard of the mine thereafter.

The workings of the mine were in two distinct groups. To the north and east at least six adits and four shafts worked three parallel veins, and to the south-west (Pultheley) a further two adits and three shafts, one of the adits being driven in 1832.[3] Of the equipment of this mine we have little information, except for Mr Briscoe's cabins.

Fig. 9.2 (top) A view in May 2007 of Cefn Gunthly's three adits running diagonally up the hillside, taken from the slopes of Heath Mynd. (Author)
Fig. 9.3 (lower) Looking across the mine's largest adit back towards Heath Mynd

There are several adits visible including what could be the 1860s mine's three adits, these latter are most readily visible at a distance from the slopes of Heath Mynd (Figs. 9.2 and 9.3). The rest of the unimproved part of the hill is littered with disturbed ground, no doubt related to the mining.

Heathmynd

Though no doubt opened to find lead, this was the only mine in this part of the county to have been worked for ochre. Official returns for 1860 state that the mine had closed 30 years earlier, making it possible that it was worked with Cefn Gunthly by Briscoe and his partners. It is noted as reopening in 1862. In 1865 it was owned by Parker and Co., and was worked by Peake & Co. from 1866, although it is noted as closed in 1869 (Morton), by which time it had been worked for ochre. Ochre again provides the last reference to the mine, the *Mining Journal* informing its readers that Stiperstones Consols Ltd. had driven a level 100 fathoms long in 1873-4 searching for ochre. Over the years the mine was worked from four shafts and three levels, most in a straight line across the southern flank of Heath Mynd with one level to the north. No figures for production or employment have been found and remains are slight.

Pitcholds

Very little is known about this mine. Probably either it or Squilver Hill existed in 1714 or even in 1696 (see above) and again in 1869 when a description of the mines was published in which one or the other was described as opened to a slight extent (Liscombe). The only firm ground is that Stiperstones Consols Ltd. drove a level 100 fathoms long in 1873-4 looking for lead. Two levels are known of and were at one time visible in a quarry; one is now dammed as a water supply.

Reilth

As with so many mines very little information is available, but here it seems that there was never much to know. A lease was granted in 1836 by William Botfield to William Cross of Chester for 21 years to the mines and minerals on land at Reilth Mountain and Vron Wood. By 1870, Kelly's *Directory* notes that 'lead ore has been found and a pit sunk but has not been worked'.

Rhadley

Rhadley was the least unsuccessful of the mines in this section. Like most of them it was tried initially for lead, but what success was achieved was with barytes. The mine first comes into view with two receipts in 1825 from R.B. More, the landlord, to Samuel Naylor, in each case for driving 20 yards at 'Radeley level' at £30 and for the erection of a cabin at £1 10s. Naylor was a well known local mine agent who was involved with the Lawrences at many mines. An undated plan of South Bog mine marks Powell's Level east of the summit of Pen Rhadley, which is clearly part of this mine despite South Bog being better known as an alternative name for Rock mine. This plan also shows that the

Fig. 9.4 Underground in Rhadley mine showing a remnant of the compressor pipework.
(Kelvin Lake, I A Recordings)

mine was being developed by both More and Briscoe, each of them having parts of the mine in their names and costs separated out. Places where there was good ore and strong spar are noted, with the maximum depth of shaft at 113 yards.[4] This is presumably a development plan which predates Naylor's '40 yards' mentioned above, and also the More v Briscoe case at Cefn Gunthly as at that date not only were they in dispute but More refused Briscoe a lease at Rhadley.

The mine must subsequently have been worked as it is recorded in the very incomplete official returns as 'ceased work 1854-5' and '1861-8 now opening on Barytes 1863' (*sic*); presumably 1863-8 saw some barytes production but no owners are named. Morton's survey of 1869 reveals that that work was not a success as the mine was then standing. Rhadley Mining Co. took over the mine in 1869 and ran it until 1875 when it seems to have stood again until 1887 when a few years of more or less continuous operation began (it was standing in 1892 and probably 1893 and 1894) under a succession of owners: Edmund Wardman & Son in 1887-90, South Shropshire Barytes Co. Ltd. in 1891,[5] Alfred Haywood in 1892, M. Hulton-Harrop in 1893-4, Rhadley Barytes Co. in 1895-7, M. Hulton-Harrop in 1898-1902 (when it was worked in conjunction with Gatten and Westcott), Thomas Butler in 1903-9 and Shropshire Lead Mines Ltd.,

Fig. 9.5 Underground in Rhadley mine showing the surviving tramway.
(Kelvin Lake, I A Recordings)

in 1910-13 (for some of the time in conjunction with Rock mine). Curiously it seems to have stood unused during the First World War but was reopened by Rhadley Mines Ltd. from about 1920 to 1924. They were registered in November 1919 with a capital of £4,000 to acquire a lease for this mine and Cefn Gunthly, then held by C. McNeal and W.P. Jones who were two of the directors of the new company. The next mining was by E. Murgatroyd of Keighley, Yorkshire, who ran several mines in a small way in the early to mid 1930s. Some mining was in progress in 1940 as there is a passing reference to it that year in a statement about local mining made by the then landlord, Sir Jasper More. The mine contained good quality barytes in a vein between 2 and 12 feet thick.

Much of the work was done from six adits although at least one shaft was dug. The interior of the mine was of some complexity, with stopes descending from some of the adits to further levels. A final level was driven into the west side of the hill almost at stream level before 1915 to open up further ground and to connect with Boat Level, but this was a failure and Boat Level was not reached after several hundred yards of driving. Some opencast work was carried out at the top of the hill. The tips were reworked by Murgatroyd, who did no underground work after 1933. The mine was never a large employer with a maximum of 10 prior to Shropshire Lead Mines' involvement where-after the figures for Rock were included, the two mines employing a maximum of 21 men in 1912. Double figures were reached once more, with 11 employees, in 1924. Production was proportionately small; 9 tons of lead is recorded in 1907-8 and about 7,000 tons of barytes by 1910. Little is known of the equipment or of transport at the mine, except that in 1902 it had a short tramway which came out from an adit to a tip. South Shropshire Barytes and Lead Co. Ltd. leased land at Snailbeach, adjoining the land now occupied by the Village Hall, and built a barytes mill around about 1889, which almost certainly took any barytes the mine may have produced, but had ceased working by 1894.

Squilver Hill

About a quarter of a mile north-west of Pitcholds — their histories are virtually indistinguishable — Squilver Hill could date from as early as 1696. The key difference between this mine and Pitcholds is that Stiperstones Consols Ltd. drove their usual 100 fathom level here looking for barytes and lead, rather than just lead.

As at Pitcholds the remains are in a quarry, but here they are buried below spoil.

Whitcliffe

By far the most southerly lead mine in the county, it was tried in 1751 by the landowner, the Earl of Powis. It was visited in July of that year by Mr. O'Connor, secretary to the Governors and Company of Mine Adventurers of England. This company was set up in 1698, financed by a lottery amidst great publicity. Despite its name it does not seem to have operated in England but entirely in Wales (although the mine itself was in England). If not wholly fraudulent it was not wholly above board, its activities petering out around about 1760. The mine was a quarter of a mile from Ludford Bridge and described as a new discovery: 'A slender Tryal at the expense of £22 only, was put by his Lordship's Order to that Work, wherein a small quantity of good Potter's Ore was found.' However the shaft sides fell in and nothing except rubbish mixed with 'an unkind greyish stone' was left. A quarter of a mile further along the same road the vein was cut in a quarry and four or five small shafts were sunk to prove the vein but without success. The area was considered to be unpromising.[6]

10 Mines in the Long Mynd area

This area is centred on the Pre-Cambrian rocks which run from the Pontesbury Linley Fault in the west to the hills to the east of Church Stretton. Most of the mines lie between the Long Mynd and the Stiperstones, with a few to the east but none in the main block of the Long Mynd itself. A few of the mines are in geologically similar rocks to the north and one, Whittingslow, lies just to the south of the hills and is included on geographical grounds.

Initially prospecting was carried out for several metals including tin, copper, lead and iron. In practice no tin is mineable in Shropshire and no significant quantities of lead exist east of the Pontesbury Linley fault (hence its use as a boundary to this area) though one or two mines did produce small quantities. Copper was found in moderate quantities in a few mines but the real prize ultimately proved to be barytes.

As with most of the county it is probable that Roman and pre-Roman mining took place but thereafter no activity is known until the very end of the 18th century. As stated elsewhere, barytes was not extracted to a great extent anywhere until the middle years of the 19th century, and in this particular area extraction did not really get under way until the early years of the 20th. Intensive mining not only started late but it also finished late — the last major non-coal mine in the county was at Huglith which closed in 1945, Sallies and Gatten mines survived until 1948, and after that only small amounts of barytes, lead and calcite were extracted anywhere in the county.

Cardington (and Frodseley)

This is not a mine but a convenient handle for a series of trials and small mines some of which are really outside the scope of this book as they lie in coal measures, and leases sometimes either specifically include or exclude coal, iron and fireclay as well as the usual tin, copper, lead and zinc. The earliest mention of mining is in a lease of 1628 for Lydley Hayes which reserves all mines of tin, coal, ironstone and lead for the landlord,[1] a clause that remained in leases for this estate at least until 1770. As an aside, Lydley Hayes was the home of the noted geologist Robert Townson, who published works at the end of the 18th century covering the geology both of this country and parts of Europe.

The first dated lease for mining was granted by Sir Richard Corbett to John Wilkinson, the ironmaster, to search for copper, lead and tin ores and other metals and minerals but excluding coal, iron and building materials, for 21 years at Tutty Hill, Bradley Hill,

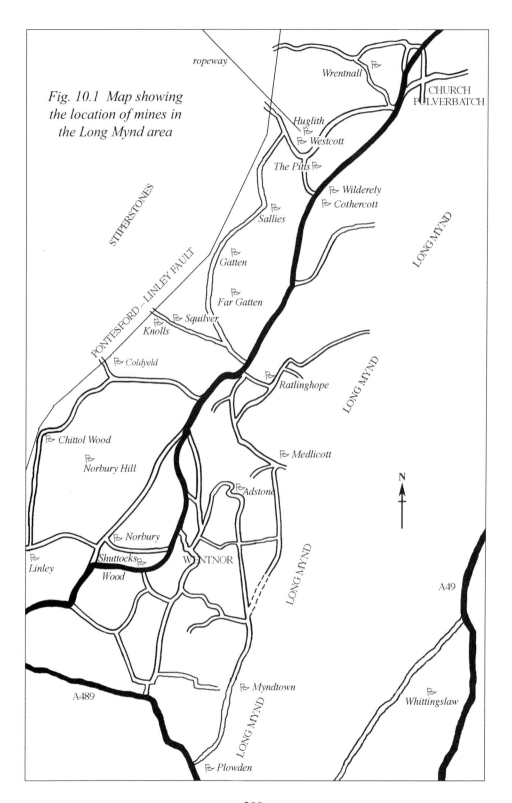

Fig. 10.1 Map showing the location of mines in the Long Mynd area

ropeway

Wrentnall

CHURCH PULVERBATCH

STIPERSTONES

Huglith

Westcott

The Pitts

Wilderely

Cothercott

Sallies

LONG MYND

Gatten

PONTESFORD – LINLEY FAULT

Far Gatten

Squilver

Knolls

Coldyeld

Ratlinghope

LONG MYND

Chittol Wood

Medlicott

Norbury Hill

N

Adstone

Norbury

WENTNOR

Shuttocks Wood

Linley

LONG MYND

A49

A489

Myndtown

Whittingslaw

LONG MYND

Plowden

Woodden Hill and Cardington Moor. The royalties were to be $^{1}/_{7}$th copper, $^{1}/_{8}$th lead, $^{1}/_{6}$th tin and 10s. per ton for lapis calaminari — calamine or zinc carbonate.[2] Clearly copper ore was found as its existence is mentioned by Robert Townson in 1798: 'Here some years ago a trial mining was made in search of copper, and some yellow copper ore was found, but of no consequence.'[3]

Reverend Plymley mentions copper ore in 1803[4] and a lode is marked as such on the Ordnance Survey map of the area surveyed between 1816 and 1836. In addition to the above, Murchison refers to trials and small workings for copper at Corston Heath and 'near Hope Bowdler'.[5]

In 1870 the Corbetts gave a licence for Edward Shepherd and John Job (of Snailbeach mine) to search for two years for minerals at Bentley Ford Farm, Frodseley, and Day House Farm, Cardington, royalties to be $^{1}/_{12}$th on coal or minerals. Shortly after this three other names were added to the adventurers, and Penkridge and Courthouse farms were added to the area to be prospected. In 1872 Corbett gave Job further time to test the shaft (interestingly the reference is to the old shaft in the Dingle and not to workings in any other place), and a 21-year lease was available if required. This lease for Bentley Ford was taken up by the South Shropshire Haematite Iron Ore and Coal Co. Ltd. who worked the mine for iron and fireclay.[6] No further history is known.

Chittol

This mine witnessed another minor attempt at copper mining. Three adits and a shaft were excavated in 1866 and 1867. Some ore was found but a low level adit did not succeed in draining the mine and it was abandoned.[7] Official returns give a different, but no better picture, and according to them the mine closed in 1859. There is little to see on the site.

Cothercott

From about 1908 until 1928 Cothercott was in local terms a fairly major producer of barytes. Production began again briefly in 1934 and 1935 and insufficiently successful prospecting was carried out in the early 1980s and again ten years later. The mine was in the Wilderley Estate purchased by the Walker family of Beverley (who were also involved in cooking oil refining at Hull) in 1905, and James Bainton Walker seems to have started the mine when he took over the estate in 1908. Little in the way of official returns were made but clearly barytes was being produced before 1913. 23,000 tons were dug in total.

J.B. Walker ran the mine as a private concern until 1920 when he became a director of the then newly formed Cothercott Company. The mine had previously traded as the Cothercott Mining Company and continued to do so, though this was never a legal name. In the early 1920s an influx of capital occurred with the arrival of Shropshire Mineral Investments Ltd. as shareholders, though they had been involved with Cothercott from at least 1920.[8] Skinner's *Mining Year Book* for the years 1921 to 24 confirm this and mention two capital projects apparently in progress. One of these was the purchase of

160 acres of Thresholds Farm and the development of a new mine, the other was the construction of a works at Saltney near Chester. Of the former there are remains of the tramway (see below), of the latter nothing more seems to be known.

All the investment did not spell success for either concern. Shropshire Mineral Investments appointed a receiver in June 1922 and Cothercott Co. followed suit a year later. The former did not recover and their furniture was sold in November 1922, although the company was not wound up until 1929. Cothercott Co. fared a little better.

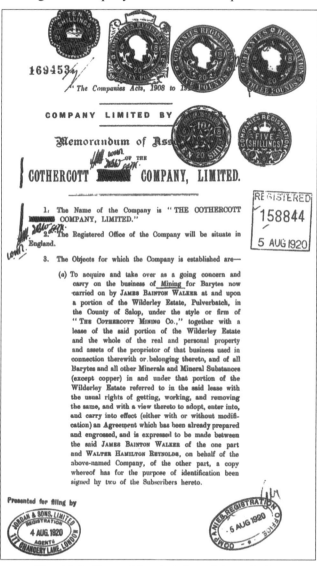

The receiver ceased to act in September 1924 and new management was installed, but the improvement was short-lived. Regular work at the mine ceased in 1928 and the company itself was wound up in 1930. Records however indicate that nine men were employed in 1934 and 1935. It is locally believed that Laportes, through Malehurst Barytes Co., were interested in the mine, and whilst there is no documentary evidence a carpenter from Huglith mine came here to work on the tramway to enable a stockpile of barytes to be removed.[9] This was presumably after the 1928 closure. No abandonment plans were submitted. It is possible that it was hoped to reopen the mine, for it was left partly equipped and boys used to play with detonators which they found in a shed, one losing two fingers.[10] During the Second World War the government were very concerned about shortages of fine white barytes (the RAF used a lot of it in paint) and associated grinding capacity, and it seems odd that Cothercott, with good reserves of quality material and a fairly recent mill, was not re-opened.

Fig. 10.2 Part of the Articles of Association of the Cothercott Company showing the 'official' alteration of the name from the Cothercott Mining Company to the Cothercott Company

202

Fig. 10.3 One of the few photographs showing Cothercott mine at work, probably taken in 1926. (coll. K. Lock)

Mining probably began at what was to become the site of their crushing mill on the side of what had been the first Shrewsbury to Bishops Castle turnpike. Some adits and possibly a shaft were dug here, and adits and shafts were also dug in the valley to the east. It was this latter site that became the more important. Cothercott is unique locally in the extent of its use of tramways and in owning a steam locomotive. Before 1915 a steeply graded line had been built to a road loading dock at the mill site using a self-acting incline.[11] The mill was under construction in 1915 and by the time this came into use the tramway incline had been replaced by a reverse and high level entry into the mill.

Production, as everywhere, fluctuated wildly. Figures survive for most years from 1910/11 (38 tons) to 1918 (1,236 tons), peaking at 3,166 tons in 1914. If the quoted figure for total production of 23,000 tons[12] is correct there must have been an average of 2,000 tons per annum between 1919 and 1928.

Employment figures likewise fluctuate. Underground they range from 5 in 1910/11 to a maximum of 16 in 1914 and average about 10 during the 1920s. On the surface the numbers are equal or greater from 1913 to 1926, with a maximum of 23 in 1923. The re-opening in 1934/35 following the 1928 closure was handled by 9 men each year.

As in many rural mines, transport of the finished product to the nearest railhead was a problem. During the First World War the mine and Shropshire County Council had exchanged correspondence with reference to the damage that Cothercott's trac-tion engines were doing to the roads, especially on the several steep hills, when trans-porting barytes to Pontesbury Station. So bad were things that the round trip of some 12 miles could take three days in adverse conditions. In an attempt to resolve this problem the mine planned to build a tramway to Dorrington railway station some 6 miles away.[13] The tramway crossed the road by the mill and was constructed for a mile or so to

Fig. 10.4 The head frame shown in Fig. 10.3 as it was in the 1960s. (Drawing by M. Newton)

Fig. 10.5 (this page and opposite) A view to the east from Cothercott hill in March 1997 showing the principal mining area and the lines of the tramway which splits right centre with the lower branch going to the left-hand edge of the photograph. Adits and shallow shafts were dug below the tramway, in the valley by the junction and to and off the left. (Author)

a point near Outrack. For reasons now unknown, but probably partly financial and partly improved roads and motor lorries, the tramway was never finished. It was, however, used for a time with the bagged barytes being transhipped to a tractor and trailer at

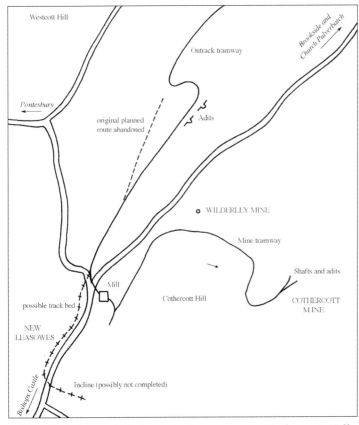

Fig. 10.6 Map of Cothercott, the arrow on Cothercott Hill indicating the approximate viewpoint for fig. 10.5

Outrack. The mine owned one locomotive, a Hunslet Engine Company saddle tank of 1877 purchased second hand in 1919 from Dinorwic Quarry in North Wales. The locomotive, at one time called 'George', was renamed 'Minstrel Park' after one of its original owner's racehorses. But it was not successful at Cothercott, regularly de-railing — it was a 1 foot 10½ inch gauge and the track would have been 2 foot gauge! It finally turned on its side, probably in the mid 1920s, and stayed there until scrapped in 1942. One further length of tramway was started to serve the proposed new mine at Thresholds Farm. Some 500 yards of laying

out work can be seen alongside the road before it would have gone under the road and up an inclined plane. It seems that virtually no other work of any type took place on the mine at Thresholds.

Little evidence has come to light on where the ground barytes went to from this mine. There were paint and varnish manufacturers on Humberside who, given the Walker family connection with the area, may have received some. The Cheshire/Merseyside area is always a probability and certainly in 1922 some was sent, via Dorrington Station, to Orr's Zinc White Ltd., on Merseyside.

The remains are extensive but spread out. The mill site is readily visible with foundations, a retaining wall, the remains of the reservoir and tramway and, at the time of writing, some mill stones. The tramway to the main mining site is visible in places round the hill and Wilderley mine is passed. To the east the tramway is now mainly a farm track with two branches visible. The area was landscaped after the recent prospecting and although much ground disturbance is visible it is difficult to interpret. There are several areas of former activity where stoping is visible, as well as the sites of adits and shafts. The tramway to Outrack is traceable for part of its route where it is near a public footpath, and passes two levels from Wilderley mine. What appears to be a branch leaves the line. This was the intended route but was abandoned as it would not have maintained a continuous downhill gradient for loaded trains, taking the line too low at one point, and resulting in a subsequent uphill gradient. The later route used a very tight 'S' bend to get itself to Outrack, the vestiges of which are still just visible. Parts of 'V' tipping wagon are now preserved locally. One building has been relocated a mile or so away and is now used as a barn (Fig. 10.9).

Fig. 10.7 The ruins of the grinding mill at Cothercott in July 1970. (S.M. Sonsino)

Fig. 10.8 This photograph of Cothercott was taken in July 1929 by an employee of the Geological Survey of Great Britain (now the British Geological Survey) from New Leasowes. By 1929 the mine was not being worked though the tramway tracks look very clean for even half a year's neglect. The tramway from the mine crosses the lower right corner with the reverse being out of sight below the picture. It then returns to what appears to be a transhipment point opposite the reservoir. From there lines go to the mill and to the loading bay. The light coloured building between the mill and the loading bay is the stable. On the other side of the main road the beginning of the Outrack tramway can be seen. The level crossing, which may have gone by this date, would be hidden by the mill buildings. The tramway itself does not seem to go beyond the fence line. Also in the photograph are Callow Hill Quarry, at that time providing most of the Snailbeach Railways traffic. It is the whitish area on the intermediate skyline directly above the mill. The ropeway from Huglith mine to Minsterley is just about visible due to its line of pylons climbing towards the top left of the photograph. (British Geological Survey)

Fig. 10.9 The one building from Cothercott mine to survive is in re-use at a nearby smallholding in June 2004. (Author)

Fig. 10.10 The remains of a 'V' tipping wagon alongside the track bed of the Outrack tramway by the 'S' bend (see Fig 10.6), March 1997. The remains have since been preserved locally. (Author)

Gatten and Far Gatten

Known references to mining at Gatten go back to a lease granted by Noel Hill to Messrs. Lowe and Potter for an illegible location in 1752.[14] In 1782 a lease was granted to Messrs. Lovett and Smith to mine for lead and copper in the Manor of Gatten in the parishes of Pulverbatch and Ratlinghope, but nothing more is known of these phases of activity. Copper was apparently mined there as in 1870 Kelly's *Directory* records that 'At

Fig. 10.11 A photograph of the barytes vein outcrop at Gatten. (British Geological Survey)

Gatten there are copper mines'. The precise location of these operations is not known but it could be at what was to become the barytes mine or of any of the sites listed as Far Gatten. In 1887 the then landowner M. Hulton-Harrop developed a barytes mine. He appears in the official returns as owner and sometimes as agent until 1902, during which period he also ran Westcott and Rhadley mines.

The mine was standing from 1903 to 1905. When it re-opened in 1906 it was being worked by Thomas Butler, who carried on until 1909, when Shropshire Lead Mines Ltd. took over for one year. Mr. Butler again appeared in the returns for 1911 as owner before Shropshire Mines Ltd. worked it intermittently.[15] In a newsletter to staff in December 1919 the firm stated that 'These old mines [Rorrington was also being referred to] are being opened out and it is hoped that they may give considerable employment in the future. Both promise well.' In 1922 they dug a new shaft and were considering installing an aerial ropeway to take the barytes from here and from Huglith mine, presumably to Malehurst, but Gatten was never connected to the ropeway. There is no evidence of any working after 1922 when much of

Fig. 10.12 In contrast to other explosive magazines illustrated, that at Gatten, photographed in June 2007, is part underground and constructed of brick. (Author)

the company's activities ceased, until Shropshire Mines Ltd.'s successors, Malehurst Barytes Co. Ltd., took a 20-year lease in 1944 from the Hulton-Harrops, the mine being referred to as Brownhill.[16] The lease stipulated that no buildings should be visible from the landlord's house, 'Gatten Lodge', or from specified parts of the drive, and that a weighbridge had to be provided. The mine was closed in November 1948 and the lease surrendered the following year.

Lead was also tried for at Gatten as the plan accompanying the above lease is clearly

209

Fig. 10.13 The remains at Gatten mine in June 2007. The main shaft is below the square of 'turf' at the left-hand end of the slab with the bolts for the winder behind it. The base of the diesel tank is visible on the right in front of the concrete slab. (Author)

marked with 'trial level (lead)' and 'trial shafts (lead)'. As the site was to the east of the Pontesford Linley Fault, economic quantities of lead would have been improbable. The activity presumably took place some time between 1881, when the large scale Ordnance Survey map shows no sign, and 1902, when it does. Perhaps the barytes was found whilst searching for lead *c*.1887.

In 1891 Gatten mine was proposed as the terminus of an extension to the Snailbeach Railway. Plans were made for an Act of Parliament for the 11 miles of new route which would have served many of the (by then failing) lead mines. It received the Royal Assent but was never built.

Barytes mining started when a large mass of the material was discovered alongside a track, and was worked open cast followed later by an adit. In 1922 a 170 foot inclined shaft was dug and a vertical shaft in 1945. Quantity was quite good, with 9,700 tons produced by 1912, 7,500 tons from then until 1920 and 1,600 tons in 1944, figures for the remaining years being unavailable. The numbers employed at the mine were usually in single figures, rising to peaks of 16 in the First and Second World Wars. Unusually for this area, U-shaped wagons were used above and below ground with only the bodies being wound up and down the shaft. It is believed that some processing of barytes from this mine and Rhadley and Westcott was done here during the 1880s and 1890s.[17] The site of shafts and collapsed adits are visible on the site as are the bases for the electric winder, a fuel tank and, at an appropriate distance, the ruins of a magazine.

Far Gatten was a much smaller barytes mine about a third of a mile south of Gatten. The vein was proved over quite a distance by three adits at an unknown date or dates. No production figures are available. There are the remains of collapsed adits and filled shafts at the site but little else.

Hazelor

A minor copper mine, this was developed by a person or persons unknown. According to the official returns made from 1860 to 1865, during the mid 19th-century copper boom, the mine had ceased working about seven years earlier. If no facts are known about this mine, at least it has a ghost story. In September 1881 a man saw the ghost of Sarah Duckett, who had disappeared several years earlier, near Old Hazel Gate toll-bar, Church Stretton. The apparition disappeared near an old mine shaft known as Copper Hole, and the shaft was dug out to see if her body could be found, but to no effect.[18]

Huglith

Mining at Huglith had begun by the late 18th century. A 31-year lease was granted on 20 November 1795[19] by Thomas Pemberton of Millichope, John Probert of Copthorne and others to William Hitchcock to search for and take away lead, tin ore, copper ore and any other ores, metal or metals from a large tract of land including what later became Huglith, at a $^{1}/_{8}$th royalty. In 1801 a land sale included '**The Pitts**' just to the south-east of the later Huglith and Westcott mines and south of the lane to Castle Pulverbatch.[20] Nothing more is heard either of these ventures or of any other activity at the mine until official returns from 1845 onwards mention Huglith as a copper mine which closed in 1859, although the mine still existed, as incomplete returns were made until 1865. Land at Huglith 'with copper under' was advertised for sale in the *Mining Magazine* of 1860, but it must have been a poor speculation as it was not reopened even during the 'copper

*Fig. 10.14 The engine house for Main Shaft at Huglith in 1926 showing the vertical headgear before the digging of the angled shaft. (*Industrial Chemist, *February 1926)*

211

Fig. 10.15 A 1926 photograph of the main adit at Huglith. The winch is presumably the one which powered the tramway to the ropeway terminus. (Industrial Chemist, *February 1926)*

boom' of the 1860s. Nevertheless, a small quantity of ore is known to have been mined from a shaft 1,200 feet south of the later Main Shaft in about 1880.

In 1910 the Wotherton Barytes and Lead Mining Co. Ltd. began working barytes on the site and this became the biggest 20th-century mine in Shropshire outside the coalfields and one of the most efficient. It was the county's biggest producer of barytes and was of national importance, producing nearly 300,000 tons during its lifetime. It was developed adjoining and ultimately incorporating the one-time copper and barytes mine at Westcott. By 1912 the returns list the owner as Thomas Butler, as does the British Geological Survey report of 1915. By the 1916 edition the Wotherton company are noted as owners, though what the relationship was between Butler and the Wotherton company is not known. Shropshire Mines Ltd. was

Fig. 10.16 The vertical head gear seen above was replaced when the new angled main shaft was dug in the late 1920s, the new winding arrangement is seen here with the mine manager Mr. Pidwell. (coll. K. Lock)

formed in 1916 (incorporating the Wotherton company and Shropshire Lead Mines Ltd.) and took over Huglith and other mines. The firm went into liquidation in 1925 and a new company, Malehurst Barytes Co. Ltd.[20] was formed. A controlling interest in that company was obtained by B. Laporte Ltd. in 1932 who ran the enterprise, using the Malehurst name, until the mine was effectively worked out in November 1945 despite local hopes of 10 more years' employment.[22]

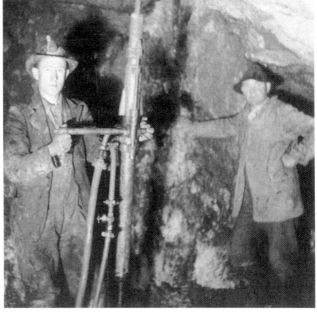

Fig. 10.17 *A photograph probably from the 1930s showing a compressed air drill. Whilst this technology speeded drilling and incidentally improved ventilation, the dust was a killer. The drills were known as widow makers. 'Happy' Adams, seen here on the left, had to retire due to silicosis in 1953. His doctor's certificate is shown in Fig. 10.18. (coll. SMT)*

TELEPHONES:
PONTESBURY 25.
MINSTERLEY 216.

WHITEHALL.
PONTESBURY.
SHROPSHIRE.

3.2 1953

I certify that, in my opinion, Mr A. Adams
residing at Snailbeach.
is unable to follow his/her employment, owing to
Silicosis

W. B. BALLENDEN, M.B., M.R.C.S.
J. H. S. PERRETT, M.R.C.S.

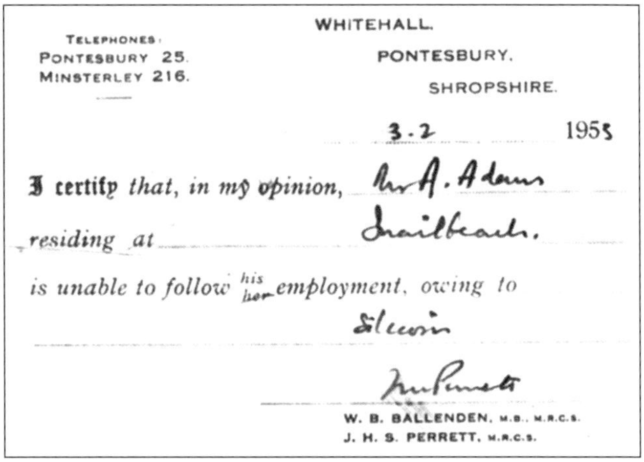

Fig. 10.18 *'Happy' Adams' doctor's certificate (see Fig. 10.17). (coll. SMT)*

For some years, possibly until the digging of the crosscut in the early 1930s, there were officially two mines at Huglith which almost alternated in their productivity. The development of the mine falls into four parts: 1910-1916, 1916-1925, 1925-1930 and 1930-1945. The first saw the Wotherton company develop Number One mine adjoining the erstwhile Westcott mine, where the inclined Main Shaft and its adit were developed later. From 1916 to 1925 Shropshire Mines Ltd. ran the mine with partial success. During this period Number One mine was closed and Number Two opened near Huglith Farm, but this latter was not a success with the ore disappearing 80 feet below ground and it was closed in about 1918 and its equipment sold to Wrentnall Baryta Company. Number One mine was reopened. Shropshire Mines Ltd.'s *Annual Newsletter* to employees refers to the mine being opened up rapidly with a new shaft and changing rooms — Mr. Pidwell, the manager, and his team were thanked for the

shaft. It was to be made a model mine. 1925 saw substantial investment by Malehurst Barytes.[23] The 1930s saw a further period of investment with the digging of a new Number Two mine in 1931 and followed over the next four years by a substantial crosscut at the 250 foot level linking all the veins. Despite the crosscut a shaft was dug at Huglith Farm in 1938/9, though it probably did not reach the level of the crosscut. The barytes from this area was shipped out, at least some of the time, by Mr. Jones the farmer, who moved it as far as the road for a company lorry to collect.[24] The ground under Huglith Farm, abandoned in 1918, had the final say as large reserves were found at lower levels there from the crosscut and it became the last area to be worked.

The whole hill on which the mine stood is criss-crossed by mineral veins, a few with some copper but the great majority of barytes, all of the significant ones running for about half a mile from the Habberley

Fig. 10.19 Riddleswood Upper Adit, photographed by Mr. Bailey in 1931. The miners are Harry Lewis and Jack Lewis.
(coll. K. Lock)

Fig. 10.20 A view of the principal area of the site in the 1930s with the rope worked tramway from the loading area to the coal pile in the foreground. It is possible that this was the original tramway to the road prior to the building of the ropeway in the mid 1920s. On a slight ledge to the left is the tramway to the ropeway terminus. The engine house, boiler house and chimney are in the centre. The corrugated roofed building to the right is the smithy. (coll. K. Lock)

Fault in the west to disturbed ground in the east. Three of these proved economic: Main, Riddleswood and Mud veins, in the best cases being several feet thick and in at least one case having 20 feet of solid barytes. The quantity of ore diminished with depth, a maximum of 440 feet below the main adit level being worked. The greater part of the ore produced was pink to red in colour and very hard, in some cases unusably so, when it was used to repair the road to the mine. Sufficient good white barytes was found along with some stained blue from copper or black from mineral pitch. The pink and blue ores could be bleached but the black was discarded. In addition to workings from the main adit and main shaft, parts of the site were worked opencast and part from other adits, notably Badger Level, and several other shafts. When Laportes took over, a report on the mine was commissioned as a result of which they dug the cross cut connecting all the veins

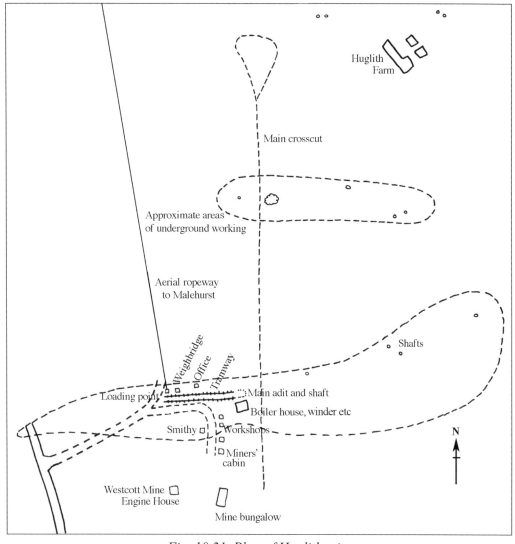

Fig. 10.21 Plan of Huglith mine

215

and equipped it with a main and tail haulage system for the trams. Winding was via Main Shaft with a single cage and initially a steam winder, the boiler for this having begun life at Milne Shaft on the abortive work at Leigh Level. This was replaced by an electric winder which went to The Sallies mine at closure. The mine also had a Sentinel compressor for the rock drills, later replaced by Holman's electrically powered ones initially run on DC from a mercury arc rectifier, this latter equipment joining the winder at The Sallies. Pumping was usually by electrical means but at least in 1940s when the electric pump failed the former steam pump from Round Hill mine was used, powered by compressed air.

Fig. 10.22 A photograph in June 2004 of the collapsed boiler house chimney. (Author)

Production and employment figures for any copper mining are not available. From 1910 to the First World War about 1,000 tons a year of barytes was dug, which stepped up to an average of about 2,500 tons until 1924 when Malehurst's investment began to come on stream. Annual figures have not been found but the average increases from 10,000 tons in the late 1920s to 15,000+ during the Second World War, with total production at 295,000 tons. Employment figures show a similar pattern, not reaching 20 until 1917 then falling off until 1925 when it climbed to 40. Figures of 60 plus were employed in several years between 1935 and 1941; thereafter numbers fell off to closure.

Initially the crude ore was trammed to a road loading point on a rope worked line powered by an oil engine. From here it was hauled in four-horse drays to Pontesbury Station and thence taken by train to the company's mill at Hanwood. As part of the investment in the mine in the 1920s an aerial ropeway was constructed to Malehurst. The site also had tramways from the mine to the aerial ropeway terminus, and for coal from the delivery lorries' stockpile to the boiler house.

The mine's water supply was from a hydraulic ram in a field to the west of the road, the concrete base of the header tank still being a local landmark. The product from the main part of the mine came up twice a day, mid-morning and early afternoon.

There are extensive but not very spectacular remains buried in thick, private woodland. Several underground parts of the mine can be accessed with permission and appropriate insurance cover. The steel chimney for the boiler and the footings of various buildings also remain, as do the sites of several adits and shafts.

*Fig. 10.23 A prominent capped shaft at Squilver from the 1930s barytes trials
photographed in May 2004. (Author)*

Malehurst Barytes Company trials

With Huglith mine possibly coming to the end of its life in the late 1930s, the Malehurst
Barytes Company carried out a series of searches for barytes. Some, like The Sallies and
Gatten, were developed, but others did not live up to hopes and were abandoned having
produced only smallish quantities. Three such are mentioned below, each established as a
result of local prospecting. **Coldyeld** produced 800 tons of the material. Initial mining in
the 1930s was opencast, by local men, Tom Evans and Jack Lewis, until one side of the
excavation caved in. Then in 1943 Malehurst Barytes Ltd. began an adit to intercept the
vein under the opencast pit. The difficult nature of the ground coupled with the suspicion
that the quality of the barytes was reducing led to the abandonment of the mine. There
are no remains. **Knolls**, like Coldyeld and Squilver (below) was an extensive barytes
trial during 1943 and 1944 when some 1,350 tons of ore was produced. The mine was,
however, being worked in 1937 and probably earlier by Tom Evans and Jack Lewis from
at least one shaft. The later mining opened up two adits and a series of trenches within
600 metres west and north-west of Squilver Farm. There are few remains, except that
the site of one of the adits is visible as is a very prominent shaft to the north of the road.
At **Squilver** the same men carried the initial development here as at the previous two
undertakings. Malehurst subsequently dug trenches and veins were located including one
in Squilver Farm yard. A trial adit established that the vein died out at a depth of 40 feet.
1,357 tons of ore were produced in 1944. The site of the adit is said to be recognisable.[25]

Linley

Like several other entries this is a convenient handle for several actual and possible
mines. Aerial and archaeological evidence was said to have pointed to an area to the west
of Norbury being mined by the Romans using hushing (see p.15). Traces of copper were
found in the immediate locality though it does not appear to have been worked. Some
was noted in the cellar of Squire Hall but for whatever reason was kept quiet. On the
other side of the Pontesford Linley Fault lead trials were conducted at The Butts, Hayes
Wood north of Linley Hall, though not apparently with success.[26]

Outlying trials

It is clear that most if not all hilly areas of the county have been prospected. Generally these trials are long forgotten and the successful ones were obliterated by later mining. Some, however, are remembered and the following serve as examples of the spread and nature of such searches. **Lyth Hill**, though not geographically part of the Long Mynd, is geologically similar and contains traces of copper. Rumours of Roman mining are given credence by some historians[27] and the existence of several trials is recorded in 1833 in Thomas Poole's diary and in 1925 in an official geological publication.[28] There is no evidence of actual mining taking place. Similarly a series of trials (see Fig. 15.3) are noted in various sources on **Pontesford Hill** and near by at **Lyd Hole**[29] and **Radlith Wood** (these last two could conceivably be the same). At Radlith Wood the 'mine' was offered for sale with the rest of the Longden Manor estate (*c.*1902). Two adits were mentioned but were disused, although the tools were still in them. History records no more of this venture.[30]

Other trials are known at the south end of the Long Mynd — copper was sought at **Whittingslow**, where two shafts 10m apart have been noted as old trial shafts in White Birches Wood. It is reasonable to assume that no useful quantity of copper was found.[31] Barytes was recorded and possibly mined at two sites near Hillend Farm at the very southern tip of the hills; one of the sites may well be that referred to as **Plowden** in the gazetteer.[32]

Mines on the western edge of the Long Mynd

Copper outcrops in a number of places and it is confidently assumed that these provided small quantities of copper for Bronze Age and Roman use. None were ever of much significance and only one appears to have been worked for other than copper. From north to south the known ones are Ratlinghope, Medlicott, Adstone and Myndtown.

At least two trials for copper took place at **Ratlinghope**. Mr. Hawkins of Ratlinghope 'made trials near that village' in which a small amount of copper ore was present.[33] Evidence points to a second mine site to the south-west of the village where the remains of trial pits, shafts and adits have been noted.[34] An early 19th-century date is assumed for this mine, although it may originate from any of the copper booms from 1680 to 1860. The principal information on **Medlicott** comes from Murchison who states that the copper vein ran from north of Ratlinghope to Medlicott and that it had been worked by the Snailbeach company.[35] The remains are scanty — a filled shaft, a collapsed adit and a tip. **Adstone** was probably just a trial — an adit by the road was opened at an unknown date to search for copper and, later, no doubt, barytes.[36] Nothing else is known of this mine, even the adit has now been obliterated. **Myndtown** was a more substantial venture than any of the others. Documentary evidence seems to be totally lacking but the remains cover sufficient ground to suggest a mine rather than a trial. It is said to have been opened for copper and remembered to have been at least tried for barytes. The bulk of the remains consist of disturbed ground but the location of at least two adits and their tips are clear.

Norbury

As with so many entries several sites are included in the location. Several small copper veins outcrop in and around the village and at least three sets of workings are remembered. They were noted by Murchison as being 'formerly much worked' and money was lost on them in the 19th century by Thomas Harrison who lived at Lee Farm. There was a 100 foot shaft at Hall Farm which went down to a 60-yard long adit, the shaft collapsing in 1957. There was another adit in the same field behind the Methodist Chapel, yet another adit went under Lee Farm itself and there was an adit further up the hill at grid reference SO 366935 which was gated to keep the sheep out. Local tradition also says that there were workings under the track to Nurton. There are now no visible remains. Post-war prospecting has revealed low grade ore containing a little copper, zinc and antimony.[37]

Also in the parish were copper mines at **Shuttocks Wood**, about which even less is known. Although there are reported to be several shafts, the sole remains are small areas of disturbed ground.

When mining at any of these sites took place is open to conjecture, but the 'copper boom' in the county in the 1860s is a clear possibility. A good local source stated in 1924 that copper mining had ceased at Norbury and at Shuttocks Wood about 10 years previously.[38]

Norbury Hill

Murchison describes a copper mine about a mile north of the village on top of Norbury Hill. No doubt some such exploration was done here but it seems not to have produced much apart from a small barytes mine. The first reference to the latter is in the particulars of the sale of the Scott Estate in 1920 when lot 24a was the mineral rights. This confirmed that a tack note or licence had been issued to Thomas Hutton and Son of Minsterley that expired on 8 September 1920 with an option for a 21-year lease if requested. E.C. Gray, sometime acting general manager of Shropshire Lead Mines Ltd. and a Spar Gravel Merchant working part of the Snailbeach site, visited the site in 1921 and surveyed it, and the 21-year lease must have been taken up as the mine is remembered by locals as working well into the 1920s. A weighbridge and attendant's hut were built in the village and a loading platform erected for transhipment where the village phone box now stands. The product was said to have been of poor quality and sold for £1 a ton, about a third of the price of good barytes. It was sent initially to Cliffdale Mill and subsequently to Malehurst, this latter fact indicating that the mine was still open at the beginning of 1925 when that mill opened. There were at least two shafts and an adit. The shafts were filled with stone when the hill top field was improved in about 1946 though their locations are still clear.[39]

The Sallies (or sometimes just Sallies)

One of the last mines to be developed in the orefield, The Sallies was trialled for barytes from 1937 and a 21-year lease was granted in 1942. The mine was developed as a result of a search for barytes to supply Malehurst Mill when it was realised in the late 1930s that

Huglith mine was becoming worked out. The mine was worked principally from adits which had rises to the surface for ventilation, although a 200 foot shaft was sunk in 1944 to prove the vein at depth.[40] The mine was always very wet, with the miners working up to their knees in water. It was served from Malehurst Mill where the headgear was fabricated and the tools were sharpened. The mineral produced was taken by road to Huglith and went to the mill on the aerial ropeway having been weighed at the weighbridge by Riddles Wood, this weighbridge being a condition of the lease. A Holman compressor and

Fig. 10.24 The Sallies mine during construction. Note the incomplete building behind the head frame. Photographed during a visit by Laporte's staff. (coll. K. Lock)

Fig. 10.25 An inspection of The Sallies mine by officials of Laporte Ltd. in 1947. (coll. K. Lock)

an electric pump went from Huglith to The Sallies when the 1944 shaft was being sunk. Figures for the mine are scarce, no doubt due to most of its life being during the Second World War. However, nearly 1,400 tons was produced in 1943/4 and more than 20 men were employed below ground in 1945 and 1948, with less than half that number on the surface. The quantity of barytes available and the expected reserves of this mine and Gatten were insufficient to be economic and it was closed on October 1948. It was the last mine of any significance in the area and the last in the area operated by Malehurst Barytes Co. In 1978 a prospecting licence was granted to Elenith Mining Co. Ltd. and B.W. Mud Ltd., but no action is recorded. The remains are few, just disturbed ground where there have been shafts or adits and some concrete bases and foundations.

Fig. 10.26 The surface buildings photographed during the demolition of the main mine in 1948, the tramway rails in front of the building having already been lifted

Westcott

This mine and Huglith's underground workings sometimes overlapped (probably unknown to the respective landlords) with the north of Westcott being the south of Huglith. Major development occurred earlier at Westcott and its unmapped workings reduced the area of ground which Huglith could ultimately work. Westcott set out to be a copper mine but some barytes production is recorded; conversely, Huglith was a barytes mine from which small amounts of copper were recorded. Westcott is only known to have been worked for two periods, 1858-70 and 1890-4, despite copper being noted in the south of Pulverbatch parish in sale particulars of 1801. The only possible clue is a field called The Pitts near Westcott.

The earlier activity occurred during the 'copper boom' in Shropshire. It was briefly worked by John Harrison and Co. following a lease from the Harrops to John and Edward Harrison and John Job in 1858, but success clearly eluded them as the lease was surrendered in 1861 although the company still appears in official returns for the mine until 1866. A new two-year lease was granted to Joseph Cooke in January 1864 and a full lease to Humby and Curwen in December 1865. By 1867 the mine was being worked by them as the Westcott Mine Company (floated as the Westcott Mining Co. Ltd. in 1869) and involved two notable mine captains — John Kitto and James Nancarrow — who were successively mine agents. When approaches were made to the then landlord of Huglith for a lease it was refused, leading to the closure of the mine in 1870 and a loss of £7,000. Nancarrow was remembered as being dissatisfied with the local workforce (with the exception of a Mr. Wellings, who had been at sea and knew about pumping) and imported miners from his native Cornwall. They may have known how to mine but they were a rough lot who got drunk in Pontesbury every night with serious consequences for the mine.[41]

No further activity is recorded until the late 1880s when the landowner worked it as a barytes mine in conjunction with Rhadley and Gatten mines which he also owned, the material going to Gatten for processing. This activity was over by 1894 and the mine effectively ceased to exist when it was incorporated underground into Huglith. Production was never great, the only returns made indicating that from 1866-68 180 tons of ore yielded 17 tons of copper and that between 1891-94 1,000 tons of barytes was mined. The engine shaft was about 100

Fig. 10.26 The ruins of Westcott engine house chimney c.1952 with Esmond Betton returned from National Service. Mr. Betton lived as a boy within site of this chimney and later worked at Huglith mine and Malehurst Mill. (coll. E. Betton)

yards deep and the ore was worked to the north and the south, the best ore being got to the north towards Huglith. At least one shaft was filled on closure.[42]

What remains still exist are in a private garden. Parts of the engine house, chimney and boiler house survive, along with several collapsed levels and shafts.

Wilderley

Probably the last new copper mine to be tried in the county, Wilderley was developed by the Anglo-Rhodesian Investments Company. This company was formed in 1914 to acquire and develop Wilderley mine (as well as having interests in what was then northern Rhodesia, now Zambia). W.H. Reynolds, the managing director, received shares when the company was formed, suggesting that he had carried out some development or proving works before the war, as shown on one of the promotional photographs mentioned below, which is captioned '1916 View above road showing original adit and dump now site

Fig. 10.27 Wilderley mine 'Engine house, washing & grading table [site of original adit and dump] main shaft etc', Summer 1917. Note the construction in progress behind engine house

Fig. 10.28 View from the office veranda, 1917

of new main shaft'. The photo is not at all clear but the work does not look currently active. This phase of work is presumably that inspected by H.F. Collins noted below. The land was part of the Wilderley Estate and belonged to J.B. Walker who owned and ran the adjoining Cothercott mine. The mine was surveyed by H.F. Collins who visited the site during the First World War and noted that about 8 tons of hand-picked ore was at the mine, representing the mine's total production. The percentage metal in the ore is not estimated but would have been somewhat less than 10%.[43] Figures available for 1916-18 give an average of 15 employees.

Fig. 10.29 'Winch and boiler before covered in', 1917. Note incomplete sheeting to main shaft building

Development work was well under way by late 1916 (see Figs. 10.27 to 10.32 produced by the company to accompany a share promotion) by which time two adits and two shafts had been commenced. A year later the company were circulating possible subscribers with a description of the mine and a set of photographs. At this stage the main shaft was said to be 110 feet deep and

Fig. 10.30 The office in 1917. The young lady may have been Miss Rosa Hubbard who was, by 1920, Company Secretary of the Cothercott Company

expected to reach sulphide ores 'at quite an early date', the main level was being driven and a boring was to be made to prove the vein below the depth of the main level. Great enthusiasm was expressed, expert opinions quoted and the possibilities of sulphuric acid becoming an indirect by-product from the ore were noted. This latter would possibly have been economic if any ore had been found at depth. Potential customers were also informed that 'Outside our Northern Boundary … level headed businessmen are opening up the same lode and spending money like water in Mining operations upon a big scale and in installing costly and large plant' — it was just a shame that it was barytes that the level headed businessmen looked for and found at Huglith! By sometime in 1918 work had been abandoned, the shafts never reaching the stated depth let alone far enough down for the adit to have intersected it.

Fig. 10.31 The reservoir with Westcott Hill in the distance in 1917. Note the horses and cart possibly delivering building materials, the bicycle by the shed, and the portable engine beyond the engine house

Fig. 10.32 General view showing the main shaft, engine house, cabin, reservoir and office in 1917. The Cothercott tramway should be in the background

Fig. 10.33 Wilderley in March 1997. Remains of the expensive construction include a cracked concrete reservoir, a few building platforms and tips where the shafts were. (Author)

That the mine was quite well equipped is clear from the promotional photographs several of which are reproduced here. For such a short lived venture the remains are good. On the main site the location of the two shafts, now filled, is clear as is the concrete reservoir and the platforms of some of the buildings. In the valley to the west of the road the main level and the trial level are visible alongside the tramway remains from Cothercott mine.

Wrentnall

As with so many places there were two separate periods of activity in the vicinity of Wrentnall, one in search of metals and the second for barytes. Mining at Wrentnall probably began in the late 18th century. A 31-year lease was granted by Thomas Pemberton of Millichope, John Probert of Copthorne and others to William Hitchcock to search for and take away lead, tin ore, copper ore and any other ores, metal or metals at a ^{1}/8th royalty on 20 November 1795.[44] The area covered includes Lawn Hill which later was mined in conjunction with mines on Broome Hill, along with Huglith. A property sale document of 1856 for Lawn Hill refers to a field called 'Level Mouth' and to a mining lease of 1832 for that level.[45] Nothing further is known of this phase of activity. Any success which might have come the mine's way would have been with copper, of which traces were noted later; lead would not have been present in economic quantities.

Fig. 10.34 The barytes vein at Wrentnall with Broome Hill in the background. (British Geological Survey)

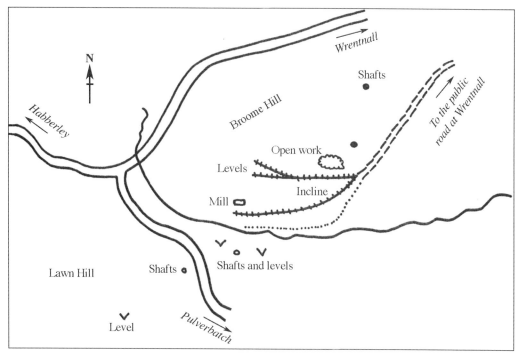

Fig. 10.35 Plan of Wrentnall mine

Information becomes somewhat firmer by the end of the 19th century. From 1890 the mine was worked for barytes by Shropshire Barytes Co. By 1892 when the mine closed it had passed through the ownership of Shropshire Barytes and Lead Mining Co. into the hands of Wotherton Barytes & Lead Mining Co. Ltd. and had produced 840 tons of barytes. The mine then stood until 1908 or 1909 when it was run for two years or so by Thomas Lewis. He in turn was superseded by William Bennett and Co. (of which he was part) in 1912; they worked the mine until 1916 when Messrs. Orr, Reid and Orr formed the Wrentnall Baryta Co. Ltd. who ran the mine until final closure in 1925. Some prospecting took place 'north east of Lawn Hill'[46] in 1938, possibly by Malehurst Barytes looking to replace Huglith. 1908 to 1918 saw 13,500 tons produced and thereafter about 50 tons a week.[47] The quality of the material was not particularly good, some being pink-stained and some

Fig. 10.36 A general view of Wrentnall mine looking towards Broome Hill. The mill is in the foreground with an adit on the extreme right and surface workings visible on the left. The photo was probably taken in the early 1920s. (British Geological Survey)

227

contaminated by mineral pitch. The numbers employed were never great — it was 1918 before numbers exceeded 10, and the early 1920s before they rose into the mid 30s.

Little evidence has come to light on where the barytes went to from this mine. The Cheshire/Merseyside area is always a probability and certainly when Orrs were involved barytes was sent (presumably unground), via Plealey Road Station to Orr's Zinc White Ltd. on Merseyside. Prior to this, from 1890 to 1909, the material would have gone to Hanwood Mill.

The barytes mine occupied two sites: two shafts and two levels on Lawn Hill, which could possibly have been the site of the first and last mines, and on both sides of a valley on the slopes of Broome Hill. This latter site had at least eight shafts and six adits as well as opencast workings. The 1909 mining was well up the slopes of Broome Hill and consisted of two or three adits connected by an 18 inch gauge tramway to a loading dock on a trackway which led across to Wrentnall village. Wrentnall Baryta Co. clearly invested heavily in the site including buying redundant winding gear and other

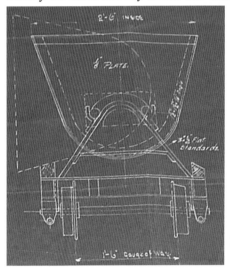

equipment from Huglith. Additional shafts and levels were dug nearer the stream and on Lawn Hill, a mill was built on Broome Hill between 1916 and 1922 and the tramway extended down an inclined plane to the mill. From the loading dock the product was hauled to one or other of the local railway stations by traction engine, in 1924 the county council receiving a payment of £82 10s. to cover repairs to the roads.

The Lawn Hill part of the site is visible from the road and some of the Broome Hill site from a public footpath. The foundations and some walling and machine bases remain at the mill, and the sites of some of the shafts and adits are recognisable.

Wrentnall Baryta Co. (after 1930 as part of the Imperial Smelting Corporation Group) remained in business at least up to the Second World War and ran major barytes mines at Gass Water in Ayrshire and Cow Green and Dubby Syke in County Durham. Cow Green mine had a Wrenthnall Shaft which remained in use until the closure of the mine c.1953, and a row of eight cottages built

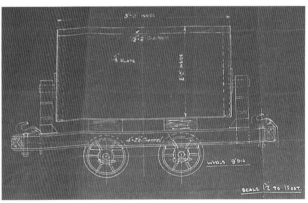

Fig. 10.37 A supplier's drawing of an 18" gauge wagon for Wrentnall mine. (SA 2338)

for the workforce are still called Wrentnall Cottages.

11   Lead and Copper Mines of Corvedale

The title of this chapter flatters, for its subjects are minor trials with one or possible two exceptions, and even these were at best just very small mines. It also misleads as its subjects are not all in Corvedale but fit no other category. The slight known history is documented for well over 600 years and some say that the Romans mined in the area, which cannot be ruled out. The area does have a fine history of sandstone and limestone extraction for building, agricultural and industrial uses, not covered in this book.

Hayton's Bent and Little Postern

Hayton's Bent is the one mine of this group to have a real history although it probably never produced much copper. The mine first comes to notice in the copper boom of the late 1680s, which swept much of the county. A lease was granted to Talbot Clerke in 1687, followed by one to the Governor and Company of Copper Miners in England (generally known as the English Copper Co.) in 1693 with which he was involved. The timing of both leases when related to the two Acts of Parliament removing the royal monopoly on copper mines suggests that Clerke was willing to take the risk of his mine being appropriated, an outcome which was much less likely if he was reworking an earlier mine than if he was opening a new one. The English Copper Co. made it very clear before the second of the Acts that they would not get involved in new mines.[1] Given that copper was mined in the county before the Civil War it must be possible that mining occurred here earlier, but this is not known, and nor is any more heard of Clerke's venture.

Further mining is said, from local information (apparently backed up by now lost documents), to have taken place about 1730 but no further definite history occurs until John Lawrence (I or II, both were alive at this date) took a 21-year lease in 1754 from Lord Craven to mine copper and other minerals at Upper Hayton's Bent. The lease had the usual conditions and gave the usual powers, though Lawrence was not permitted to smelt there. Royalties were 1/5th on copper and 1/8th on other ores. A mine, no doubt Lawrence's, is shown on an estate map of 1770. The site was visited by Murchison in the late 1830s, when he recorded that it had been abandoned 100 years before and that there was no profit nor records, just trial shafts and galleries.[2] This conflicts with the evidence given above but does give some credence to trials in the 1730s. Could there have been two distinct sites?

Local information then cites development by a William Lovett Mining co. around 1850. This was said to have been backed by the Earl of Powis, Marquis of Bath and the trustees of the Earl of Tankerville, 'all fresh from their success at the Westcott Copper Mine', and the technical side was dealt with by two Cornish mine captains — L.R. Carleson and T.J. Penfold. Unfortunately nothing else is known of this venture and it is presumed to have been short-lived and even less successful than Westcott. The land was sold by the Craven estate to the Powells of Sutton Court who, though not having the mineral rights, were involved in some of the later attempts at this mine. The first of these was in about 1870 when either 50 men or two men and a wheelbarrow — depending on which local source you believe — drove a level to intersect the old workings. The 50 men are much more likely to have been involved in the 1850 activity as this apparently involved work such as alterations to watercourses and the construction of a dressing floor. In 1901 the New Inn stated that the nature of its trade was 'mining, agricultural and roadside' though no active mine is shown on the contemporary Ordnance Survey maps. The mine's last fling was in the First World War, and activity finished in 1919 or 1920. The area has been looked at since, most recently in 1995 when the unsurprising verdict was that 'all the explorations produced nothing worth recording'.

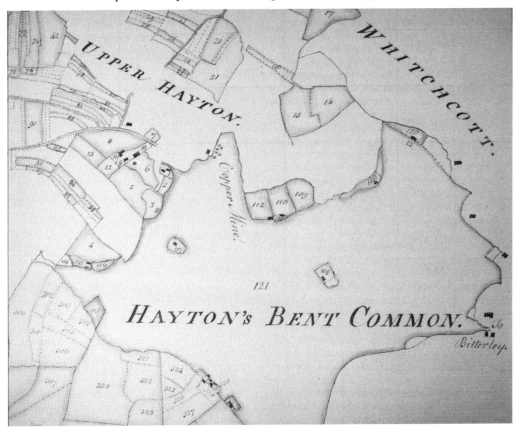

Fig. 11.1 An extract from a map of the Craven Estate in Stanton Lacy of 1770, which shows six copper pits. (SA 6001/2480)

As the location of the earliest mining is unknown so is its extent. The Lawrence mine of 1754 is no doubt the mine marked on a Craven Estate map of 1770; this shows six shafts. At some time(s) adits have been dug from the roadside to intersect shafts, and leatwork constructed from Collects Well to a dressing floor, perhaps during the 1850 campaign. The remains of the mine are slight — there are a few depressions where shafts have been, the sites of two or three adits are visible in the bank at the side of the road and a house, now called Mine House, could conceivably include what may have been an engine house. The best remains are those of the leat which passes almost under Mine House and crosses under the road in a culvert from where it runs at a shallow fall on top of a raised earthen bank at an increasing height as the road falls sharply. This passes the site where the dressing floor was and passes under a track called Mulberry Lane using a siphon.[3]

The 1882 Ordnance Survey marks a shaft for copper at **Little Postern**. No documentary evidence exists for this but a reasonable suggestion has been made that this would be a trial following any success that Lawrence had had at Hayton's Bent.[4]

Rushbury area

A mine is said to have existed at **Blackwood** but no details have emerged. In the 17th century some prospecting was done as on 29 January 1666 an agreement was made between Richard Cleverley of Luschcott and Edward Lutwyche of Lutwyche that Timothy Baldwin of Stokesay might dig in the lands of Lutwyche in Eaton and Rushbury, now occupied by Cleverley, for veins of mineral coal, lead, copper, tin ore and allum of vitriol, Lutwyche having leased the minerals to Baldwin for 16 years. Nothing else is known of this venture, certainly not the locations of any adits or shafts; presumably it was not a success.[5]

Shipton area trials

When the Reverend Plymley was collecting information for his book[6] in 1793 he was informed of two sets of trial workings in or near Shipton. William Reynolds, the ironmaster, knew of small quantities of lead being found and an unnamed source spoke of a trial in progress for lead. Reynold's information may have been related to work he carried out in 1788 when he wrote that 'Cornish men here soon to attempt working mines ...', although the number of men he expected (he asked for 40 beds and 200 pairs of trousers) suggests a much larger enterprise.[7] At some date in the late 18th century William Smith of the London Lead Company took Flintshire miners to a trial near Much Wenlock.[8] Murchison noted copper minerals in the vicinity in the 1830s.

Quite how, if at all, the known remains relate to any of this evidence is unclear, but the existence of a level near Shipton Hall to a shaft some 500 yards away is likely to have been one of them. The level has been partially explored and has been ascertained to have been dug by hand with picks rather than explosives. The level was remembered locally and, given that Shipton belonged to Wenlock Priory, was assumed to be a secret passage from the hall to the priory. None of the above seem to have led to significant discoveries.

If Murchison was right about the copper it is a slim possibility that this could be James Mynour's mine, see Wenlock entry below.

Within a mile and a half of Shipton there are two other shafts on the 1882 Ordnance Survey map, one at **Larden** about a mile north and the other at **Oxenbold** a mile and a half east. They all belonged to different families but it is probable that the prospect of a local find prompted other trials *c*.1790. No doubt these represent many others in this and other localities of which no record survives.

Wenlock

In 1394 James from Derbyshire, described as a 'mynour', sought royal consent to work a copper and silver mine on land belonging to Wenlock Priory.[9] This was granted 'without prejudice to anyone ... and without the demolition or destruction of houses or gardens nor to permit the work to be carried on unless under supervision of one of themselves or some sufficient person for whom they will answer, certifying the King in Chancery from time to time of all their proceedings'. The only clue to the location of the mine is the condition that no houses should be demolished or gardens destroyed, and it may therefore have been in or near a settlement, possibly Much Wenlock itself. Traces of copper (and lead) were recorded over the years, notably by Murchison in the 1830s at various places in the limestone of the vicinity. Little other record exists of the mine although Hugh de Burnell, a leading Shropshire knight who had supposedly been commissioned by the king to supervise the mining, was released from this duty by a Writ of *supersedeas omina* (i.e. he was let off the above supervision, which he denied ever being asked to do) in 1397, and also at some date there was a Patent of Richard II for the Sheriff of Shropshire to dig a royal mine in land which had already been granted to the Priory of Wenlock.[10] How these two sets of requirements relate to each other is not known. The status of this mine and its relation to royal control of mines which could produce gold or silver was cited in the lawsuit Regina v the Earl of Northumberland in 1568 — 'The Case of Mines'. This suggested that the mine at Wenlock produced gold, which is so grossly unlikely as to be effectively impossible.

Even further away from Corvedale is **Little Wenlock**, where an entry in the Shropshire Sites and Monuments Records suggests that there was a post-medieval copper mine. Nothing further seems to be known and, whilst a trial is clearly possible, a successful mine is not.

12   Mines in the Breidden Hills

The Breiddens are a small, almost isolated range of hills which straddle the Shropshire/ Montgomeryshire (Powys) border. The largest of the mines in them, which traded under various names but is usually known as Bulthy, crossed the border both below and above ground. The rest of the mines are wholly in Wales but are covered here because the geology does not change at the border and the histories and names of some of the mines are interrelated.

There have been suggestions of Roman mining activity in the hills but there is little evidence to back up that suggestion. It is quite possible that significant exploration began in the late 17th century when several of the other mining areas were being developed but no firm dates can be given before a lease of 1729. Mining continued, though with little continuity, until the late 19th century. It was then revived at Bulthy *c*.1910 for a few years.

Initial prospecting in these hills was for lead, copper and tin but in the event, though a little lead was found, barytes was the principal product; this was dug before 1836, so the Breiddens must have been one of the earliest centres of production in the area. Feldspar, china stone and other minerals were subsequently won from mines and quarries.

It is impossible to be definitive about how many mines existed, especially on Middletown Hill, all of which seems to have been dug over at some time. Bulthy has been the site of much activity, some of which can no longer be identified, whereas Dingle, West Middletown and New Piece are a little more definite.

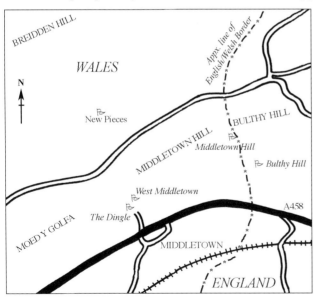

Fig. 12.1 Location map for mines in the Breidden Hills

233

Middletown Hill

Often incorrectly called Middleton Hill, this should not be confused with Middleton Hill in Chirbury parish, 9 miles south, which had mines of its own. In the following I have used whichever spelling was used in the source material, usually Middleton.

The first definite reference to mining in the Breiddens is a lease from Richard Corbett of Longnor to two gentlemen from Devon for 21 years from 1729.[1] It gives them permission to mine lead, copper or other ores, but not coal at Cefn-y-Castell Hill in the parish of Alberbury. Cefn-y-Castell is an alternative name for Middletown Hill, referring to the hillfort on its summit. The lease implies that there were already mines in the area and makes it certain that prospecting, under the authority of a take note or similar, had taken place. The precise location of adits and shafts at this mine is not known, nor is its success or otherwise, although no continuation lease has been found. The next lease from the Corbetts was to John Wilkinson, the ironmaster of Bersham, on 30 November 1763;[2] the mine is described as being at Middleton Hill but may well have been the same mine. This lease specifically excluded spar, which at this date could have been barytes and leaves the possibility that another leaseholder was working it. This lease was renewed for a further 21 years for all metals in 1786 but immediately passed on to a Mr. Briscoe.

Mr. Briscoe may not have been successful as the next known lease is not until 1819 when James Ryan (for whom see p.45) was granted 21 years for all mines and minerals and all clays, earths, stones and 'ffossils'. The mine does not appear to have been a success; Ryan's short-lived school of mining was not successful either.[3] Buildings he erected were included in a subsequent lease of the property. In 1825 a 36-year lease was granted by the Corbetts to Sir Robert Hill, but this lease, at least initially, is described as 'inoperative, Ryan refuses to surrender former lease', Ryan staying into the 1830s. Sir Robert may never have put his lease into operation as in 1836 the Middleton Hill Mining company, a cost book company, were operating. This company had a strong Welsh connection, with three of the directors being from Wrexham and Flint, the fourth, J.H. Walduck of Birmingham, having mining interests in several parts of the country.

The Corbetts granted a 2-year lease in 1841 to Alexander Bower (who had been involved in mining at Bulthy since at lease 1836) to prospect on the hill for green and white feldspar and barytes. This lease included a cottage and a building erected by James Ryan. Royalty was set at 1/8th and a further 14 or 21 years would be available if wished.

The next recorded activity, in 1857 was a 21-year lease to Messrs. Burls and Dunsford for all mines on Middleton Hill. The primary material to be mined was barytes, the royalty for which was 1/10th as against 1/15th on other metals and earths. Only the draft lease survives and it is quite possible that the actual lease was never signed, as a year later Thomas Orchard and James Richards received a 2-year licence to mine the 'wastes and commons on Middleton Hill', followed in 1861 by a 21-year lease. Orchard changed partners as in 1862 the terms of a lease to be granted to him and a William Watts were discussed, and the following Lady Day (25 March) they received a 21-year lease for mines and minerals under Middleton Hill, and worked both barytes and china stone. The latter was sent by road and boat to Tunstall to a Mr. Malpas to be ground.[4] The china stone, though of acceptable quality, was much more difficult to grind than the Cornish product and damaged the grinding mills, meaning that Middletown Hill's china stone was not much of a success. The rent was increased a year later, but 18 months after that the lease was surrendered.

Thomas Davies and two partners (who were already working next door at Bulthy) received an agreement for one year in 1872 to search a portion (now unknown) of Middleton Hill for minerals, including china stone which was then being worked at the Shrewsbury end of the hill. In 1874 the interest in the china stone lead to a lease being granted to the agent for the Middleton Glaze Stone and Lead Mining Company Ltd. for Middleton Hill china stone quarries. Under the lease they were granted 21 years for the mines and quarries, to work silver, lead, copper, zinc, cobalt, barytes, china stone, stone, (zinc)blende, ochre and other minerals, at a royalty of $^{1}/_{14}$th, but it is not known to what extent this enterprise was involved in mining rather than quarrying. They received a further 21-year lease two years later presumably for other parts of the hill. This last lease, at least, was abandoned in June 1875.

Thomas Davies again sought a take note in 1878 (this time with two different partners) for one year, later extended to two, to the same part of the hill for minerals. They must have found something as the royalty on the first note was $_{1/15}$th and on the extension $^{1}/_{12}$th. By this time the mining on the hill and at Bulthy was in the hands of Thomas Davies and as early as October 1872 the mines at the eastern end of Middletown Hill and Bulthy were being called North Snailbeach Silver Lead Mine. From this period on these mines seemed to use either name, in the case of Middletown (with or without the 'w') or the 'Hill' and sent in government returns under both Montgomeryshire and Shropshire. This vagueness may have had fatal consequences in the 1920s (see below), and the mine's subsequent history is given under Bulthy, below.

Remains of mining on the hill almost all date from the Bulthy period after 1870, although some long-filled adits on the northern slopes may be earlier. Before the coming of the Shrewsbury to Welshpool railway in 1862 the lead ore, barytes and other products from these mines would have been carted to the River Severn, probably at Criggion. Once the railway was opened ores were taken to Middletown Station for onward transmission. Production and employment figures have not survived for any of these operations.

Bulthy to 1871

The English part of the range of hills was known as Bulthy and owned for most of the period of mining interest by the Gardners of Sansaw, who are recorded as granting leases from 1836 onward. It is clear from the 1836 lease that mining had previously taken place as the lease between Rev. Gardner and Sir Robert Hill and Alexander Bower of 'all mines, pits & veins of lead ore and the strata called barites connected with the said lead ore', refers to 'where the mouth of the level now is'. The royalty was to be 'every 8th dish of lead and an eighth of all the barites to be handed over in a state ready for sale'.[5] This is the earliest specific reference to the mining of barytes in the county but the wording implies that it was still considered an unusual substance. (The London

Lead Company's extraction of the material at Nether Heath in 1729 was presumably for research rather than commercial extraction and its mining at Wotherton at the end of that century is assumed rather than stated.)

The next involvement of the Gardners seems to have been a lease to Pegg, Darke and company sometime before 1867, when the tenants gave three months' notice during which they should have removed their plant but did not. There followed a series of letters from the landlord to his solicitors about the action taken by one Williams, the tenant farmer, who tried to refuse to allow Wilson the haulier access to the site to remove a boiler. On its removal Williams was assured that no more would be taken away and the gates would be locked. The mine was reopened in 1871 when Thomas Davies, W.J. Sennett and Evan Evans were given a take note for one year with the offer of a 21-year lease if required, an offer that was taken up.

Little is known about the size or scope of these mines though railways, railroads and waggon ways are all mentioned in the 1836 lease, some of which clearly predate that lease, suggesting a mine of some size. The transport arrangements for Bulthy would have been as for Middletown Hill.

Bulthy from 1871

Within a year only one of the original partners was involved. Evan Evans had died and his widow sold out to Sennett at about the same time that Davies sold his share to R.L. Wright.[6] In 1877 a lease was granted to Beales and Schooles who either retained their bit of the hill or reappeared in 1889 and renegotiated the lease to reduce the dead rent from £60 to £40 p.a.[7] From 1880 a series of short lived companies and individuals owned and/or operated it:

1880 North Snailbeach Lead and Barytes Mining Syndicate Ltd.
1881 North Snailbeach Company
1881-2 Bulthy Lead Mining and Barytes Company
1883 Bulthy Mining Company
1884-6 Bulthy Mine Lead and Barytes Works Co. Ltd.
1889 Beales, Patchett and Schooles
1891-3 Bulthy Barytes and Lead Mining Company
1894 Bulthy Barytes Company

At this point the mine was abandoned, having produced 5,587 tons of barytes since 1881,[8] and one ton of dressed lead ore and 4 tons of undressed.[9]

During this period the mine suffered one of its two known fatal accidents when on 1 April 1885 James Sennett, described in the newspapers[10] as the mine agent (though E.O. Ferguson appears as such in the official returns), tried to apply oil with a knife to the mill whilst it was in motion and became caught in the mechanism. The one witness, Edwin Poole, said that that had been the normal practice. Mr. Sennett was taken to the Infirmary but died later of his injuries. In the reports the mill is described as both a spar (barytes) mill and a lead mill though at this date very little, if any lead was being dug. This is the only reference to this mill, whose location is not known.

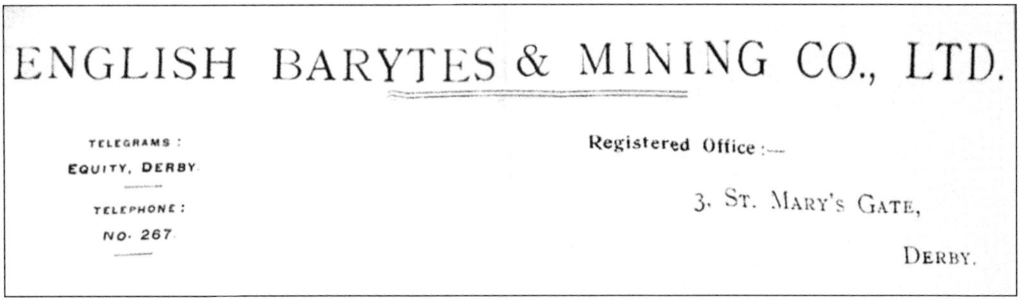

ENGLISH BARYTES & MINING CO., LTD.

TELEGRAMS :
EQUITY, DERBY

TELEPHONE :
NO. 267

Registered Office :—
3. ST. MARY'S GATE,
DERBY.

Fig. 12.2 English Barytes and Mining Co. Ltd. letterhead. (SA 5154/3/209)

The mine was active again in 1910 when a J. Beamond briefly took it over. By the time that the Bulthy Estate was offered for sale in 1914 Wm. Oldfield (of Snailbeach mine) and W. Wilson-Barnes (involved at Cothercott mine) had rights to search for minerals on specified parts of the property. The enterprise employed only two people, both underground, though production figures for the period — 106 tons from the dumps[11] — suggest that not too much of the work was actually underground.

The mine was again reopened 1914 when the English Barytes Mining Co. Ltd. of Derby obtained a 2-year lease followed by a 21-year one in 1916. 2,700 tons of barytes were produced by the end of the war and nearly 6,000 tons before they went into liquidation in 1922. In addition several tons of shale were sent to their Derbyshire works for an unspecified purpose, possibly to do with paint manufacture.[12] The 1916 lease signed in 1917 stipulated that the mine was not to be worked with adjoining mines, but the condition does not seem to have been honoured as the mine passed out of the Bulthy Estate below ground, and the accident report below states that the mine crossed the England / Wales border below ground — i.e. into the adjoining property.

The mine's second fatal accident occurred during the English Barytes and Mining Company's tenure. A petrol engine was being used underground to pump the mine dry when boring for new work tapped into old workings, and a compressor on the surface was providing some air to the workings. Five men were down the mine when fumes began to build up. Robert Paddock rescued the foreman, Bennett, got him to the foot of the shaft and returned to look for two others — William Grant and William Whittall — before collapsing. Joseph Chidley then took Bennett up to the surface and returned to look for the other two but collapsed himself, whereupon Paddock and Bennett went back down to rescue him. William Grant was found collapsed 170 yards into the mine and was put on a bogey to be pushed out but both his rescuers then collapsed. Grant did not get out alive despite a local youth named Pryce getting to him before also succumbing. Two local farmers rescued Pryce and Bennett and a doctor tried unsuccessfully to revive Grant. William Whittall had gone to stop the petrol engine before he had collapsed, but fortunately fell by the discharge pipe from the compressor, which kept him alive. Sometime after he had been given up for dead he reached the shaft bottom and was wound up in the kibble.

This incident did have one positive aspect, as it led to two men, Robert Paddock and Joseph Chidley, being awarded the Edward Medal 'for together saving a foreman overcome by petrol fumes'. This medal, known as the miners' VC, was very rarely awarded to other than coal miners and is thought to be the only such award in connection with the mines covered in this book. The mining company, English Barytes Mining Co. Ltd, and the mine agent were both fined for permitting the use of a petrol engine underground. The mines inspectors in both England and Wales each denied knowledge of the mine, which consequently had not been inspected.[13]

Fig. 12.3 Upper Adit at Bulthy photographed in July 2007. (Author)

The liquidation of the English Barytes and Mining company in 1922 did not quite spell the end of mining. On liquidation the lease was assigned to Bulthy Mines Limited. An adit going north from the valley south of the main road was opened in 1923 and reported on by Mr. Hocking, the manager of Huglith mine, as being in calcite for 200 feet, But despite being opened up for several hundred feet, no lode material was found. Presumably this work was carried by Bulthy Mines Ltd., to whom the lease was assigned, but whether Mr. Hocking was working for his employers, Shropshire Mines Ltd. or as a consultant is not known. Local information suggests that some small production from underground and from re-working the tips took place in the late 1970s.

The mine was quite extensive. The British Geological Survey reported in 1922[14] that the barytes vein was followed north-west to south-east for 1,300 yards, and that a level had been driven into the south side of Middletown Hill which followed the vein for 614 yards. The vein was four to eight feet in width and produced two grades of barytes. This was dispatched unground but hand sorted into best white and a lower quality dark-stained spar. The main shaft was said to be 165 feet deep and there was a second shaft north of it. A low level adit opened below the main road though it is said that this was not productive.[15] Around the area of the upper adit are a series of smaller adits and shafts no doubt dating from various periods in the mine's history. The mine had a steam winder at the main shaft at one time, as well as the compressor referred to above. A tramway followed the contours round the hill from the upper adit until it reached an inclined plane where trams were lowered to a loading point just short of the main road. The phases of development are unclear, although the upper adit appears to date from the post 1914 period which would make the tramway of the same date.

During the period from 1880 to 1894 a maximum of 15 men and a minimum of three were employed, usually the great majority on the surface. The only figures available for the 20th century are two in 1910, three in 1913 and the five referred to above in 1921.

The remains are not extensive. The lower adit is blocked and used as a water supply, the upper adit is visible but blocked and the group of trial adits and shafts around it have left many traces, but the whole area is a thicket of brambles and gorse. The route of the tramway and incline and below it the mine road are just about traceable. Little is visible on the English side of the border, much of the area at the time of writing being a quad biking track.

New Piece (now New Pieces)

This is a hill to the north of Middletown and Bulthy Hills where Thomas Briscoe and others must have thought minerals existed as they obtained a 21-year lease from the land owner, Thomas Eyton of Wellington to mine lead, copper, tin and other minerals on land occupied by Thomas Griffiths[16] in 1786. Nothing more is known of this or any other mines on this hill.

West Middletown

This mine is in the valley (the Dingle) between Middletown Hill and Moel-y-Golfa and was always primarily a china stone enterprise. A one-year lease was granted to William Evans to search for feldspar, greenstone and other spars, earths and clays in the west part of Middleton Hill on 14 June 1852, at which date a pit was open and power was granted to drive levels, as specimens of the stone had been sent for trial earlier in the year. Despite this the mine was not a success and the lease was not renewed, the problem probably being the quality of the mine's china stone. The area of the mine has been quarried but some remains of an adit could still be seen in the mid 1990s.

Dingle

This was a small mine which produced calcite a little further down The Dingle at Middletown than West Middletown mine. The fact that it only appears to have produced calcite suggests a late 19th or 20th century date. Work carried on into the mid 1920s.

It had one shaft and some opencast working accessed by a short tunnel. It had a steam winding engine and the reservoir to supply the boiler still survives in the woods. The shaft area has been landscaped.

13 Oswestry area Mines

This area of the county is best known, in mineral extraction terms, for its coal mines and limestone quarries, but it includes a small number of metal mines with a history going back before the Romans. The principal of these lie along the hills north-west of Llanymynech, with Carreghofa to the south, Llanymynech in the middle and Crickheath Hill/Llynclys at the north. The first two of these are now just on the Welsh side of the border but in the past at least parts of them have been in Shropshire. The story is complicated by the fact that a lot of information quoted refers to Llanymynech when the context makes it clear that Carreghofa or even Crickheath is the probable location. Of the other mines in this chapter Treflach is in Shropshire, Craignant is just in Wales and the border runs through Moelydd. These latter represent a no doubt significant number of other, now unknown sites.

Carreghofa

As was seen in chapter 1 a mine of this name played its part in British history. It was not heard of after 1195 until the late 17th century, though there is a possibility that mining took place here in the 14th century.[1] Then it surfaced in 1678 as Y Graig Wen and was leased to two miners by Sir Richard Myddleton. The extent of work is unclear and in 1692 gunpowder is recorded as being used to open up old workings, said to be the earliest recorded use of the material in Wales (the earliest recorded use in Britain being at Ecton, Staffordshire in or just prior to 1686).

Nothing further is known until 1753 when Slaughter and Richardson, Deeside smelters, surveyed the area but no work was apparently done until 1760 when Lord Powis encouraged exploration. Even then little was done or won. At similar dates work was tried on the hill away from the Carreghofa area, perhaps for copper as well as lead. The mine next appears in the early 1840s when large developments were supposedly under way. In about 1853 the mine was worked profitably by individuals and in 1855 by the Carreg Hova Copper and Lead Mining company who were raising ores of lead, copper and zinc. By 1857 a further cost-book company, the Carreghofa Mining company, had been set up (according to the letter writer) by 'crooked speculators whose directors never attended meetings' and then dissolved. Proper accounts were not kept, ore sent for sale was not recorded and when the company was dissolved the directors admitted to owing the shareholders £150.[2] The captain at that date was John Lester. The New

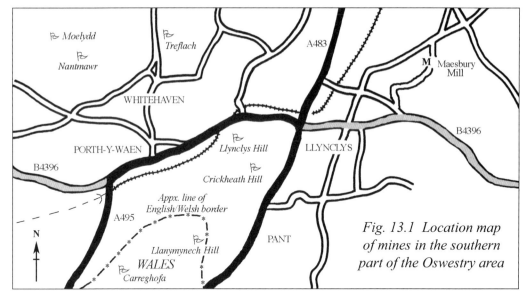

Fig. 13.1 Location map of mines in the southern part of the Oswestry area

Carreghofa Mining Company was then formed to take over the mine, which was said to be good and well placed for land and water transport. During the 1857 'crisis' small quantities of copper ore and a little lead were being dug, probably during development work, the copper ore being sent either to Messrs. Newton, Keats & Co. of Liverpool, 'a small works at Runcorn' or 'via Amlwch'. The mine was not being regularly worked, however. In September 1857 a shareholder visiting the mine expressed surprise to find it not working, the agent apparently having gone to open a mine near Wrexham. The scale of mining was clearly not great. In April 1857 two men were digging a new shaft whilst others were clearing out the old winding shaft, but at no stage is the level of employment or output given.

Any remains there may have been are now covered by a golf course.

Craignant

Nothing is known of this mine. It is just in Wales and was found by members of the Shropshire Caving and Mining Club in December 1962 after information from a local farmer. There was evidence for several shafts and two adits, one of which was explored; it was unusual in that its roof was of limestone and its floor of clay. Apparently the locations of some of the shafts are still clear. There is also what could be the remains of an adit in a disused quarry behind the lime kilns on the English side of the road.

Crickheath Hill

That copper ore was being gathered in the township of Crickheath by 1799 is evidenced by a statement of the quantities of ore on which royalties of $^1/_8$th were due to Lord Powis. This mining was being carried out by two sets of men, William Edwards and Edward Dyke, and Ellis Jones and (?John) Thomas, the former pair having 'gathered' the greater amount of ore (5.4 tons as against 2.6) and working two sites (see below). The ore was

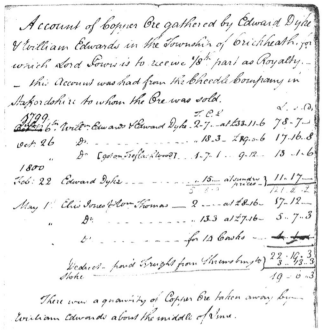

Fig. 13.2 A statement of copper ore sold to the Cheadle Company in 1800 from land owned by the Powis Estate in Crickheath and Treflach. (SA 552/18/8/7/14)

sent to the Cheadle Company in Stoke, Staffordshire. The quality of ore varied considerably, ranging in value from more than £23 a ton to less than £8. During a similar period a John Lewis had raised lead ore at Crickheath and no doubt paid royalties to the Lords Powis.

The British Geological Survey, writing in 1929, record that all metalliferous mining had been long abandoned and that even by 1868 had been in decline for some years. Despite this (or perhaps relating to a different, nearby location) two companies were floated with names that suggest that they intended to mine on Crickheath Hill — the Crickheath Lead and Copper Mining Co. Ltd. of 1874 and the New Crickheath Lead and Copper Mining Co. Ltd. of 1875. They may have been inspired by the (comparative) success of the adjoining Llynclys mine. There are remains of shafts and adits on the hill.

Llanymynech

Amongst the oldest mines in the area, the evidence for bronze age mining and metallurgy and for Roman working is compelling. The best known mine here is now called The Ogof, Welsh for 'cave'. It may be in part natural but the bulk is not. Signs of human activity from the Bronze Age onward have been discovered including numerous hammer stones and antler picks, along with coins from the Roman period. Human and animal remains have also been found and paint a picture not only of early mining but of human habitation, whilst local Bronze and Iron Age encampments show signs of metallurgical activity. The Ogof forms a figure of eight circuit of passageways and chambers about 600 feet long of varying widths and heights, the smallest being very tight — now called the 'Agony Crawl'.

Though it is probable that the memory of the mine stayed alive and that it would have been worked as necessary to supply local needs, especially as the adjacent Carreghofa mine was worked in the late 12th century, nothing specific is heard of it until 1602. Thereafter a series of mentions appear in various documents making it clear that at least small scale mining was taking place. When Carreghofa was reopened in the mid

Fig. 13.3 The mouth of Llanymynech Ogof in 1986 (with a member of the Shropshire Caving and Mining Club in the background). (Kelvin Lake, I A Recordings)

century it is probable that Llanymynech was worked either separately or in conjunction. Intermittent work continued into the 18th century and a survey of 1753 shows several old shafts. The work in the 18th century was perhaps carried out by unemployed quarrymen in the winter, and in 1791 there are records of lead, copper and zinc ores being got. There was increased activity between 1795 until 1804 with some of the ore being exported by canal to Macclesfield and Birmingham. After 1797 and before 1862 (when navigation of

Fig. 13.3 Two members of the Shropshire Caving and Mining Club in Llanymynech Ogof in 1968. (Kelvin Lake, I A Recordings)

the Upper Severn finished) other products went out by river from Clawdd Goch on the Vyrnwy. The final fling on the hill seems to have begun in 1841 and petered out by about 1870, in 1868 the mines being described as having been in decline for some years. After that occasional working probably occurred, most probably by unemployed quarrymen.

In addition to The Ogof the whole hill was littered with pits, shafts and opencast workings. Frequently shafts would enter old workings and on one occasion a new adit was driven below the known Roman workings and up into them. No information has survived as to output or employment at these mines. Apart from The Ogof, surface remains are scant as the area is now home to a golf course, but much remains underground and is explorable with the appropriate insurance, equipment and consent. One other very tangible reminder from about the end of the 17th century is a specimen in the Woodwardian Collection in Cambridge's Sedgwick Geological Museum. The catalogue entry for item A17 11 f73 records: 'A whiteish brown sparry crust striated across consists of severall Incrustations and shewing the successive Application of each to other in the Formation of the body by water running down the side of ye Fissure of stone, on which this crust was form'd & affixed in Slany Monack Cave near Oswestry in Shropshire'.[3]

Llynclys Hill

Bagshaw's *Directory* of 1851 carries the comment that 'It is the opinion of many that minerals abound in this township. A party of gentlemen have commenced works in search of copper ore but none had been found when our agent visited.' The optimism may have been well founded but, assuming that the above refers to Llynclys Hill rather than Crickheath Hill (see above) it was to be nearly 20 years before commercial scale mining began. In 1870 a group of partners, including John Job of Snailbeach and James Yelland, obtained a take note for one year from the Powis agent, Thomas Newill, to seek lead, copper and zinc at 'Llyncklys' Hill. This led to the formation of the Llynclys Lead and Copper Mining Co. Ltd. in 1871, with John Lester[4] as Captain. The company, incorporated in March 1871, was to have capital of £12,000, 5s. per share was to be paid on application and allotment, whilst calls were not expected to exceed 2s. 6d., at intervals of at least 3 months. The prospectus, issued in August, told potential investors that the company was formed to work under land at Llynclys near Oswestry and that it had 300 acres of rights. The mine was near Llynclys Station and was able to have deep adits levels, thereby reducing the costs of steam pumping. In addition to lead and copper, iron oxide and limestone could also be worked. Accompanying the prospectus were two reports, one by John Lester and the other by a national figure who appears at several Shropshire mines, James Nancarrow. He reported that two lodes were present, the Ranter lode on which several pits between 3 and 16 yards deep had been sunk along with 100 yards of 'drivages', and the North and South lode (later called the Redfern) which had been proved by a 25-yard deep shaft. In addition to the metal ores he noted a 4 foot thick 15 to 20 yard wide bed of iron oxide which could be mined at a profit, and also that limestone dug out could be sold for burning and other uses. All in all he expressed himself impressed. For the rest of 1871 there were weekly reports by Lester of the sinking of shafts and the getting of lead.

Despite the promise, all this work must have been carried out on take notes as the lease was not prepared until January 1874, by which time a new company, the Llynclys United Lead Copper and Oxide Mining Co. Ltd., had been incorporated. Correspondence refers to further leases in 1876 and 77. The New Llynclys Lead, Copper & Oxide Syndicate Mining Co. Ltd. was incorporated on 8 July 1881 to acquire the mine from Messrs. Job and Yelland who had a take note in 1870 and a lease in 1877, suggesting that the mine was being worked in two parts for some of this period. This last company probably never worked the mine. In January 1883 legal action was threatened by the Powis estate as no payments had been received for five years and the company were standing in the way of those who wanted to develop the mine. In 1884 the mine first appears in the official returns when a dozen men working for R. & C. Gill produced 85 tons of lead and 60 tons of zinc ores with a value of nearly £800. That was it, for the mine was abandoned in 1886.

Ultimately, although unsuccessful, this mine was more than just a scratch, with over 4,000 feet of workings on three levels, in most cases accessed from quarries. A series of adits still survive in quarries and the sites of several filled or blocked shafts are also recognisable.

Treflach and Moelydd

There is evidence on the ground that mining may well have occurred in and around Moelydd but no documentary evidence has yet been found.[5] A mile or so to the east is Treflach where a little evidence has survived. In 1799 two of the men mining at Crickheath were also getting ore here, but judging from the price received it was of lesser quality and it was sold to the Cheadle Company. Additionally lead and zinc was worked in unspecified locations to the west of Oswestry. John Gibbons was a local businessman with substantial interests in various industries including coal, lead and zinc mines, the latter on land owned by Sir Watkin Wynn, the Powis estate, Miss Whilton, Mr. Dorsett, Mr. Hollins and Mr. Hughes, the last named also being the mine manager and an equal shareholder with Gibbons ([6]/16th each). The ores were mainly worked opencast but with a few shafts (the deepest known being 14.5 yards deep) and headings. 'Old pit' was cleaned out in 1788/9 at a cost of 10 shillings; quite how old 'old pit' was is not revealed nor whether the cleaning out opened up any new production. Water seems to have been a problem. After mining the land was trenched to return it to agriculture. The only figures quoted suggest an annual production of 40 tons of ore on Sir Watkin Wynn's land and 2 tons on Powis estate land. The zinc was sold to the Cheadle (Brass) Co. The few tons of lead ore also dug was sent to Minera for smelting. Though Gibbons was active in the area from the mid 1780s until his death in 1811 no metal mining involvement is recorded after about 1790.[6]

In 1854 the Powis Estate granted Benjamin Davidson of Birmingham a take note to search for ore at a $^1/_{10}$th royalty, with a 21-year lease being available if wanted, but there is no evidence that it was.

In the same vicinity a series of shafts along a vein have been noted at **Nantmawr**.

14 Copper Mines in north-east Shropshire

The mines in this group are geologically related to each other and to copper mines in Cheshire and Staffordshire, whose fortunes they tended to follow. Suggestions of Roman or earlier mining have been made for several of the mines in this group but the first record of mining is from Pim Hill during the reign of Charles I. There was something of a boom in the late 17th century, a short-lived period of expensive activity in the 1860s and a final hiccough in the First World War. One or two of the sites have been re-examined in recent years but further activity is very unlikely.

Other metals and minerals were found in small quantities and occasionally exploited. Thus Clive produced cobalt, iron and barytes, Pim Hill vanadium, Rednal cobalt, iron and manganese and Wixhill lead. Listed below are mines or places where some record has survived of mining or prospecting. It is more or less certain that trials would have taken place everywhere that the sandstone outcropped and it is quite possible that some of these now unremembered sites were more successful than many set out below.

Clive

This is one of the few mines where archaeological examination has suggested the dates of the earliest works. The similarity of some work at Clive to known Roman mining at Llanymynech gives good grounds for accepting that the Romans mined here. Other archaeological work and finds indicate a period of activity in the late 17th century which would not be at all surprising given other local activity; there are remains such as tobacco pipes and tools and indications that a substantial amount of ore was removed.[1]

The first known records date from shortly after 1709 when Thomas Oswin went to Ireland to work copper and returned not long after to develop a copper mine at **Drepewood** (towards Wem) which he claimed contained gold.[2] This has always been considered to be part of Clive mine, though Drepewood is over a mile north. The next reference to activity in the area is when Roger Atcherley took a lease in 1711 at **Spendiloes** copper mines near Grinshill Church, the precise location of which is not known. Thomas Spendlove sought a lease in 1739 for the above mine from the Varnons of Clive via a Mr. Brazier (or Bresnor) of Hanbury Hall, Droitwich.[3] This was not the only Droitwich connection as a lease was held by John Payne of that town at some time in the 18th century.

Though it is probable that work continued at least intermittently, the next definite information comes from a short spell as a well-capitalised mine in the 1860s. The success of Alderley Edge copper mine in Cheshire led to a renewed interest in copper mining in Shropshire and several mines were developed in this period. The Gardner family of Sansaw granted various leases to individuals who sold out to the Clive Mining Co. Ltd. in 1862 and 1863. Amongst those whose interests were acquired was William Henderson of the British Metal Extracting Co. Ltd. who held a patent for ore treatment which was also purchased. Further changes of proprietor occurred and in 1865 the New Clive Mining Co. Ltd. was formed, with much of its capital coming from Birmingham, the previous company remaining in existence until 1882. The new company obtained leases for additional land, again from the Gardner family, and sank money into the mine to very little effect, most of the best ore having been removed much earlier. By 1869 the company was beginning to sell off plant and the mine had closed by the following year. The only subsequent use for the mine was as a water supply for Hadnall, a shaft being deepened on several occasions and pumps installed. The water supply is still used, though only for animals.

The mine or mines would have been small affairs, except during the 1860s when up to 40 men were employed, many recruited from Alderley Edge and Cornwall.

Fig. 14.1 A view along the northern stope of Clive copper mine in 1986. (Kelvin Lake, I A Recordings)

The mine at its maximum was centred on Clive village opposite the church where there were trials in the 18th century, but it spread to the north and south with early activity at both ends. In all there are believed to have been 29 shafts spread over about a mile. The maximum depth of the mine was 80 yards though the productive levels were mainly at the 60 yard level, the lower level being used for the purpose of collecting the ore for tramming to the winding shaft. At least one part of the mine was solely developed for cobalt and some barytes and iron were also produced. It is impossible to estimate production of any of the minerals mined, for although official returns were made in the 1860s no production figures are given.

The copper ore, at least during the 1860s, was broken in cog crushers at the surface and screened, that which passed the one inch screen being treated in stone tanks with hydrochloric acid and then precipitated on scrap iron. The precipitate was then dried in a kiln, barrelled and sent to the smelters, presumably in Swansea.

There are not a great deal of surface remains though two shafts exist: the Well Shaft and the Rubbish Shaft. This latter can on occasions be entered and access gained to a substantial area of the old workings down to a hundred or so feet, below which the mine is flooded. Some of the Yorkshire flagstone processing tanks were sold in 1869 to the Bryntail mine in Montgomeryshire, where several remain at the restored mine near the Clwedog dam three mile west of Llanidloes.

Fig. 14.2 Surviving leaching tanks from Clive mine, now preserved at Bryntail mine, Powys. (I. Cooper)

Hawkstone

The excavation of a Bronze Age founder's hoard together with the proximity of Bury Walls, a major Bronze Age site where early tools have been found, makes it a reasonable supposition that copper was mined here in prehistoric times even if only from outcrops. It is also believed that the Romans mined here, as there was a villa in the vicinity. Mining in historic times probably began when five gentlemen reached agreement to share costs and profits of any ores found in Weston-under-Redcastle and Wixhill.[4] There is no plan with the agreement and it is not certain where in Weston mining was intended (see Weston Heath below) but it is very likely that Hawkstone was included. Certainly the landowner, Mr. Tenison, mined copper on the estate as he sent samples to John Woodward, an early collector of geological specimens (see also Llanymynech). He sold the estate to the Hill family in 1737 by which time all mining had ceased.

The extent of mining was never great. There was a shaft, now filled, which was 3 metres deep with two short levels opening in the face of the Terrace in the gardens of the house. There is a grilled shaft lost in rhododendrons half a mile further west on the Terrace and there is the suggestion that the Grotto is the remains of a Roman mine. The are other known unexploited veins in the gardens including one to the north-west of the Red Castle.

If the extent of mining is unimpressive the remains are interesting. The Grotto and the Terrace are in the gardens which are regularly open to the public and two samples of rock, referred to above, which were sent by Mr. Tenison to Mr. Woodward in the late 17th or early 18th century, remain with the latter's collection at the Sedgwick Geological Museum at Cambridge University.

Fig. 14.3 A member of the Shropshire and Mining Caving Club in the underground folly at Hawkstone Park in 1986. This is believed to be or to incorporate a Roman (or earlier) copper mine. (Kelvin Lake, I A Recordings)

Pim Hill

One of the first written records of copper mining in the county is at Pim Hill. In the early 1640s an amount of blue stone was dug on Haremeare (now Harmer) Heath, but the works were abandoned when the miners joined King Charles I's army in the Civil War in 1643. In that year the stock of stone was carted to the Warren House (no doubt the dwelling of a local official, logically the Warrener but possibly the constable) and it was declared to be treasonable to touch it. The stone was finally used for road-making. When the royal monopolies were progressively removed between 1688 and 1693 the Lord of the Manor (the Earl of Bridgewater) invited a group of Derbyshire miners to dig a shaft, but it was not a success and work had ceased by 1700.[5] In April 1710 the Bridgewater family granted a lease to Abraham Darby and Company of Bristol to seek copper at Harmer Heath and Myddle Hill, but this must have proved unprofitable as by 1714 copper ore was being sent to Coalbrookdale from Cumbria for brass making.

No further activity is known of until the Shropshire copper 'rush' of the 1860s. Only little is known of this phase of the mine's life, when between 10 and 20 men were employed and some cobalt and vanadium were found in addition to a small amount of copper. The highlight of the mine's existence, no doubt, was reached in 1878 when the *Mining Journal* mistakenly informed its readers that platinum was found here — presumably the journalist knew that an uncommon metal had been found but could not remember that it was vanadium. The final words were written in the early years of the

20th century when prospecting for cobalt took place, needless to say this added another chapter to the history of this not exactly successful enterprise.

At its maximum the mines consisted of three shafts 400, 500 and 600 yards north of the summit of Pim Hill, and an adit connecting with one of them, but little remains. It is also likely that shafts and/or adits existed between Pim Hill and Newton-on-the-Hill about a mile to the north along the vein.

Rednal (or Eardiston)

As with all the other mines in this group, hopes were much higher than results; however, unlike many of the others, Rednal did produce some rich ore. In the 1840s samples of ore were found to contain 18.5% copper, much better that usual for the county, where a figure of less than 10% was normal. The landowners hoped that the royalties from this mine were going to financially endow a church by raising £200 p.a. for five years, but whilst it may have helped it did not fully achieve the aim. In the event the income from the royalties were replaced by the sale of fishing rights on a lake at Pradoe, the country house of the Kenyon family who owned the area mined and built the church.[6]

The first recorded mining was the sinking of three shafts in 1827 by David W. Jones, 'the lime man' of Oswestry, who was granted an 18-month search note in August 1827 with a 21-year lease to follow, if wanted. He dug down about 10 metres and encountered water problems which he could not afford to resolve. He also encountered evidence of earlier mining.

In June 1836 group of businessmen and gentlemen, mostly from Liverpool but including a David Jones, presumably the one involved in 1827, took a lease. Initial success proving the lode prompted the company to obtain a search note on the adjoining Tedsmore Estate to the north. Though the lode was found at a shaft dug here a lease was not taken up and work concentrated on the main site near Lane End. An adit was dug to drain the 1827 workings and ore was raised by a hand winch. Work continued until 1839 when the mine was sold, the new partners then falling into dispute and forfeiting the lease.

A report had been made on the mine in 1837 by a Mr. Henwood which was forwarded in 1840, following the above failure, to a London businessman who then sold shares in a new company, the Eardiston Mine company, raising sufficient capital to equip the mine properly and pump out water from below adit level, where the best of the ore lay. New shafts were sunk on each side of the road just south of Lane End, one in March 1841 with a three horse whim to the east and the other to the west of the road equipped with a steam pumping engine which was in production by November. Significant amounts of ore were now being raised but not sufficient to be profitable. Royalty payments were late and difficulties were occurring with shareholders who did not receive information to which they were entitled on the sales of ore. In the end the information the company refused to supply was supplied by the landowners. Despite further capital being raised by a call on the shares the mine could not be run profitably and the company gave up the lease in September 1844. Work had ceased in the spring and the engine was dismantled and removed. A total capital of about £8,000 had been used and though much good ore had been raised it had never been sufficient — even so, it was the most profitable period in the mine's history.

The mine retained a reputation as a rich mine and it is not surprising that it was amongst the first Shropshire copper mines reopened during the boom of the 1860s. Negotiations had begun in 1859 with Messrs. Wright of the Ruabon Spelter Works who wished to mine the lower grade ores left in the previous campaign. The proposal was to treat these ores on site by calcining and acid leaching; however, agreement could not be reached on the provision of a calcining furnace and a lease was not granted.

The next approach was from Sir Jocelyn Coghill and partners, this time with no mention of calcining as the lower grade ores were to be treated by acid leaching — the same process as used at Clive mine. This company took the precaution of interviewing an employee from the (relatively) successful 1840-41 activity who confirmed that ore was available but that water was a problem. He was also of the opinion that the mine had failed through lack of financial backing, internal and external quarrelling and general rascality! A 12-month lease was granted in December 1862, followed by a 21-year lease in 1863. Various trials took place around the area, a previously filled shaft was re-excavated and a new vein containing cobalt was discovered. The warnings about water proved correct and work on parts of the mine were delayed until the new steam engine was pumping. This 12 horse power engine had to pump night and day to keep the workings, by this time 30 metres deep, clear of water. By October 1863 the partners had invested £1,000 and had had enough. They surrendered the lease.

Fig. 14.4 Underground stone-arched level at Rednal mine

Next to try was Alexander Alison of Chelsea, chairman of the British Copper Co. Ltd., who purchased the mine for £1,000 and took up the lease from 1 January 1864. Shares were advertised for sale in the *Mining Journal* in March 1864 to raise capital for new buildings and a 60 hp engine. This engine and two boilers arrived via Rednal Station in August and a blacksmith's shop, carpenter's shop and engine house were constructed. Whilst the mine was adequately equipped, finances and management were not sound. The June 1846 rental on the lease was unpaid and safety conditions stipulated in the lease had been ignored, miners were not being paid, bills were not met and Alison was not answering letters. Work at the mine stopped in September 1864 and by the December the mine was flooded again and the boilers lay untouched on site. Demands for money were made throughout 1865 and the British Copper Co. Ltd. was made insolvent. The Kenyons subsequently received part payment of their rent and gave consent for some of the plant to be sold and removed, following advertisements in the *Mining Journal* between March and September. Included in the adverts were two new boilers and an incomplete 60 hp engine.

Enquiries were made about the mine in 1866, 1880 and again in 1906. This latter got as far as a draft lease which contained a requirement by Robert Kenyon that the lessees, the Northern Mercantile Company, must not adversely affect the quantity or purity of the water from wells and springs within a mile of the mine. This requirement stemmed from the fact that previous mine companies had pumped so much water out of the mine that springs and wells dried up, whilst the mining had also caused pollution. This water clause proved a final stumbling block not only to the 1902 scheme but to others in 1908, 1912 and 1917. The 1917 scheme was proposed by UK Mineral Developments Ltd. who obtained leases on two Cheshire copper mines, Alderley Edge and Bickerton, and hoped also to reopen other Shropshire mines including Clive and Pim Hill.

The water problems were resolved by the provision of mains water and in 1966 one last attempt was made to test the extent of the ore-body. Surface and borehole samples were taken and geochemical analysis carried out. The lode was found to die out at depth and though malachite was found, it was a long way short of economic viability.

The mine consisted of a number of shafts up to 30 metres deep at three sites: Mine Pit Field, Lane End Field and Tedsmore Bank. Both surface and underground workings extended to at least 1,800 feet in length running south-west to north-east and there was a 500 foot adit. A horse whim was constructed in Mine Pit Field and the steam engines were (or were to have been) in Lane End Field. Some opencast working was carried out which was later extended to form the stone quarry which provided the stone for the church.

It has been claimed that 2,500 tons of ore were raised in total from the mine[7] but information contained in the Kenyon family papers suggests that the figure is closer to 500 tons, half of that in 1842 and almost all the remainder between 1836 and 1844. The ore was sold to various copper companies in Swansea, Liverpool and, possibly, Cheadle.

Little now remains. Engine House Plantation in Lane End Field recalls the engines and there is some stonework from the engine house, whilst on the other side of the road the quarry is visible. All the shafts have been filled in and a little of the adit has been explored, with some fine stone arch supports noted.[8]

Sandford

The Society of Mineral and Battery Works[9] issued licences to work minerals. In 1667 an offer to take up a joint lease in the 'parish of Sandford, Shropshire within 5 miles of the church' was submitted to the society on behalf of Dr. Underhill and Mr. Manley. This was then converted into a concession to cover an area within a radius of one mile from a pillar of wood or stone to be erected on the site, but whether the lease was finally sealed is not indicated. There are two Sandfords in the county, one near West Felton, the other east of Preece; neither has ever been a parish or has a church. If the site is really in Shropshire its location remains a mystery.[10]

Wixhill area

Included in this are known mines at Wixhill itself, trials at least at Weston Heath and trials at Lee Brockhurst. Copper ores in this area may have been known in Roman or even prehistoric times. It is reasonably suspected that early activity at Wixhill predates 1697 as in that year a lease was sought by Sir Phillip Egerton, owner of Bickerton mine in Cheshire. This was not apparently taken up as in the following February a lease was granted to Richard Larkins. Between these dates, on 14 October 1697 Richard Corbett, Thomas Sandford, Thomas Hill, John Gardner and Jonathan Browne agreed to share all expenses and profits in any ores or metals found in Weston-under-Redcastle and Wixhill. Quite how these enterprises related to each other is not known, for in no case do any records survive. Wixhill does not feature again until a brief spell of activity in the 1860s when a shaft was opened or reopened at the south end of the hill. Again little is known of this enterprise. Remains are scanty, just two filled shafts and two adits.

It is believed that miners from Wixhill were responsible for mining at Weston Heath where a mine is said to have been worked up to or at least in 1728.[11] In about 1800 it was wryly noted that the Rev. Snelson 'expected to find hidden treasure at Weston'[12] — he did not.

If Wixhill miners opened up Weston Heath it is possible that the activity at Lee Brockhurst was also theirs. Two trials for copper are noted[13] in the upper mottled sandstone of the Lee Hills, one was still visible in 1925, 200 yards west-north-west of Moston Park, whilst in a cutting on the main road half a mile north of the house there was a trial level. Nothing now remains. 'Pits (dis)' are also marked on the current Ordnance Survey maps to the north of Lee Brockhurst (and the west of Wixhill) which may also be connected with copper prospecting or mining.

Yorton (or Broughton)

Like most of the other entries in this section Yorton is not a mine but a useful name for a number of shafts spread over quite a distance and clearly related to Clive mine a mile to the east and Pim Hill to the south. Like all the mines in this group the copper ore was sought in long but poorly mineralised faults.

Records of this mine are slight. The lease of 1710 mentioned at Pim Hill could have involved Yorton, Murchison notes its existence in 1839 and leases exist from three different landowners — Viscount Hill, Gardners of Sansaw and the late Major Bailey — in 1863. The mine adventurers involved are Harries and Co., Henderson, Morris and Procter, Williams and Wright, most of whom were also involved at Clive and outside the county.

The best recorded of the shafts is near Alderton. It was still locatable in the 1920s when it was noted as being covered by a grille at the roadside and acting as a drain for the highway. It was 150 feet deep. This site may also have been called Yorton Bank and Shotton Hill. There is another possible shaft 140 feet to the north. The 1863 activity covered a larger area running south from this latter shaft almost to Harmer Hill. There are now no known remains.

15 Non-Mining Sites

Whilst the extraction of ore had to take place where that ore was found, the treatment of the ore did not. A balance had to be struck between the transport costs of the ore and the power required to treat it. This section covers the sites where ore treatment took place away from the mines themselves, namely certain lead smelthouses and barytes mills. Similar facilities on mine sites are dealt with in the section on that mine.

Between *c*.1780 and 1895 much Shropshire lead ore was smelted locally, whilst at other times ore was sent to other parts of the country for smelting. Snailbeach for instance sent ore to Thomas Smith's (a partner of the Snailbeach proprietor, Lovett) smelter at Minera in Denbighshire in the 1780s before they built their own smelter,[1] and to Dennis' at Ruabon from 1895 after the closure of their on-site plant. Ore was also sent from other mines to Deeside and Chester for processing. Products other than lead and barytes were almost always sent out of the county having received initial dressing at the mine.

Four other groups of features are included in this section: barytes mills, aerial ropeways, large drainage levels and the Snailbeach District Railways. These generally went (well) beyond any individual mine site boundary and most of them served more than one mine or other concern, though not always at the same time.

Smelthouses

Until at least the mid 17th century Shropshire lead would have been smelted in small quantities using wood or charcoal and the locations would have been chosen to balance the need to move lead ore and timber as well as to pick a site with a good natural draught. Such 'boles' are known from excavation to have been used on the Stiperstones and Pontesford Hill and will have existed in many other places. More urban sites would have been widespread though presumably only for production of goods from lead pigs and scrap lead rather than smelting the ore. Lead was being smelted on industrial sites (for example see Leighton in chapter 1) during the Civil War, but the extent to which it was an industrial process is not known.

Two principal areas of the county subsequently became involved in smelting — the Ironbridge Gorge and the coalfield around Pontesbury — though the first recorded smelter in the vicinity was built at Pool Quay near Welshpool in 1710 by the Earl of Powis. This is relevant because although it was primarily to treat ore from the Earl's Llangynog mines it is probable that the ore from the London Lead Company's mines was treated here.[2] This smelter closed in 1762.

Smelting reduced in Shropshire in about 1860 when rail transport meant that ore could be sold and transported to the bigger firms away from the ore-field, though Snailbeach bucked that trend by smelting near the mine almost to the end of lead mining.

The Ironbridge Gorge

In the 18th century this area was a centre of all types of industrial activity, most famously coal and iron working, but it is believed that before the 1750s the lead industry may have used as much coal and employed as many people as the iron works.[3] In 1753-5 ore was coming from 'Pannels' (presumably Pennerley) to be smelted in the gorge at the 'Salop company's' smelter.[4] Quite where all the activity was is not certain but at least four sites seem to have been active at some time between 1730 and the early years of the 19th century. It seems an obvious place — the river provided transport for the lead, from Shropshire and mid Wales, the gorge provided coal and the river transported the pigs to Bristol, then a principal centre of the lead industry. Lead smelters first appeared at Ironbridge around 1730, when debts mentioned in papers of John and Robert Myddleton of Chirk and the Coalbrookdale Company are concerned with equipment for a smelter. The Coalbrookdale Company's records also make reference to a smelter at Madeley

Fig. 15.1 An engraving by Francis Chesham (1749-1806) based on a painting by George Robertson (1724-1788) of the Iron Bridge; of particular interest in the present context is the depiction of the Bower Yard smelter on the right hand side of the picture. Published 1 February 1788

Wood on the north bank of the River Severn which adjoined land they leased in 1756. A document of 1774 mentions a smelthouse adjacent to the company's land at Dale End. Whether these two are the same and whether one of them is the Myddleton smelter is not known.

The first clearly dated reference to a lead smelter was to one on the south bank of the river near Broseley. The land was leased in 1731 and the smelter was in operation by April 1732. It was built by the London Lead Co., whose history is given briefly on pp.69-70, to process ore from their mines in the Marches.[5] In spite of its location near plentiful coal, markets and transport it was out of use by 1736. The proprietors of Bog Mine, Mathew Dore (or Dove, the writing is not clear) and company, took a lease from 1740 which they held until 1748. This smelter was probably sited just downstream of the Iron Bridge and was later used as a malthouse.

Also in the same vicinity was a smelter shown in Bower Yard on various plans, notably on a plan of proposals in the late 18th century for locks to improve the navigation. It is also illustrated on several contemporary paintings and prints as it stood within sight of the bridge (Fig. 15.1). Nothing is known of its users or period of use but in 1788 materials from a smelter in the gorge, possibly this one, were sold to the proprietors of the Arrow Smelter at Aberystwyth.[6]

In 1760 The Bog Mining company sought land at The Lloyds on the north bank of the river:[7] 'The Bog Company intends having a smelthouse down at the coals for the smelting of lead'. The building was expected to cost about £200 and 'very likely may consume 400 or 800 tons of coal a year'. It is not known if this was built but Bog certainly had a smelter in 1761 as documents refer to it, though not to its location,[8] and a smelter was certainly in operation in the vicinity in 1790 when William Reynolds developed the new town of Coalport. This smelter was pulled down and re-erected by Reynold's executors in 1810. By 1849 Smelthouse Row was shown on the Madeley Tithe Map, but there is no sign of any smelter.

The Pontesbury Coalfield

Small quantities of coal had been dug in this locality for centuries. In 1402 Shrewsbury Abbey Cartulary[9] refers to a case where revenues of a pit at Winsley may have been misappropriated. Mining is recorded in the 17th century but the beginnings of large scale development are in the second half of the 18th century. Whether the development of the coalfield led to the relocation of smelting from Ironbridge Gorge to this area or whether the desire to make this move led to an increased and successful search for coal is moot. Smelting began at four sites in the last quarter of the 18th century, and a further site came on stream in the second quarter of the 19th century, but all these sites are called Pontesbury by contemporary writers which has led to some confusion. To add to that confusion, two of the sites adjoined each other at Malehurst and a further two in Pontesford, an eastern outlier of Pontesbury. These last were major employers, in 1851 providing work for 90 men and 35 boys. Both of them had substantially closed by the mid 1870s. Both buildings remain and have been converted but the 150 and 180 feet high chimneys were demolished in the early 20th century.

Malehurst

The first smelter at Malehurst, sited in Engine Field adjoining the colliery, was erected in about 1778 by Jonathan Scott and Edward Jeffreys who had a colliery lease.[10] By 1783 the smelter was leased for 14 years to a group of businessmen under Francis Lloyd, possibly the White Grit company.[11] The 1783 lease gives specific consent for another smelter or other buildings to be constructed and a second smelter on the colliery site was built in 1792 or 93 by or for John Lawrence on a field 'called ye Bridge or Engine Field'. By 1795 the lease condition that coal or the smelter used should come from the landlord's (Thomas Boycott) mines, was being breached by Lawrence, who was bringing in coal from a mine of his own at Limehouse Gate in Pontesbury (north of the turnpike to Minsterley, the colliery that the White Grit company were leasing when the land was sold in 1794).[12] Scott and Jeffreys lost the resultant case and had to pay Boycott the lost royalties in 1797.

Both the smelters were gutted during March 1796 by Lawrence's men and this appears to have been the end of smelting at Malehurst. Little is known of the smelt-houses, except that they were built of brick from brick pits on the colliery site (in breach of lease conditions) and had brick ore bins. One of them had a steam blowing engine for the slag hearth, a water course and 'basin' constructed to service it. A tramway was laid to it from a coal pit. The location is not precisely known — the tithe survey of 1842 shows two Engine fields and no Bridge fields, though other documents imply that Bridge field was where the Minsterley Brook joined the Rea Brook. At the same time as the smelthouses were gutted, the beam was removed from a steam engine, presumably that of the smelter, although as the colliery seems to have closed at the same time it could have been one of possibly two other engines.[13]

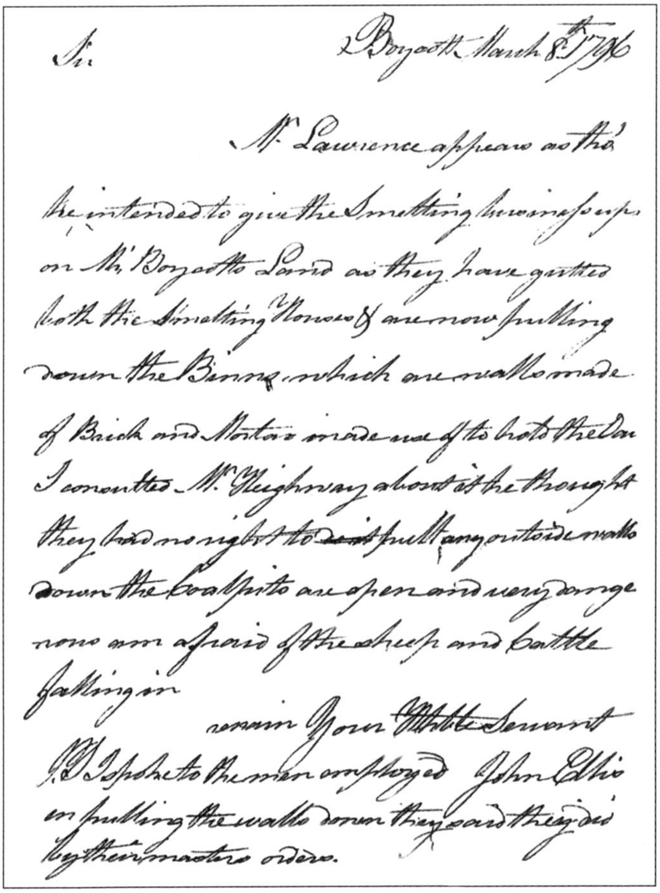

Sir, Boycott March 8th 1796

Mr Lawrence appears as tho' he intended to give the Smelting business up on Mr Boycott's Land as they have gutted both the Smelting Houses & are now pulling down the Binns which are walls made of Brick and Mortar made use of to hold the Ore I consulted Mr Heighway about it he thought they had no right to ~~sai~~ pull any outside walls down the Coalpits are open and very dangerous am afraid of the sheep and Cattle falling in

remain Your ~~Hble~~ Servant

P.S. I spoke to the men employed in pulling the walls down they said they did by their masters orders. John Ellis

Fig. 15.2 Correspondence establishing something of the number and nature of the early smelters at Malehurst. (SA 6000/13914)

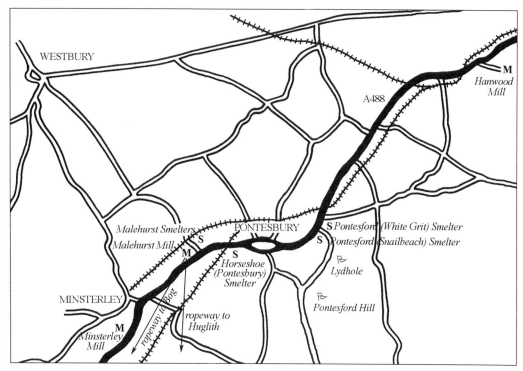

Fig. 15.3 map showing the location of sites in the Pontesbury area

Pontesbury

When John Lawrence was party to the dispute with Boycott at Malehurst, amongst the issues was that Lawrence was bringing coal from his own pit 'in the neighbourhood', no

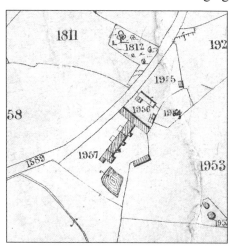

Fig. 15.4 The Pontesbury tithe map of 1842 gives some indication of the size and layout of the smelter near the Horseshoe Inn. (SA PF220/3/3)

doubt the Limehouse Gate one which must have been virtually opposite the smelter he built. It is also a reasonable assumption that he purchased Coalpit Croft, which had been sold in 1794,[14] and may have been on the next plot to his own house and near the later site of the Horseshoe Inn.[15] As Lawrence seems to have continued smelting as agent for the White Grit company, it is reasonable to assume that when the Malehurst smelters were being gutted, the Pontesbury one was being built and equipped using parts from its predecessors. By 1814 the White Grit company had a smelter and ancillary buildings in Pontesbury when a valuation was carried out. Lawrence was still using the smelter after his bankruptcy in 1830 and carried on smelting, at least for Pennerley Mine company, until the autumn of 1831, the smelter (*inter alia*) being auctioned in the November. (The smelter, at least, does not seem to have sold as Lawrence is still recorded as the owner in 1842.) The Pennerley Mine company had a lease until the August 1832, but by the time of a visit by Thomas Poole in 1834 it was leased by Bog mine company, and by the tithe survey of 1842 by William Cross and company. Bog and Pennerley were being worked together during this period by Walker, Cross and company and it seems probable that they had effectively taken over Lawrence's smelter when they took on his mines following bankruptcy. The end for the smelter came in 1845 when Walker Cross were wound up by order of chancery (see Bog mine entry) and the smelter again auctioned. The only item known to emerge from the wreckage was a 4 horse power steam engine and boiler which John Lawrence IV purchased for £55 from John Bowen of the Lea who had purchased it as lot 92 at the auction. It probably went to one of Lawrence's collieries.

The 1831 sale advertisement contains limited information on the equipment of the smelter. It had hearths (furnace(s) and slag), a blacksmith's, ore bins and buddle house with a fire engine for working the latter. There was also a steam engine with a 33 inch cylinder, 50 yards of 12 inch pipe and sundry items which were to be offered for sale separately. By the time of Thomas Poole's visit in 1834 the Bog company had three 'draft' (reverberatory) furnaces and a slag hearth with a blowing engine, all with flues that ran across a field to a 53 yard high chimney which was 12 yards in diameter at its foot and 2 yards at its top, giving a total flue length of 150 yards. It seems to have been known as 'the tower' and was so shown on the tithe map. The furnaces were capable of producing 24 pigs of lead in 24 hours.

The building survives as two cottages a few doors east of the Horseshoe Inn. Across the yard from these, and making a semi-detached pair with Lawrence's own house, is the cottage of the smelthouse foreman.

Pontesford, Snailbeach

When Thomas Lovett and partners reorganised Snailbeach mine in 1782 they wasted little time in acquiring coal and a smelter. The coal mine was leased from Samuel Jones

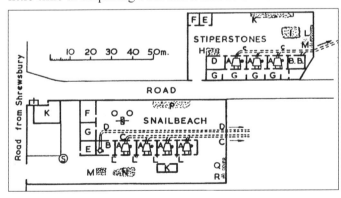

Fig. 15.5 *A drawing by a contemporary French visitor,
M. Moissonet, of the smelters at Pontesford,
published in 1862*

(forebear of Heighway) on land near the Nags Head at Pontesford, a lease that also provided for the smelt-house which was built on the same landlord's land a few yards away. Both mine and smelter were running by 1784. The smeltworks was extensively rebuilt in about 1828. Snailbeach used these premises until 1862/3 when they moved their operation to a new plant adjoining the mine. There is no evidence that the Pontesford smelter was reused, although in October 1877 there were discussions as to whether Lazarus and Sons, who had considered refurbishing the works, would take it for the remainder of the lease until about 1884. In the event, they declined.[16]

Ultimately the smelter had the usual complement of reverberatory furnaces, slag hearths and ancillaries. The slag hearth blower was worked by a waterwheel and the flues discharged into a chimney over 180 feet high via a flue running across a field which was presumably built in 1832, the same year as the chimney for White Grit's works (see below).[17] When Thomas Poole visited in 1834 he noted that the flue cost £2,000 and that there was £7,500 worth of lead in stock. The chimney was 63 yards tall, 16 yards in diameter at the base and was cleaned

15.6 Part of the Snailbeach Company's Pontesford smelter, May 2007. (Author)

by discharging a cannon up it. At the time of his visit, workmen were constructing cavities at the base of the chimney 'for the vapour to deposit their soot'.[18] The building survives in agricultural and domestic use. It is possible that some lengths of flue survive underground behind the smelter and this possibility has given rise to various stories about secret tunnels and underground passageways.

Pontesford, White Grit

The White Grit companies had Lawrence both as a member and as their agent, and it would seem likely that he would have smelted their lead ore at Malehurst and subsequently at Pontesbury. When the Grit company changed hands in the mid 1820s over the Leigh Level issue, they and Lawrence were on opposite sides of four lawsuits and it seems unlikely that Lawrence would still have been smelting their ore. By 1834, when Thomas Poole visited, the company is known to have had a smelter over the road from Snailbeach's. An 'inclosure' plan of 1828 which happens to show the smelter's site also shows a much smaller building which could either have been incorporated into the smelter or just possibly have been a smaller one. One interesting feature to survive on a timber in the building is a quality control mark applied at a Baltic port prior to export. Research is as yet insufficiently advanced to give a date or port, but comparison with other such marks on a warehouse in Manchester (built in 1830) and Pontesbury church (restored in 1829) are not inconsistent with a date of *c*.1830 for the smelter. The more likely ports of origin include Gdansk and Riga. The chimney was built in 1832 which is possibly after the smelter had begun production.[19]

White Grit had ceased to use the smelter by 1844 when the landowner Heighway Jones leased it to Ward and Lloyd for £35 p.a. These men subsequently worked White Grit mine, but could have been doing so as early as 1844. In 1852 the smelter was referred to as being leased to Stainsby and Horton, the Stiperstones company who still held the plant in 1870.

Fig. 15.7 The Pontesford smelter built for the White Grit company now in use by an agricultural merchants, May 2007. (Author)

In 1843 it is recorded as having three furnaces (reverberatory), a slag hearth and a 4 h.p. blowing engine.[20] The following year the lease to Ward and Lloyd refers to a weighing machine, a slag hearth with a steam engine, a 5 h.p. boiler, two hearths, pumping apparatus, a smithy and an office. By 1852 a Heighway Jones family document refers to three smelters; perhaps one was 'down' at the time of the 1844 lease. Sometime before 1870 Burr Bros. of Shrewsbury took over a Pontesford smelter, despite being very good customers of Snailbeach, which must have been the former White Grit one as Lazarus and Sons had the option of the Snailbeach smelter in the 1870s when it was clearly not useable. Burrs used the smelter until at least 1880, when their letter heading still referred to a smelter in Pontesford, and possibly until they closed their Shrewsbury factory in 1894. The building is now used by a transport contractor.

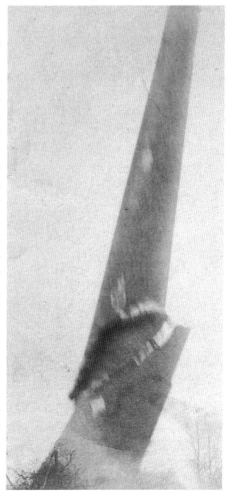

Fig. 15.8 Action photographs of chimneys are not all that common, but this poor photo must fit the bill. It is said to be the chimney of the former Snailbeach smelter, demolished c.1919. (Shropshire Archives)

262

Snailbeach smelter

The arrival of Stephen Eddy at Snailbeach mine saw a series of improvements at the mine and at the company's smelter at Pontesford. Despite these improvements the company built a new smelting complex within a mile of the mine in 1862. That year they surrendered the lease on their colliery,[21] to enable them to use the much superior coal which could be imported via the new branch railway to Minsterley. The new smelter complex consisted of a walled enclosure with an office and staff facilities, a slag-house, a building housing a range of five reverberatory furnaces and the usual ancillary buildings. The site was served by a tramway from the mine and had a small reservoir and three settlement tanks stepped down the slope of the site. The slag-house and each of the furnaces had underground brick flues (Fig. 15.10) which met in a 'beehive condenser' (Fig. 15.9) from where a main flue went over a mile to a chimney on Resting Hill. The original chimney became dangerous and was rebuilt in 1885. The operation of this condenser remains a mystery though it is known from correspondence that some part of the system could be washed down using water from the reservoir to take the minute pieces of lead and zinc which condensed on the flue to the settlement tanks and been scarped off,[22] the lead recovered this way being specifically noted in the official return

Fig. 15.9 The remains of the circular 'beehive condenser' at Snailbeach smelter on the early 1970s. This has since been filled, though access to the very edge can be obtained underground via the flues. (K. Lock)

Fig. 15.10 A photo in June 2005 of Shropshire Caving and Mining Club member Peter Eggleston in the brick flue from one of the furnaces to the condenser. (Kelvin Lake, I A Rcordings)

263

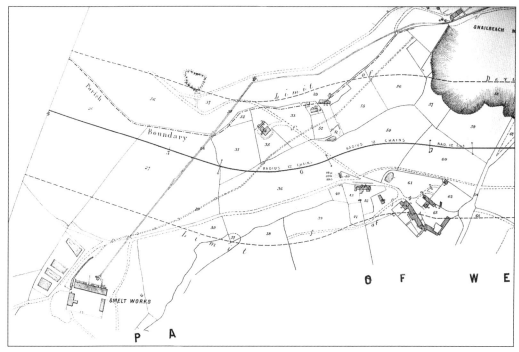

Fig. 15.11 The early layout of the Snailbeach company's 1860s smelter is shown on the plan for the Snailbeach District Railway in the early 1870s. (SA DP474)

for 1873. The tramway went out of use when the Snailbeach Railway was built (see Fig. 15.11). The site went out of use in 1892 just before the mine's principal customer, Burr Bros., closed their plant in Shrewsbury. One furnace was briefly resurrected in 1897

Fig. 15.12 The occasion pictured is the funeral of Derwas Owen Jones of Pontesford House on 11 May 1907. The cortège is passing the Nags Head and the notes on the reverse of the photograph imply (geographically) that the chimney in the background was that of the White Grit smelter, but call it the Snailbeach company's. (Shropshire Archives)

no doubt to re-smelt the beds of the other four furnaces which would have contained a significant quantity of lead.

The site is now a private house and garden. The remains of the offices have been converted into a house. All that remains of the furnaces are the foundations, but the flues are fairly intact. The condenser was demolished above ground and filled-in below some years ago. The main flue is not traceable at the smelter end but can be followed down for some distance from the chimney.

Maesbury

In 1837 the county boasted one more smelter. The *Shrewsbury Chronicle* for 27 October 1837 advertised 'for sale or let by auction on 15th November' a Lead Smelting Works at Maesbury which the advert explained had a new design of flue which would cause no nuisance to locals. It went on to mention that lead and coal was raised locally, it had good canal and turnpike connections, that there were six furnaces, one of which was complete, a dwelling and workshop and another dwelling to be completed. Nothing further is known of this smelter, not even whether it was used.

Llanyblodwell

The List of Buildings of Architectural or Historic Interest for the area refers to a small flue chimney built of 'red engineering brick (English Garden Wall bond). Square section tapering to top. Stepped plinth and moulded capping. Segmental arch to furnace and remains of brick-lined flue to south. Forms a prominent feature in landscape.' It is dated to the late 19th century and its location in the middle of a limestone quarry suggests that it was probably for a lime-kiln and not a lead smelter.

Pulley

A lease was granted in 1766 for coal and lime workings in Pulley, Pulley Farm and Hanleys with permission for a smelter at The Hanleys or on other waste ground of the Powis Estate. The parties mentioned were all either shareholders in the Pennerley or the 1758 Snailbeach mine and the lessor was also a principal in both companies. Though coal was raised at Pulley there is no evidence that the smelter was ever built (or that it was not).[23]

Barytes Mills

Such mills away from mine sites fall into three categories: existing small mills, existing 'factories' altered to this use, and purpose-built mills, the latter becoming increasingly important as barytes production expanded. The following entries are in alphabetical rather than chronological order. There were clearly more mills involved than are now known of, for example in 1855 barytes was shipped from Pool Quay presumably by river (see East Wotherton) possibly to Shrewsbury, although by then the old Abbey Mill had become defunct and no other mill is known to have been grinding barytes at that date.

Fig. 15.13   Abbey Mill as it may well have looked when it ground barytes

Abbey Mill, Shrewsbury

Small quantities of barytes had been mined in Shropshire since at least 1729 but it was not until the early years of the 19th century that technology enabled the product to have beneficial uses and not until after 1850 that it became of significant commercial importance. The first specific references to mining and milling in the county occur in the later

Fig. 15.14   The mill wheel at Abbey Mill revealed (then re-covered) during recent excavations

1830s when it was being mined at various places including Bulthy and Wotherton, milled at Abbey Mill in Shrewsbury and samples of it (and witherite) given to the proposed museum of the Shropshire and North Wales Historical and Natural History Association. The reference to milling is brief. On 13 March 1841 an indenture for the sale of land and buildings to William Cooper from James Hiles includes a reference to Abbey Mill 'used for grinding barytes leased to William Heighway Jones for 7 years from 4 May 1838'. The ore may have come from Bulthy, which had reasonable access to the River Severn and thus to the mill. The use of the product is not known though it is likely to have been in the manufacture of paint or bleach, the local textile industry requiring the latter. The mill probably fell into disuse after the miller's son fell under the wheel in 1851. It was burnt down in the early 20th century. The remains have been briefly uncovered during recent archaeological excavation and buried under the gyratory road system adjoining the Shropshire Wildlife Trust's premises.

Cliffdale Mill

When Snailbeach installed their 60 inch pumping engine at Lordshill in about 1848, the 36 foot diameter water wheel on the Minsterley Brook near Wagbeach Level mouth became redundant. In 1858 an approach was made by the proprietors of the newly formed Cliffdale Barytes Company to use the waterwheel and either the older mill building or a newly erected one to grind their product. They rented the mill until 1863[24] when they took a lease at £20 p.a. for 21 years from the Marquis of Bath, the landowner. Further leases were obviously granted as the company were still milling in 1915 when improvements were made, with the installation of additional millstones and a gas engine to supplement the waterwheel.

The company gave up the mill in 1926 although their mine functioned for a further decade. Barytes from Cliffdale's Calcot mine was dealt with here as was that from Ridge Hill between that mine's founding and 1926. Towards the end of its life the mill broke up the crude ore in a mortar mill consisting of 'two heavy rolls and a revolving horizontal pan'.[25] The resulting coarse sand was bleached in sulphuric acid in lead lined wooden tanks to remove the iron oxide and calcite. This took four hours using heat from perforated steam coils. After washing and kiln drying the product was milled. There were two sets each of three pairs of horizontal stones, one operated by the waterwheel and the other by the suction gas plant. Much of the barytes passed through only two stones, the third set produced very fine material described as having 'a silkiness of touch which was not always required'. The *Shrewsbury Chronicle* for 13 September 1929 notes that during the demolition of the mill the waterwheel was removed, but there are partial remains of the structure which supported it. The site is now occupied by a dwelling.

Hanwood Mill

During the cut and thrust of Shrewsbury's textile industry in the late 18th and early 19th centuries John Marshall and Sons, a company operating nationally, acquired a small paper mill in Hanwood in 1810. The mill was rebuilt, possible after a disastrous flood in 1811 which caused havoc all the way along the Rea Valley. The new mill was a four-storey factory used for flax manufacture, canvas weaving and, interestingly in view of the uses to which barytes could be put, bleaching. Marshalls went bankrupt in 1886 and the mill remained empty until 1890 when it was conveyed complete with a 300 hp Robey engine, boiler, 18 sets of stones and other equipment to the Shropshire Barytes Company, who conveyed it the following year to the Wotherton Barytes and Lead Mining Co. Ltd. who supplied the mill from their Wotherton mine.

The mill did not lead a charmed life, as within just over a hundred years of the 1811 flood it had had two further disasters and had closed for good. On 11 December 1897 a mill stone on the top floor came off its bearings, demolished a pier and brought down the roof and three floors, killing a 5-year-old boy who was there with his father. There was a further accident on 29 December during the clearance work when two men, including the 5-year-old's father, were injured when an arch collapsed. The mill was rebuilt, only in 1915 to be devastated by a major fire. It survived and in 1919 was the location for a series of improvements in barytes processing carried out by a Dr. Watson for Shropshire Mines Ltd., who had taken over the Wotherton Company. Yet further improvements were to have been carried out by the company although it is not known if they were put in hand before it was closed for good and subsequently demolished following the opening of a new state of the art mill in Malehurst in 1925.

The site suffered from transport problems. The ore was shipped in by traction engine and trailers from a number of mines, principally Wotherton, and when that closed (production fell off there around 1912) ore of a lower quality came from Bog mine by train to Hanwood station for final delivery by road. Outgoing drums of ground barytes left via the station. In an effort to reduce the damage to the lane to the mill a tramway was constructed sometime after 1901 to the main road.

Fig. 15.15 A postcard of Hanwood Mill early in the 20th century; the tramway from the main road runs down the centre of the picture

The arriving ore was crushed in a jaw crusher and passed via an endless bucket-belt into the bleaching vats. These were in the shape of inverted curved cones about 12 feet deep heated by perforated steam coils. The original intention had been to treat large quantities of ore, but the stirring necessary to enable all the ore to be bleached abraded the lead sheet vat lining. After eight to ten hours bleaching the material was washed and dried and then passed into the mill. Here it was reduced to a fine sand in a mortar mill and then ground to the required fineness by two or three pairs of French Buhr millstones. In 1916 there were 24 pairs of such stones which along with 'edge runners and tube mill'[26] had treated between 5 and 6,000 tons of ore in the previous year.

Maesbury

The River Morda south of Oswestry has over a very long period provided power for a number of mills, one of which in 1862 became Maesbury Paint Mill, run by a Mr. Edward Peate. What little is known of this operation comes from *Industries of the Morda Valley* by R.D. Thomas published in 1939, which states that the mill's 'supply of white barytes came from the slopes of the Stiperstones at Snailbeach, reaching Oswestry by rail, going thence by road cartage to the mill for grinding. Paints and varnishes were made here for wholesalers in Liverpool and elsewhere'. Mr. Peate died in 1888; all use of the mill then ceased and it became derelict.

Malehurst

In the years after the First World War Shropshire Mines Ltd. carried out a major capital programme which initially included improvements to Hanwood Mill. At some point it was decided that a new mill with railway sidings would be a better bet and the site at Malehurst between Pontesbury and Minsterley was used. The company seems to have occupied the site since about 1917 as the aerial ropeway from Bog mine terminated there. The mill was opened (though only half finished) early in 1925 and purchased shortly afterwards by Malehurst Barytes Co. Ltd.[27] In 1932 they were taken over in turn by Laportes, who continued to use the Malehurst barytes mine.

During the Second World War, when Laportes considered that some of their other plants were at risk of bomb damage, the scope of Malehurst

Figures 15.16 to 15.21 were published in The Industrial Chemist and Chemical Manufacturer *for May 1926. The captions (and capital letters) are theirs.*
Fig. 15.16 'The Washing Plant showing Trommels and Jigs, etc.'

Fig. 15.17 'View of Washing Plant with Jig in Foreground'

Fig. 15.18 'The Bleaching and Acid Tanks'

Fig. 15.19 'The Drying House with Dryer in Foreground'

extended to produce ammonium perchlorate and potassium perchlorate for tracer bullets and flares. The government had requested a similar plant at Kingsway, Luton but after bomb scares Laportes offered a site in front of Malehurst mill; consequently a government funded plant was quickly built and in production by 1942. Its daily capacity was sufficient to treat an incredible 5.25 million tracer bullets a day.[28] The function of the new plant was surrounded in secrecy and rumours soon spread — vats were said to bubble and hold heavy water needed for nuclear experiments.[29] Whether the plant did produce anything else will probably never be known; only five or six men per shift were employed on this side of the work, all of whom are now dead. The plant had a cork floor and was worked on a three shift basis. It was mothballed during the Cold War until it was removed in 1959 and one bay of the building demolished.[30]

After the war the site returned solely to its original purpose until the closure of the last mines in 1948. It was used briefly to grind a lorryload of Brobat washing powder a week, the employees remem-

270

bering this as being a very unpleasant substance to handle. The aerial ropeway was dismantled in 1950/1 and the site was sold in 1956. The mill remained in use into the 1980s for preparing animal feed, and after a period as a builders' merchants and a transport depot is at the time of writing an industrial estate.

In addition to the advantage of a site by the railway and at the end of a ropeway, the choice of a greenfield site enabled the company to establish its mill unhindered by the constraints of an existing building. They took full advantage of this to build a mill equal to any in the country. It was visited by a journalist from *The Industrial Chemist and Chemical Manufacturer* in 1926 whose report in the May issue that year is headed 'A Short Description of the up-to-date Methods Employed by the Malehurst Barytes Company at Minsterley, Salop'. A later article in the same journal (February 1927) sums up the company's ethos: 'The mining and subsequent treatment [of barytes] is rising only now from the morass of haphazard rule of thumb methods to the realm of scientific practice.'

Fig. 15.20 *'The Raymond Pulveriser'*

Fig. 15.21 *'Power House, showing Boiler and Gas Producer'*

Fig. 15.22 Malehurst Mill in 1968 whilst it was an animal feed mill. The building is still much as it was when a barytes mill. The hoist up to the mill is on the left-hand edge. The group of buildings at the right-hand edge were a 1942 shadow factory though the first bay (off the photo to the right had it still existed) was demolished in 1959. (Shropshire Archives)

The 1926 article gives an excellent description of the then new plant and provides the information given below and the illustrations reproduced here. The crude ore was transferred to a 50 ton storage bin as it arrived from the ropeway. It was then washed and broken down to ¾ inch size in a jaw-breaker and passed to two rotating trommels, the second of which screened the material into five sizes from ¹⁄₁₆th inch up to ½ inch and above. Each of the sizes was passed to its own set of hydraulic jigs where the heavy barytes particles were sorted from the lighter waste and fell to be collected from the bottom of the jig (Fig. 15.17).

Malehurst produced four grades of final product, No. 1, HRB, HS and HB. When No. 1 grade was required a special, but unspecified, ore was used. The No. 1 and HRB crude products were the top qualities obtained and were further treated in the bleaching plant (Fig. 15.18). The bleaching tanks were filled with 20 tons of barytes into which 15% by volume sulphuric acid was pumped, steam was passed through the tanks and the acid dissolved out the impurities. The acid was drained off for reuse and the barytes washed once in hot water and several times in cold. It then passed to the drier which consisted of a slightly conical circular plate rotating over a furnace (Fig. 15.19). Three sets of fixed ploughs spread and moved the barytes from its feed in the middle of the plate to the outer edge where the dry produce was scooped off into a receiving bin.

All the products, whether they had been bleached or not, were dried and passed into the grinding house. The critical factor in barytes production is the fineness and Malehurst produced a product which passed through a 300 mesh (300 holes to the square inch) and used a Raymond mill to grind it (Fig. 15.20). This mill coupled grinding with a system of air separation which eliminated over-sized particles from the ground aggregate. The uniformly fine material was blown into a cyclone collector from whence it was bagged ready for transport. One of the strengths of Malehurst was their quality control. Every 15 minutes samples were taken and sent to the laboratory for testing for fineness and colour. The earlier methods of testing for fineness had been either to see if a sample felt gritty between the teeth or to place a sample on a tile and rub it with a steel spatula, but in the latter case the presence of an insignificant quantity of silica made it feel gritty even if it were more finely ground than the barytes. A Malehurst director therefore devised a micro-photometer to establish the fineness of grinding. A further test required for the paint industry was that for colour, and again Malehurst seems to have led the way. The older test relied on dropping a small quantity of turpentine on to a sample and noting the change in shade, the less the better. Malehurst developed a 'comparator similar to a tintometer' which not only quantified the change of shade but enabled a given shade to be maintained, thus offering a more reliable product. At the time the article was written the company were experimenting with a grade of barytes finer than their current No. 1 grade which was to be even whiter.

One further report of the mill survives from towards the end of its life. In 1946 the British Geological Survey published their Wartime Pamphlet No. 46 on barytes which dealt with both the state of the industry and the reserves. It is a valuable document for information on individual mines and shows what changes had occurred at Malehurst in the previous 20 years. Standards appear to have slipped slightly, possibly due to wartime needs. The screens of the rotating trommel still delivered 5 sizes but the finest was now $^1/_{12}$th inch as against $^1/_{16}$th. The hydraulic jigs had been replaced by Malehurst Paddle Classifiers for the finer grades, the lower grades passing through one of two types of Harz jigs. By now the plant was equipped with a continuous rotary gas-fired drying and bleaching furnace in which the barytes decrepitates to a white powder.[31] From the furnace the product passed to a vibrating screen; the finest particles passing the screen were ground to produce the No. 1 grade, while the rest was ground in a Raymond mill and marketed as a lower grade material.

Minsterley Mill

Taylor Gilbertson and Co. began grinding barytes in a mill on the west of the Bishops Castle road south of the village in 1893. The premises they used had become a creamery by 1909. This flourished and finally became part of Eden Vale whose successors now have large premises at the north of the village.

Minsterley Barytes Mining and Milling Co. ran the mill by 1897 and were presumably grinding barytes from their Great Roundtain mine. By 1901 the mill was being operated by Minsterley Baryta Co. Ltd. It is not known where they got their raw material, but it may well have been from one or more small mines in Perkins Beach, for one of which they took a 12-month licence in June 1906. They did not renew it and July 1907 seems to have marked the end of their Minsterley activity.

Snailbeach Mill

Lower Works, below the white tip and adjoining the railway, was the site of a brickworks and later tip, both out of use by the late 1880s, at which time a small barytes mill had been erected on the part of the site nearest to the road bridge over the railway. Alfred Haywood, who built the mill, occupied the site from 1889, receiving a back-dated lease in March 1891. Later that year, the enterprise was taken over by the South Shropshire Barytes & Lead Co. Ltd. The company purchased barytes from Snailbeach and also presumably initially from the South Shropshire company's own mine at Rhadley, though no production is recorded from that mine between 1891 and 1895. The mill may have closed by October 1894; certainly no rent was paid after that date until a new company, the Barytes and Lead Co. Ltd., formed in 1895 with Haywood again involved, took it over in 1896. The company limped on, locked out due to non payment of rent and breaking in again until they went into receivership in July 1899. J.W. Walker took the mill from 1901 to 1904. F.W. Read trading as 'Read F W (Snailbeach Barytes Co)' took over in 1906. He held the lease in 1911 and may have still done so when Snailbeach Lead Mining Co. Ltd. ceased trading, but the mill had closed and was demolished by 1914.[32] E.C. Gray's spar gravel works used the site from the 1920s.

Sutton Mill

The Rea Brook was used to grind a lot of barytes (as well as blowing slag hearths, grinding corn and making paper). From Cliffdale Mill it ran through Minsterley and Hanwood and on to Shrewsbury, where it powered Abbey Mill and Sutton Mill. Milling at Sutton has a long and complex history but in recent times there have been three mills — Old Mill and two at Lower Mill, one on each side of the stream

Fig. 15.23 An undated photo of Sutton Mill. (coll. D. Trumper)

in the parishes of St. Julian's and St. John's (Sutton). It is this latter which ground barytes. Little is known of this operation, said to date from the late 19th and early 20th centuries. The evidence for the activity is, however, compelling as bags of ground barytes were found dumped in the race at the time of an archaeological investigation in the early 1970s. The mill had had an earlier industrial connection when it was owned by Herbert Mackworth of Betton Strange (whose father had south Wales copper and coal connections) from about 1730 to 1780. Mackworth converted it into a forge, but the subsequent owners, the Berwicks, rebuilt it as a mill and it was this building where the barytes grinding took place. The mill was demolished in the 1960s.[33]

Major Drainage Levels

Virtually every mine in the county was able to use at least to a limited extent an adit or level to help drain the mine. Most of these were short, wholly within the immediate locality of the mine and used only by one mine.

Boat Level

By the 18th century the principle of draining mines by levels or soughs was well established and the idea of taking boats right into the mine along such a level was being considered. Pennerley mine was dug in the 1720s with a 'Great Level', the location of which is not known. One possibility is that it was this level that was extended to Bog mine and became Boat Level. Certainly from about 1809 to 1812 John Lawrence IV and partners were extending a level from Pennerley to Bog.

It followed a twisting course for 2.167 miles from its mouth at 892 feet above sea level just south of and well below Stiperstones village with offsets to serve Burgam, Tankerville, Potters Pit, Pennerley, Bog and Nipstones. At some of these mines, notably Bog, more than one shaft was served. Boat Level intersected Bog mine at the 52 fathom level and was around 500 feet below shaft top level by Nipstones.

In 1844 the *Chester Chronicle* reported that consideration was being given to extending the level eastwards to open up new ground. Unless a short length to serve Weston's Shaft is meant this was presumably not done as work ceased at the mine in that year. In any event, it would have gone under the Stiperstones ridge, which was barren of ore. The 1858 Gravels Mining Co. Ltd. prospectus mentioned the possibility that this level could be used to drain a proposed mine at Benree, but there is no suggestion that this ever happened.

The level was extended south to the site of the future Ramsden's Shaft probably during the First World War and carried on to terminate near Nipstones Rock at Nipstones mine. During the early years of the 20th century Bog mine was opened and closed several times and the level periodically became partly blocked although regularly patrolled and maintained and remaining in 'use' until the final closure of Bog mine in 1932. Before the First World War Shropshire Lead Mines Ltd. proposed to connect Boat Level with a new level being dug at Rhadley mine, but in the event that level, though long, was abandoned, at least in part due to its failure to open up new ore-bearing ground. By 1950 Boat Level's portal had collapsed and a late 1960s exploration got less than half a mile before meeting an impassable blockage.

Little is known of the working of the level or even if the use of boats was thought of initially. If they had been, the curves in the level would probably have been somewhat less sharp. Boats were floated out with the flow and hauled back hand over hand using a rope fixed to the level's sides. At least two types of boat were used, as three wooden and iron boats were offered for auction when Bog mine was sold in 1830. It is possible that the use of boats had reduced by this time as a new house built near the mine in 1832 was given stables due to the increased need for horses to draw wagons of ore to Shrewsbury, but when visiting in 1834 Thomas Poole[34] describes Boat Level (calling it a natural canal used instead of a railroad) and implies that it was still in use. He does, however, comment on the amount the new proprietors had spent on improving the road from the mine. It is assumed that no processing such as ore dressing took place at the level's mouth as there is no sign of any spoil in the vicinity. Indeed, at the time of Thomas Poole's visit he noted workmen filling casks with ore at the mine.

The level itself was narrow and far from straight. The first 60 feet is lined with drystone walling to about 5 feet which then carries a brick vault, 3 foot 9 inches wide at the springing and 6 foot high at the centre. Two sections of vault were replaced (possibly in 1907) with flat reinforced concrete with a headroom of 5 foot 4 inches. This lined part takes the level through the looser shallow deposits, and as far as is known beyond that point it is cut into natural rock and is coffin-shaped in section: the minimum width of the roof is 1 foot, at shoulder level it averages 4 foot 4 inches, at the invert, 2 foot 6 inches.[35] However small, the boats must have been a tight fit. No doubt the job of hauling the iron boat back to the mine was considered a treat which the management had to allocate by drawing lots. The only visible remaining part is the mouth, situated on private land.

Leigh Level

There was a brief boom in the mid 1820s, the recession following the end of Napoleonic wars having ended and there was what John Lawrence IV later described ruefully as an 'unparalleled Rage for Mineing in 1825'.[36] He and his partners had been developing mines *inter alia* in the Hope Valley and Shelve areas with the Earl of Tankerville and Mr. More of Linley as their respective landlords. They had drained some mines with the Wood Level (see below) and seem to have planned a much deeper and longer level. In the event both landlords refused to renew Lawrence's leases, granting them instead to a company of 32 gentlemen, some of whom were local but many (and most of the capital of £39,000) coming from the north-west of England. The Earl of Tankerville had commissioned a report from Thomas Fenwick, a mining engineer from Gateshead, on the state of the mines on his land in 1820, which though not critical played a part in the decision not to renew the lease. Lawrence applied in 1825 to have his lease with Mr. More renewed, but this was also refused. Lawrence challenged both landlords in the courts and four suits later and bankrupt, won. The 32 gentlemen, also known as the Farmers Company,[37] suffered financially and ultimately ceased trading, the concern being wound up in 1835, and the landlords ended up losing law suits, royalties and rents.

The intention was to drain Batholes, East Roman Gravels, Roman Gravels, Ladywell and Grit mines, a distance of about 5 miles, at a maximum depth of 270 yards. At Lords Stone it was to have split, one route going via Batholes, East Roman Gravels

Fig. 15.24 A photograph at Milne Shaft on the Leigh Level, possibly at the completion of work on the shaft. (coll. K. Lock)

276

and Roman Gravels and the other cutting off a corner direct to Ladywell. As this served no intermediate mines it may well have been intended to open up new ground. In practice even Batholes mine was not reached. An undated and untitled section contains precise measurements and appears to be a survey rather than a proposal as it seems that it was produced when work was abandoned after 2,045 yards had been driven. The shaft depths given are somewhat different from the proposed plan, the biggest discrepancy being at Lords Stone where the actual shaft is 16 yards deeper at 176 yards than the initial survey expected.

Local pressure to complete the level grew in the late 19th century. William Oldfield of Snailbeach mine wrote to the *Shrewsbury and Wellington Journal* in April 1898 advocating the continuance of the level though not following the earlier proposal. He suggested that from Batholes it went via Nick Knolls, 'Sheffield' (?Shelfield), Roundhill, Tankerville and Pennerley to 35 chains west of Bog mine and from there to drain the Gravels and Grit district. Nothing happened then but later the idea was picked up by Wotherton Barytes and Lead Mining Co. Ltd. and their successors Shropshire Mines Ltd. as a lease was obtained in 1916 to clear the level out and extend it. Work commenced in 1919 simultaneously at the existing Blue Barn Shaft and the new Milne Shaft, the excavation between those two being completed that September. A report to staff in December states that cages were being put in Milne Shaft (just short of Batholes mine) and that the level was generally being put in good order. They hoped to reach Wood mine (as East Roman Gravels was then called) 100 feet below Wood Engine Shaft by the following September. In the event despite substantial capital input the level did not get as far as Wood mine before work was again abandoned having reached within 144 yards of their objective by 4 November 1920. It is probable that no further work was done, certainly by March 1922 the lease was to be surrendered. The final length was just over two miles.

Physically the early part of the level was (and no doubt is) narrow and convoluted. The 20th-century work is clearly much bigger, for two battery-operated electric railway locomotives were purchased in 1920 for use on the contract, whilst Milne Shaft was provided with substantial headgear and a steam winder, the boiler from which went to Huglith mine when Leigh Level was abandoned. Visible remains are few. Some years ago the entrance was still extant in private woodland though it was in danger of collapse, and it is possible that the location of some of the shaft tops can still be identified.

Wood Level

In about 1790, under John Lawrence III, Wood Level, also known as the Hope Valley Level, was to drain Batholes, the often renamed East Roman Gravels, Roman Gravels, Ladywell and Old Grit mines. Progress was slow. Roman Gravels was not reached by the end of the century when a lease was granted to a group of men including Lawrence, a condition of which was that Wood Level should be extended to Shelve Gravels (as its landlord called it) by 25 March 1802. This is presumed to have happened as Lawrence was working that mine thereafter. He concentrated on working well drained mines and neglected Grit which was still not met by Wood Level, a neglect that could have been part of the reason why Mr. More did not renew Lawrence's lease in 1825. The new lessees of 1839 are said to have extended Wood Level sometime after 1844[38] and before 1848. This was the full extent of the level.

Its much rebuilt outlet is visible almost literally under the A488 near Hope. The collapse of the shallowest part of the level below that road has at the time of writing just been repaired after causing several years of single file traffic over a temporary 'bridge' across the level.

Transport

The Snailbeach District Railways
The main line railway companies did not see sufficient benefit to justify building branch or mineral railways to serve the lead and other mining districts; the nearest they came was Minsterley. After the opening of this line in 1861, Snailbeach mine would have become aware of the benefits which a connection to the national network could bring, and when Henry Dennis took over they decided to become involved in the promotion of narrow gauge lines to serve their and other lead mines. Surveying commenced in 1872 and an Act of Parliament was obtained in August 1873 for what was officially the Snailbeach District Railways, sometimes known as the Snailbeach Railway.

Though the earthworks were built to accommodate standard gauge tracks, the line was laid to the unusual gauge of 2 feet 4 inches. Two lines were authorised, No. One at 3¼ miles long from Pontesbury to near Crowsnest and No. Two a further 1⅞ miles to a point close to Tankerville mine. The Snailbeach Mine Co. was limited as to how much of the capital it could subscribe, and not surprisingly raising the balance was difficult as few other mines were willing to invest. Sufficient capital was raised for Railway No. One to be built and this was open in July 1877. Passengers were never catered for and general goods traffic was light. Lead and coal for smelting were expected to be principal traffic and this proved to be the case, at first. Ore was brought to the railway by road from Tankerville, Pennerley and Bog mines (all in the same ownership) until their closures in the mid 1880s.

In the early 1890s a new scheme was proposed to tap traffic from other mines. To be called the Shropshire Minerals Light Railway, it would have almost followed the route of Snailbeach's Railway No. Two to approach Tankerville, where it would have set off to serve Bog and thence passed round the southern end of the Stiperstones to Gatten. Its Act of Parliament received the Royal Assent in 1891 but capital was not forthcoming and the line was never built.

Further proposals for extension were put forward at two now unknown dates to serve a site at Buxton. If as suggested elsewhere[39] the first was in the early years of the 20th century the purpose could have been to serve a proposed quarry at Buxton which did not materialise, possibly the development of Granham's Moor Quarry rendered the scheme at Buxton less attractive. The second proposal to serve the same location could have been put forward during or after the First World War, either as the quarry at Buxton was finally developed, to serve the existing quarry after the closure of the Bog line ropeway in 1925

Fig. 15.25 Locomotive no.4 crosses the main road at Pontesbury

(if the quarry was still open that late), or to try to divert the quarry traffic to the railway, probably after Colonel Stephens took over the line in 1922. In two of these cases it is odd that the proposed plan did not show the ropeway whose path the line would have had to cross.

Lead traffic fell sharply in the 20th century until production effectively ceased when pumping was stopped in 1911, although small quantities were carried at least until 1922. Zinc ore never provided as much traffic as barytes, but even this dwindled, the last being carried in 1930. The last major traffic from the mine was calcite spar, which was carried until 1940.

The line as built ran from a transhipment siding just west of Pontesbury station to Crowsnest, then a branch reversed to gain height to reach the mine where it spread into sidings to serve various locations, finally ending up, via an inclined plane, at the Lordshill engine house. Two further branches were constructed, one to the smelthouse and a later one to serve Granhams Moor Quarry, in Eastridge Wood near Habberley, which used the railway from 1905 until 1921. Sidings were provided at various times to serve the firms working on White Tip and Lower Works. The line was almost moribund by 1922 and would have closed but for the intervention of Colonel Holman Stephens who specialised in rescuing light railways and running them with military precision on a shoestring from his office in Tonbridge in Kent. The new owners repaired the line and developed what traffic was available. Their ownership saw various improvements including the provision for a siding at Lower Works, presumably for spar gravel traffic, and a proposal, not carried out, for a siding for Gray's spar works which needed to cross Farm Lane for 'opening out of an undertaking' in July 1923.[40] Ultimately the only traffic consisted of stone from Callow Hill Quarry a mile or so outside Pontesbury. The County Council were offered the line in 1932 but declined as they would have required an Act of Parliament to run it, although they did lease it from 1947. The stone traffic for the County Council saw the line out, it closing in 1959.

The line initially had one steam locomotive, *Belmont*, built by Henry Hughes and Co. of Loughborough, later supplemented by *Fernhill* built by Barclays and Co. of Kilmarnock and hauled the traffic until 1905 when *Dennis* arrived from W.G. Bagnall Ltd. of Stafford. When Col. Stephens took over only *Dennis* was left, but it never worked again. Instead Stephens purchased, second-hand, a small locomotive built by Kerr Stuart and Co. of Stoke-on-Trent and two American locomotives which had been built for

Fig. 15.26 By the 1950s a farm tractor (or gravity) powered the railway, though only stone was being transported on the line by then

Fig. 15.27 Snailbeach loco shed in 1980, prior to restoration. (Author)

the trench railways in the First World War. These three worked the line until 1946 when all were totally worn out; they were scrapped in 1950. For the last 13 years of the line's life downhill traffic ran by gravity (not that that was new) and uphill traffic was worked from the exchange sidings and tarmac plant at Pontesbury by a tractor straddling one rail. The line had an appropriate collection of goods vehicles.

The route of the railway from the site of the road bridge at the west end of Pontesbury to Callow Lane has since been a lorry route to the quarry, and from there to Snailbeach much of the line has been ploughed out. However, through Snailbeach to Crowsnest, and from there to the mine and up to the engine house it is mostly visible and in some parts walkable. At the mine the locomotive shed has been restored and a short length of track which was never lifted still remains. No locomotives survived, but two wagons and a tractor similar to the one used in the last years of the line's life are stored in the loco shed. At the time of writing a scheme has been launched to re-lay part of the line for use by tourists.

Aerial Ropeways

Tramways were relatively expensive to construct, required fairly level ground or earthworks and could take up valuable ground space. With developing technology in the second half of the 19th century came improvements in wire ropes. Not only was this important in terms of winding shafts for men and minerals; it also enabled the development of aerial ropeways. A patent was taken out for such in 1856-7 and an improved variety was patented in 1868. They began to become widespread in a great variety of industries early in the 20th century and were still being installed in the 1960s.[41]

Bog mine to Malehurst and branches

Road conditions had always been problematical and in about 1917 the newly formed Shropshire Mines Ltd. decided to install an aerial ropeway to convey ore from the mine to the railway at Malehurst and to carry coal back. It was built in 1918-9 using, amongst

Fig. 15.28 The ropeway junction, or transfer station, on Beach Hill. At the time of the photograph (c.1920) the branch from Perkins Beach had gone and the line to Buxton Quarry was running

Fig. 15.29 A view down the Buxton line from the transfer station

others, German prisoners of war. A railway siding was agreed at Malehurst on 23 July 1919,[42] but is said not to have become operational until 1922. Initially a branch was put in to the lower part of Perkins Beach Dingle to serve mines there, but it was not a success, probably due to the gradient up which the buckets had to be hauled. By December 1919 it seems to have closed, as a light railway was being considered to connect that valley's mines to the ropeway, presumably behind Stiperstones School.

Fig. 15.30 The remains of the trestle pictured in Fig. 15.29 photographed in May 2004. (Author)

At the same time it was expected that the ropeway branch to the quarry then being developed at Buxton would be finished by April 1920. The line was used until the closure of Bog mine in October 1925 and was dismantled in March 1927. Some at least of the equipment was not scrapped but exported to Spain for re-use.[43]

The line ran from the mine towards the top of the Stiperstones to Beach Hill where the branches joined. From there it descended sharply to an 85 foot high pylon in the field behind Stiperstones School, crossed the road to Minsterley by the Stiperstones Inn and ran along the valley below Central Snailbeach mine. It continued straight to an angle

Fig. 15.31 Huglith ropeway terminus. (coll. K. Lock)

station north-west of Snailbeach and followed its new, equally straight line to Malehurst. En route it ran either close to or across the back gardens of 7, 8, 9 and 10 Little Minsterley (owned by Shropshire Mines Ltd., and their deeds contained a clause giving access to the line), crossed the main road and arrived at Malehurst where the ore was tipped out by hand. The stone from Buxton Quarry was dropped at Poulton, where the line crossed the main road, and was collected from there.

The ropeway being about five and a half miles long, the principal rope was 11 miles long. This rope was carried on a series of trestles, mainly of wood but with metal ones in critical places such as road crossings. Generally the buckets were well above the ground except in cuttings, where they were low enough for locals to empty them of their coal. The buckets were supported on and moved by the same rope which was powered by an engine at Bog mine. At termini and junctions the buckets ran off the rope and onto sloping rails which either guided them into their new alignment or sent them for filling or emptying. They were held on the rope by gravity and friction. Runaways, especially down the very steep gradient from the junction station to the field behind the school in Stiperstones, were fairly common, rather noisy and very inconvenient. Each of the buckets carried around 5 cwts of barytes down and somewhat less coal back up to the mine.

Not surprisingly, remains are now sparse, though the junction station and Bog terminus are visible as arrays of bolts projecting from concrete bases at ground level. Bases from wooden trestles have survived at a few places but most of the bases noted for steel ones have either been pushed into streams adjoining their former sites or, in the case of the one near Stiperstones School, been blown up and left.

Huglith to Malehurst

In the immediate post First World War years Shropshire Mines Ltd. invested heavily at several places, not least Huglith mine which they wished to see become a model mine. Initially ore was transported within the site on a tramway then loaded onto drays for four horses to pull to Pontesbury Station.[44] On 23 April 1921 an agreement was entered into with the County Council for a proposed aerial ropeway line to cross the Minsterley to Pontesbury road. It is not known exactly when the ropeway was opened.

The ropeway outlived Huglith mine, for when that closed in 1945 barytes was brought in from Gatten and The Sallies mines by lorry for trans-

Fig. 15.32 Little remains of the Huglith line. Pictured in April 2007 is a base for a steel pylon near Poles Coppice. (Author)

port to Malehurst. This carried on until the closure of those two mines in the autumn of 1948. The ropeway was dismantled in 1950 or 1951. The bridge over the main road (protecting it from falling debris) was demolished at 5am one Sunday morning; the village policeman who should have been there to supervise traffic was late.[45]

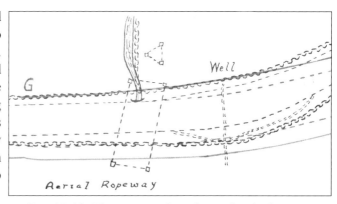

Fig. 15.33 The principal evidence for the location of the ropeway bridge over the main road at Poulton is this plan for road improvements of 1926. (SA-SCC Roads and Bridges Committee, Agreement No. 182)

The line ran from a loading station some yards west of the main adit at the mine 3½ miles straight across country to the mill where it no doubt used the same unloading facility as the Bog line. Unlike the Bog line, however, it was little if ever used to convey anything back to the mine.

Fig. 15.34 An example of the area's literary heritage: the cover of Malcolm Saville's Seven White Gates, *which depicts a highly imaginative aerial ropeway*

The most notable survivor is the pit at the mine which housed a (more or less) horizontal wheel which marked the rope's furthest point from Malehurst. Otherwise just a few trestle foundations remain.

Other Ropeways

Various published sources have credited the ore-field with three other ropeways, none of which actually existed. Callow Hill quarry was served by the Snailbeach Railway and was not far from the line of the Huglith ropeway but neither used it nor had its own. Nor was there ever a ropeway from the Gravels mine to a smelt mill.[46] There was no ropeway from Potter's Pit to Pennerley mine despite several suggestions to the contrary, the confusion probably being caused by the existence of a half mile long suspended rope or chain which worked Potter's Pit Shaft from Pennerley's engine.

Appendix 1

Page from bargain book of 1827

29 Set to James Bunting
and Co. to Drive in Lee
Level at 5t. 5. 0 per yard
to find thing own horse
&c —— 19 —   99 15

1 James Bunting
2 Josh Owens
3 Willm Bennett
4 James Price
5 Thos Lewis   } Bargain
6 Thos Bunting   } Men
7 Thos Morgan
8 John Rogers
9 Thos Bunting Junr
10 John Jones
11 John Lewis   } Labourers
12 Thos Morris

Employed as usual

Appendix 2

Extract from SAHS *Transactions* Vol. xi, 1888 from pages 278-9

The remains of their labours are visible along the whole surface of the hill, like irregular cuttings along a large cheese; but it presents the most remarkable appearance at a spot near the northern end, where, at the foot of the hill, a mine called the Roman Gravel Mine is now in operation. The way in which the Roman miners followed the veins of ore is here exhibited in the most remarkable manner. Where it did not appear to run deep they soon stopped, and have left but a shallow cutting. In some places the cutting is wide; while in others it is at the same time very narrow and very deep, in one instance sinking to a depth of, I believe, forty yards, yet not wide enough for more than one man to work in it. In other places the vein of ore has been more massive, and in following it the Romans had hollowed in the rock cavern-like chambers, from which galleries ran in different directions, which are now blocked up by rubbish. The Roman miners also sunk shafts. In one of the largest of the caverns on the line of the vein I am describing, near the brow of the hill, the vein has been followed downward by a shaft of great depth; in its present state a stone is heard rolling down for several seconds. It is not easily examined from its position, but having been carried up to the surface of the rock above, no doubt for the purpose of more easily raising weights up and letting them down, we were enabled to ascertain that it was a square shaft of small dimensions. We have, however, still better evidence of the extent to which the Roman miners perforated the mountain. I have just stated that at the bottom of the hill, just under these large Roman surface workings, there is a modern mine, which was begun some years ago, but, for some reason or other, was soon abandoned. This mine has been recently taken by a most respectable company, which has taken the name of the Roman Gravel Lead Mining Company, who, in the prosecution of their own works, have met with numerous Roman shafts and galleries to a considerable depth.[1] The antiquity of these mines has been proved, not only by the Roman pigs of lead already mentioned, but by Roman coins and pottery found from time to time among the old rubbish. Early mining implements also have been found, but none have been preserved, with the exception of a curious description of spade.

Glossary

adit	a horizontal tunnel from daylight into a mine, sometimes called a level
buddles	a wooden, stone or brick chamber into which water separates the crushed lead ore from the lighter waste
deads	unwanted rock dug but left in the mine, often in worked-out areas
gangue	minerals contained in the vein which are not wanted, e.g. barytes until the 19th century
kibble	a large bucket, at one time wooden and later usually iron or steel, used to lift ore, water or men out of the mine
level	see adit
pitches	the parts of a mine covered by bargains, see chapter 4
rises	a wholly underground shaft driven up from workings
sett	the defined area of land in which mining may take place included in a lease, a legal agreement between a landowner and a mine company setting out the term, the area covered (sett), rents, royalties and general conditions, see chapter 3
shaft	a vertical or near vertical 'hole' into the mine
stope	a vein left after the mineral has been extracted
winze	a wholly underground small shaft dug down within a mine

Bibliography

BOOKS

Angerstein 2001 — Angerstein R.R., *Illustrated Travel Diary*, 1753-1755, Science Museum, 2001

Anon 1987 — Anon, *Stiperstones Mining Area,* Shropshire Libraries, 1987

Bick 1991 — Bick D., *The Old Metal Mines of Mid-Wales,* Vol. 6, Pound House, Newent, 1991

Brook and Allbutt 1973 — Brook F. and Allbutt M., *The Shropshire Lead Mines,* Moorland Publishing, Leek, 1973

Brown 2001 — Brown I., *West Shropshire Mining Fields,* Tempus, Stroud, 2001

Burt 1984 — Burt R., *British Lead Industry,* Dyllansow Truran, Redruth, 1984

Burt *et al* 1990 — Burt R., *et al, The Mines of Shropshire and Montgomeryshire with Cheshire and Staffordshire,* Exeter University, 1990

Carruthers *et al* 1915 — Carruthers R.G., *et al, Special Report on the Mineral Resources of Great Britain Vol. II Barytes and Witherite,* BGS, 1915

Carruthers *et al* 1916 — Carruthers R.G., *et al, Special Report on the Mineral Resources of Great Britain Vol. II Barytes and Witherite,* BGS, 1916

Collins 1972 — Collins R.S., *Barium Minerals,* HMSO, 1972

Colvin 1963-73 — Colvin H.M., ed., *The King's Works,* HMSO, 1963-73

Cromarty 1993 — Cromarty D. & R., *The wealth of Shrewsbury in the early fourteenth century,* Shropshire Archaeological and Historical Society, 1993

Dewey 1925 — Dewey H., et al, *Memoirs of the Geological Survey, Special Reports on the Mineral Resources of Great Britain, Vol. XXX, Copper ores of the Midlands etc,* HMSO, 1925

Dines *et al* 1945 — Dines H.G., *et al, Barium Minerals in England & Wales, Wartime pamphlet 46,* BGS, 1945

Dines *et al* 1965 — Dines H.G., *et al, BGS Bulletin 14, The West Shropshire Mining Region.,* BGS, 1958 re-printed 1965

Donald 1955 — Donald M.B., *Elizabethan Copper,* Pergamon Press, 1955

Evans ?2003 — Evans G., *A Voice from the Hills,* Muriel Regde, Minsterley, ?2003

Eyton 1854 — Eyton Rev. R.W, *Antiquities of Shropshire,* John Russell Smith, 1854

Fowler 1994 — Fowler R.P., T*he Geology of the Shelve Mining Region*, account 21, Shropshire Caving and Mining Club, 1994

Francis *et al* 2000 — Francis P., *et al, Never on a Sunday,* Shropshire Mines Trust, 2000

Francis 2001 — Francis P., *On the High Road,* (Little Minsterley history), Francis P., Shrewsbury, 2001

Gough 1979 — Gough R., *The History of Myddle,* Caliban Books, Firle, 1979

Hamilton 1967 — Hamilton H., *The English Brass and Copper industries to 1800,* Frank Cass, 1967

Jackson 1883 — Jackson G., *Shropshire Folklore,* Trubner & Co, 1883

Jones and Mattingly 1990 — Jones B. and Mattingly D., *An Atlas of Roman Britain,* Blackwell Reference, 1990

Kellys — *Kelly's Directory of Shropshire,* Kelly, various years.

Leonard *et al* 2000 — Leonard, *et al,* ed, *Gale of Life,* Logaston Press, Almeley, 2000

Liscombe 1869 — Liscombe and Co., *Mines of Cardiganshire, Montgomeryshire and Shropshire,* Blake & McKenzie, Liverpool, *c.*1869

Lynch 1972 — Lynch N., ed., *Prehistoric man in Wales and The West,* Adams and Dart, Bath, 1972

Mate's 1906 — Mate's County Series, *Shropshire,* W. Mate & Sons, Bournemouth, 1906

McGraw Hill 1992 — *McGraw Hill Encyclopaedia of Science and Technology, 7th ed.* McGraw Hill, New York, 1992

Merry *c.*1976 — Merry D.T., *History of Minsterley,* Miss D.T. Merry, *c.*1976

Morton 1969	Morton G.H., *Geology and Mineral Veins of the Country around Shelve,* Liverpool University, 1869
Murchison 1939	Murchison R.I., *The Silurian System,* John Murray, 1839
Pearce 2008	Pearce A., ed., *Snailbeach Lead Mine* Shropshire, Peter Burgess, 2008
Percy 1870	Percy J., *The Metallurgy of Lead,* John Murray, 1870
Pettus 1670	Pettus Sir J., *Fodinae Regalis,* 1670
Phillips 1884	Phillips J.A., *A treatise on Ore Deposits*, Macmillan and Co, 1884
Plowden 1799	Plowden Edmund, *Reports (in French),* His Majesties Law Printers, 1578, (Translation 1799)
Plymley 1803	Plymley Rev. J., *A General View of the Agriculture in Salop,* Board of Agriculture, 1803
Pocock *et al* 1925	Pocock R.W., *et al, Geology of the country around Wem,* HMSO, 1925
Pocock *et al* 1938	Pocock R.W., *et al, Memoir of the Geological Survey of Great Britain, Shrewsbury District, ,* HMSO, 1938
Raistrick 1989	Raistrick A., *Dynasty of the Iron Founders,* Sessions Book Trust, York, 1989
Rees 1975	Rees U., ed., *Cartulary of Shrewsbury Abbey,* National Library of Wales, Aberystwyth, 1975
Rees 1968	Rees W., *Industry before the Industrial Revolution,* University of Wales, Cardiff, 1968
Sidgwick 1950	Sidgwick N.V., 1950, *The Chemical Elements and their Compounds*, OUP, 1950
Skinner	Skinner W., *Mining Manual and Mining Year Book,* W. Skinner & F.T., various years.
Smith *et al* 1922	Smith B. *et al, Memoir of the Geological Survey of Great Britain, Vol. XXIII, Lead and zinc ores in pre-carboniferous rocks of West Shropshire and North Wales,* HMSO, 1922
Smout 1998	Smout C., *Wur bist-ee gaw'n Siree?* (Stanton Lacy History), Flemish Press, Ludlow, 1998
Toghill 1990	Toghill P., *Geology in Shropshire,* Swan Hill Press, Shrewsbury, 1990
Tonks 1974	Tonks E., *The Snailbeach District Railways,* Industrial Railway Society, 1950 rev. 1974
Torrens 2002	Torrens H.S., *The Practice of British Geology 1750-1850,* Ashgate, Variorum, Aldershot, 2002
Townson 1799	Townson R., *Tracts and Observations on Natural History and Phisiology,* Townson, 1799
Trinder 1973	Trinder B., *The Industrial Revolution in Shropshire,* Phillimore, 1973
VCH	VCH, *Victoria County History of Shropshire,* 1908 on. Vols. I and 8 and 10.
Warter 1886	Warter J.W., *An Old Shropshire Oak,* Kegan, Paul, Trench and Co., 1886
Wedd *et al* 1929	Wedd C.B. *et al, The Country round Oswestry, Geological Memoir,* HMSO, 1929
White and Baker 1998	White R. and Barker P., *Wroxeter, Life and Death of a Roman City*, Tempus, Stroud, 1998
Whiteside 2006	Whiteside J., *The Churches and Chapels of Pontesbury Parish*, Robert Pither, Pontesbury, 2006
Wilson 1922	Wilson G.V. *et al, Special report on the Mineral Resources of Great Britain Vol. II Barytes and Witherite,* BGS, 1922

CD ROM

Cox 1998	Cox N.C., *et al, The Gloucester Port Books Database, 1575-1765,* in association with the University of Wolverhampton, 1998

References

Abbreviations used

SA	Shropshire Archives
PRO	Public Record Office
LLCo	London Lead Company (see page xx)
SCMC	Shropshire Caving and Mining Club (Shropshire Mining Club until 1976)
SMR	Shropshire Sites and Monuments Records, held by Shropshire County Council at Shirehall
BGS	British Geological Survey
SAHS	Shropshire Archaeological and Historical Society

Introduction

1. Rhadley Mine, possibly as early as the 1820s and Rock Mine by 1854 had each been known as Bog South or South Bog, in both cases geography rather than sharp practice was presumably the reason.

Chapter 1 An Overview of Shropshire Mining

1. Lynch 1972.
2. Suggested on a 6 inch to the mile OS map annotated by Lily Chitty, SA 6004/806 Shropshire sheet 48 NE.
3. L. Chitty, *Antiquaries Journal* 1925 vol. V p.409.
4. L. Chitty, *Transactions of Shropshire Archaeology and Natural History Society*, 1941-3, p.149.
5. 'The Crucible' in Hughes, G. 'Old Oswestry Hillfort excavations by W.J. Varley 1939-1940', *Archaeologia Cambrensis* 143 (1994), pp.75-79.
6. There is a view that weathering could possibly have resulted in much higher silver content in some lead ores near the ground surface than was found later and lower; this could explain Roman interest and the Carreghofa silver referred to below. Other geologists, however, consider this to be very unlikely and I know of no work on this specific to Shropshire.
7. It is mentioned in a prospectus for the Gravels Lead Mining Co. Ltd., but this must be a suspect source especially as the author of the report states that the pig was marked 'Adrian II', his quotes.
8. See R. White in Leonard 2000, pp.31-39.
9. Jones B. and Mattingly D., *An Atlas of Roman Britain*, but see 'Hush hush no longer' SAHS *Transactions* 79, 2004, where D. Pannett comprehensively challenged this interpretation of the evidence.
10. Montgomeryshire Collection, xliii, pp.36-7.
11. White and Barker 1998.
12. See *SCMC Annual Journal* 9, 2004, p.45.
13. Worthen parish is noted as having 11 outliers one of which is reasonably assumed to be Shelve; the lead mining connection is clearly somewhat tenuous. Lily Chitty's comments are at SA 6004/252/16.
14. 'Shelve' would at least refer to the Grit and Gravels mines and possibly also to Snailbeach, all these were in the Royal Forest of Stiperstones.
15. The information in these paragraphs has been taken from Eyton 1854, Rees 1968 and Colvin 1963-1976.
16. It remains an intriguing possibility that some of this lead could have been re-cast in the 17th century and still be in place, much patched, on the tower roof. It is apparently the oldest lead on any roof in the country.
17. SA 3365/309 and 10 and Cromarty 1993.
18. PRO E368/94 mb 196 and Cromarty 1993.
19. The Latin word used for a mine in the tithe charters is *minerie* or *minerio*. The word *fossatum* is known in medieval Latin used for coal-pit. The word used in this document is difficult to read but is probably *fossa* or *fosso*.
20. 'The Shrewsbury Mint in the Reign of Richard I and The Silver Mine at Carreghofa' in W.C. Wells, *Numismatic Chronicle* 5th series, vol. xii, 1932.
21. Some readings of the Pipe Roll 7 Ric I p.182 suggest that there may have been a mint at Carreghofa but not whether that would be as well or instead of Shrewsbury.
22. See above note and Powell's *Welsh Chronicle*, ed. 1584, p.209.
23. See James Lawson, 'Lead Mining' before 1815, *SCMC Journal* 9, 2004, p.45.
24. Plowden 1578.
25. Information given by Rose Lawrence to Jasper More of Linley, referring to documents then in her possession but now lost.
26. Rees 1968.

Chapter 2 The Products

1. Fowler 1994.
2. Geological time is divided into periods each of some millions of years of which the relevant ones are set out below. For more detailed information see Toghill 1990.
   Pre-Cambrian period more than 570 million years ago
   Cambrian 492-570 million years ago
   Ordovician 435-492 million years ago
   Silurian 405-435 million years ago
   Triassic 250-205 million years ago
   Tertiary 66-2 million years ago

3. For further information on the cisterns see *Shropshire Magazine* 4, 1961, pp.19-21.
4. *VCH*, 1, p.39.
5. Pocock *et al* 1925.
6. Dewey *et al* 1925.
7. At Chengkou and Ziyang.
8. The minutes of the Court of Assistants (i.e. the board of directors) for 17 June 1729.
9. From letters made available to the SCMC from Mr. Abington's descendants.
10. See Dines *et al* 1945.
11. See Dr. Withering's paper to the Royal Society of 22 April 1784, *Experiments and Observations on the Terra Ponderosa*.
12. Witherite has also been known (*inter alia*) as Aerated barytes (by J. Watt in 1790, *Mem. Manchester Society*: 3: 599), Barolite (in Kirwan, R. (1794) *Elements of Mineralogy* (1784), second edition. London: 1: 134), Sulphato-Carbonate of Baryta (Thomson, T. (1836) *Outlines of Mineralogy, Geology, and Mineral Analysis*) and Viterite (possibly Croatian *c*.1960), which probably is how witherite sounds if you don't pronounce 'w' and 'th' as in English. Even more exotic is that large quantities of viterite were mined from beneath the oceans of the planet Oaan Tar for use in/as particle shield generators. This is 'Star Wars' via 'Google', but the planet has been struck off Wikipedia's listings as being 'made up crap' (for a given value, no doubt, of 'made up').
13. Figure for 1914–18 from the Betterton Report, a report of the Departmental Committee appointed by the Board of Trade to investigate and report on the non ferrous Mining Industry, HMSO, 1920
14. Dines *et al* 1945.
15. Collins 1972.
16. Sidgwick 1950 gives a melting temperature of 830ºC and boiling temperature of 1,737ºC, and McGraw Hill 1992 1,140ºC and 1,560ºC respectively. Other sources give yet other figures, none of them stating any specific parameters which could lead to such significantly differing results.
17. Collins 1972.
18. This latter may have been a trade name, but some sources at the time used it as a word.
19. *Encyclopaedia Britannica*, 15th Ed. 1997.
20. Information from the farmer's daughter.
21. Morton 1869.
22. Phillips 1884.
23. Information from P. Lutter, 'British Oil', *Broseley Local History Society Journal* No.27, 2005 and Bagshaw's *Directory* for Shropshire, 1851.
24. From a letter from John Lawrence to John Scott.
25. Pettus 1670 quotes them as John Tugg and Henry of Wisbech whilst Donald 1955 quotes John de Inge and Henry de Bisshebury, and Rees 1968 gives the year as 1233 (presumably a typo) and the men sent as Inge and Wisbeach!
26. See SCMC Newsletter, *Below!* 2001.4.
27. Warter 1886 (but probably written *c*.1860).
28. Percy 1870.
29. *Shropshire Magazine*, Jan. 1961.

Chapter 3 The Process
1. Burt 1984, pp.52-3.
2. This practice carried on almost to the end of mining in this area, being remembered with horror at Ridge Hill mine by the mine captain's young daughter sometime in the 1920s.
3. Channel Four 'Time Team', 3 Feb. 2002.
4. *VCH*, 10, p.253.
5. B. Trinder, 'The Lead Smelters of the Ironbridge Gorge', *SCMC Annual Journal*, 1979.
6. *Transactions of the Flintshire Historical Society*, vols. 18,19 and 20, 1960/1.
7. Trinder 1973.
8. Diary Of Thomas Poole, SA mi 6750, 1833-9.
9. M. Moissenet (in translation from the French) 'Lead Mining and Smelting in the Snailbeach District Shropshire', *Mining and Smelting Magazine*, February 1862.
10. Cox 1998, Gloucester Port Books CD.
11. See note 7 above.
12. SA 261/1.
13. See note 7 above.

Chapter 4 People
1. From correspondence in the More of Linley Collection re the provision of a turnpike.
2. The turnpike as built went a long way round between Pultheley and Lydham, the proposed improvement was for the 'straight' line between these two places as is now used by the A488.
3. From an unpublished thesis 'Lead Mining in south west Shropshire 1780-1900', by Olga S. Newman, Keele University, 1984.
4. From an interview with several members of the Rowson family.
5. Kinnaird Commission Report 1864.
6. Kinnaird Commission Report 1864.
7. Whiteside 2006.
8. Information from Mrs. Trow, Elijah Parry's daughter, herself onetime postmistress of Snailbeach.
9. Kinnaird Commission Report 1864, but see also R. Burt, The British Lead Mining Industry.
10. Bolton and Watt papers, Birmingham Name Book, Birmingham City Archives.
11. The Governors and Company of Mine Adventurers of England, ran mines in mid Wales from the late 17th to mid 18th century and looked at Whittingslow and Weston Mines. The Shropshire Company of 1740 raised capital in the County but was only active in Wales. The English Copper Company were briefly involved at Hayton's Bent.
12. Rees 1968.

Chapter 5 Mines on the western flanks of the Stiperstones I

1. J. Lawson 'Lead Mining before 1815', *SAHS Transactions* No.79, 2004.
2. Also known, especially prior to the early 19th century, as Minsterley lead mine and the company as Minsterley mining company, not to be confused with East Roman Gravels at a much later date or Minsterley Barytes Mining and Milling Co.
3. SA box 800 uncat correspondence, see below.
4. Percy 1870.
5. Brook and Allbutt 1973, p65.
6. *VCH* Vol. 8.
7. SA 152/1.
8. The 'white tip' which features so much in this account has, as will be seen later, now gone but was for many years the defining feature of Snailbeach, well remembered if not loved by the inhabitants. Those who did not know it may find its scale difficult to comprehend. See Fig. 5.16.
9. The great-great grandfathers are both recorded by Sir Jasper More in 1898, the uncle is from Lily Chitty's collected correspondence SA 6004/. If Rose's great-great-grandfather referred to was on her Lawrence side it would have been John I who died in 1769; both he and his son (John II) were involved with the mine. The man referred to may, however, have been on Rose's Jones' side, or one of her other, now unknown, great-great grandfathers.
10. SA Raine Papers 851/293, this could be the only survivor of an annual series of account which enabled the cost book mine to share out its costs and profits between partners, or it could have been connected with the death that year of John Lawrence I.
11. For a detailed assessment of both the estate map and inventory see Cuckson A., 'Snailbeach Mine in the 1760s' in *British Mining* 71, 2002.
12. The Act was 30 & 31 Victoria I, c. 'An Act for facilitating the Acceptance of Stock of the Snailbeach Mine Company (Limited) in substitution for Shares in the Snailbeach Mine Company; and for other Purposes'.
13. The trade was not all one way though, as Snailbeach were approached two years later by Mr. Hawksworth of Minera asking if they would smelt 697 tons of his ore. During the 1880s they also purchased ore from both Perkins Beach and Roman Gravels mines.
14. From correspondence with Captain Oldfield SA 1950/4. Bog and Pennerley mines were also considered.
15. Kelly's Shropshire *Directory* for 1941.
16. Registered in High St. Ruabon and probably absorbed into the Gravel Trading Co., see SA 1950/37.
17. Sadly this is not the perpetual motion suggested by some; the water wheel was not powered by what it pumped up and allowed to discharge from the adit.
18. Throughout the book steam engine size is given in the inch diameter of the cylinder. The engine, known locally as The Lady Mary Deborah, had a 36 foot long unequal beam with a six foot stroke at the cylinder and a nine foot one at the pump. It worked 5 strokes a minute at 50 psi and had a capacity of 5,000 gallons per hour, much in excess of its needs and it generally pumped for six hours a day.
19. In the past various dates have been given and assumptions made about the mine drainage arrangements. For the discussion which has led to the information given here see Cuckson, A., 'Snailbeach mine: pumping and winding machinery *c*.1782-1856', *British Mining 78,* Northern Mine Research Society, 2005.
20. For a fuller discussion see Brown, I., SCMC Account 17 and Cuckson, A., 'Snailbeach Mine in the 1760s', *British Mining 71,* Northern Mine Research Society, 2002 and SCMC Account 22, p.18.
21. Sold to Gresford Colliery near Wrexham after closure.
22. It is possible that Lordshill mine referred to a different location.
23. Correspondence from Charles Moore and Co. Ltd. to Joseph Roberts at the mine.
24. Correspondence 10 February 1930 from Moores to Joseph Roberts at Snailbeach.
25. Correspondence from Charles Moore and Co. Ltd. to Joseph Roberts at the mine.
26. Local information via SCMC Account 17 by I. Brown.
27. Townson 1799.
28. SA 1950/82 & 83.
29. See Pearce 2008.
30. Kelly's 1870.

Chapter 6 Mines on the western flanks of the Stiperstones II

1. SA 103/1/8/166.
2. Notes on the Lawrence family will be found in chapter 4. Where possible the particular John has been specified or a reasonable guess made.
3. Frances *et al* 2000, p.178. At east two levels near Crowsnest were used as air raid shelters.
4. SA mi 184/3.
5. SA 2028/1/2.
6. Note in the Worthen parish registers for that year.
7. SA 2495 box 67 uncat, these leases are too fragile to open and the details on the outside are none too clear it is believed that the names quoted are accurate.
8. Possibly Heighway Jones, Horton and Stainsby, see SA 1709 box 199.
9. Information from an unpublished thesis by Olga Newman, 'Lead Mining in south west Shropshire 1780-1900', Keele University, 1984. This was not the mine's first venture into property as in 1845

Samuel Bayley of Pennerley was re-housed when his cottage fell down in one built by the Bog mine company, SA 5381/7/6.

10. The Captain of Snailbeach mine.

11. Carruthers *et al* 1915.

12. Though the location of this tunnel is not in doubt some published sources have reported it ambiguously as if it were wholly underground, for clarification see the author's 'Would the real Somme Tunnel please stand up' in *Below!* (SCMC newsletter) No. 4, 2006.

13. Despite appearing in returns no limited company of this name appears in the Board of Trade records.

14. In the event this only went down to Boat Level but opened up adequate barytes ground. It had been intended as late as 1919 to go down a further 600 feet to find the lead, which would have been too deep down to be reachable.

15. For more information on the documents up to 1761 see the author's 'Bog Mines down to the year 1760' in the *SCMC Journal* No. 8, 2003.

16. SA 1118, 26-11-1813.

17. Plymley 1803.

18. Information from K. Lock.

19. Tonks, *The Snailbeach District Railways*, p.9.

20. SA 4991/5/16.

21. Francis *et al* 2000.

22. For this and much other information I am indebted to Andy Cuckson, see his piece in *SCMC Journal* 6.

23. Geological Association Proceedings Vol. 13.

24. SA 5982/1/15.

25. SA SCC 1/A/1/17 1957-6.

26. Brooke and Allbut 1973, p.81.

27. SA mi 184/3.

28. This and other information is from an article by Nigel Chapman in the *SCMC Journal* 2.

29. Cuckson, A.,'The Parrys and Central Stores', *SCMC Journal* No. 9, 2004.

30. SA 4991/2/7.

31. It began as the name of one of four 'walks' in Hogstowe Forest in the Middle Ages.

32. Much information on these mines has been obtained second-hand from the minutes of the London Lead Company via Lewis, *Lead Mining in Eastern Montgomeryshire in 1751* in the Montgomeryshire collection vol. LVIII pt II p.114 on, and Rhodes, J.H., *The London Lead Company in North Wales 1693-1792*, thesis for Leicester University, 1970.

33. Smith *et al* 1922

34. Carruthers *et al* 1916

35. 'Old works' were noted when the lease of 1724 was negotiated.

36. The family had now lost 'Articles of Co-partnership' dated 1791, see More, Sir J., Shelve district history.

37. Jackfield Mines Ltd. were considered a shadowy concern with Mr. Chambers the manager. It has been suggested that they were criminal as at least one

director went to prison following a scam relating to new contractors plant which was driven round the Tankerville tips for enough hours to be registered as second-hand, though no one seems clear how this worked. Some mines at least seem to have been tax fiddles. Information from the late Clifford Lewis.

38. In a now lost paper reported in the Caradoc and Severn Valley Field Club Transactions for 1947-50.

39. SA 2499/1 contains on the rear some notes presumably written by P. Blight, a mining surveyor in the 1920s one of which is that the mine opened *c.*1842, this is also the only source for the information that it was sold by order of the sheriff in 1877.

40. Noted from website 'Mining Index of Cornish Newspapers' prepared by Alasdair Neill.

41. If one takes the official returns at face value then in 1866/7 the Ovenpipe Company owned Perkins Beach mine but not Ovenpipe mine which was owned by the Bog and Pennerley Company.

42. Who supplied Charles Moore and Co. of Lymm (see Snailbeach) with a sample truck of barytes via Joseph Roberts at Snailbeach in 1930.

43. Information from Harold Rowson collected for *Never on a Sunday*. Old miners including his grandfather used to use hazel twigs or a clock spring to divine for barytes or water.

44. SA 2499/1 drawn *c.*1920 marks this.

45. Wilson *et al* 1922.

46. I. Brown, *West Shropshire Mining Fields*.

47. See Bog water engine on page 104.

48. Information from Rose Lawrence, see chapter 4, page 68.

49. Although when explored recently no way through could be identified.

50. Rhadley also used the name South Bog at one time.

51. Although officially registered as the Leeds Rock House Lead Mining Co. Ltd., in 1868.

52. This and other information below is taken from a list of documents made in 1911, the documents themselves have not been found.

53. Mate's County Series 1906.

54. Although there are vestigial remains at Roman Gravels and Pennerley.

55. In operational days the upper room of this building was used as a club room for the miners and occasionally for religious services.

56. SA 437 box 17.

Chapter 7 Mines of Shelve and the Hope Valley

1. See Chapter 1, note 12.

2. In the 1831 correspondence John Lawrence distinguishes between Batholes and Shelvefield (later to be East Roman Gravels) both on the land of the Earl of Tankerville, in a letter of 1853 he states that he worked Batholes, Wood and Shelvefield all the property of the Tankervilles. This has to put some doubt on what took place at which mine, but as there

is no mention of Wood mine in the 1831 correspondence I have assumed that Shelvefield and Wood
are the same mine. This is confused by the 1853
letter referring to an unspecified one of those three
belonging to Lloyds, which ties up with nothing
else though they did own land in Shelve parish and
issued at least one lease jointly with the Mores in
1801 related to Grit.

3. From correspondence to and from Lawrence in SA
at 1118/.

4. *The Silurian System*, he had done his fieldwork whilst
the new turnpike was being constructed down the
Hope Valley presumably 1834-5.

5. Information from the late Clifford Lewis.

6. Letter of 24 June 1831, SA 1118/18.

7. Jasper More the then landlord did some historical
research and noted that Rose Lawrence, the last
member of the family and the daughter of John IV
had documents back to this period. John Lawrence
III states in correspondence that his family had
mined at Grit for 200 years, that was in 1831.

8. Lord Herbert would have had the mineral rights
under the 'wastes and commons' of the manor if
Mr. More had been a copyhold tenant, so More was
presumably a freeholder. For further details see SA
1037/2.

9. There is nothing to specify whether mine or company.

10. Presumably the Hazeldine of Coleham foundry etc.

11. SA 437 box 13. The account also included debts to a
canal carrier and wharfage charges at Gloucester.

12. 'More of Linley' papers.

13. It is tempting to speculate that White Grit East
was between Benree and Grit Farm. Palin and Co.
owned both in 1859 but did not own Grit Sett. The
two mines (if Benree ever developed as such) shared
James Skimming as their agent in 1859. These
were on or near Gritt Hill which at least at times
was a separate sett, the issue is further confused by
a statement to the *Mining Journal* of 10 Feb. 1872
by Mr. Whittall (mine agent for the More estate)
that Gritt Hill sett was south east of Grit sett when
geographically Grit sett is south east of Gritt Hill.
One possible location could be Shelve Trial, see the
end of this section.

14. Carruthers *et al* 1916.

15. Chester City records TC/P/l/423, personal papers of
William Hall.

16. Bick 1991.

17. Carruthers *et al* 1916.

18. SA 1509/44a.

19. The name of the mine in the 1858 prospectus is
given as Gravels or Roman Mine, another undated
plan shows only one sett, Roman Boundary.

20. Information from the 1858 prospectus report and see
Transactions of the SAHS XI 1888 p.272 an extract
of which, describing this mine is reproduced in
appendix 2.

21. *Ibid.*

22. Shown on a plan probably prepared by P. Blight
c.1920 for Shropshire Mines ltd.

23. It is could be that it was the order address which
was Roman Gravels mine and that the delivery address was elsewhere, the then fairly new Malehurst
Smelter being an obvious possibility. Interestingly
a 14-inch blowing engine existed at Pontesbury
smelthouse in 1831, but whether it is the same, and
if so whether it had been moved, is unknown.

24. 1858 prospectus.

25. From a paper delivered to the Severn Valley and
Caradoc Field Club in 1947.

Chapter 8 Mines to the west of the A488

1. Kelly's *Directory* for that year.

2. SA 552/18/8/4/23.

3. See Skinner's *Mining Year Book*, 1921.

4. Some information and 'colour' from Mrs Trow,
Arthur Bishop's (the mine captain throughout the
mine's entirety) daughter

5. Information from J. Lawson and Sir Jasper More's
proposed history of Shelve district.

6. SA 938/408.

7. These last two sets of figures from BGS 46.

8. SA 552/18/8/4/1.

9. SA 1950/4 uncat.

10. Evans 2003, p.71.

11. Joseph Brown's testimony under Rorrington.

12. SA 552/18/8/4.

13. The *Mining Journal*, 21 Aug. 1852 p.399.

14. Cuckson, A., 'The Cliffdale Barytes company',
SCMC Journal 7, 2001.

15. Francis *et al* 2000.

16. Though the *Shrewsbury Chronicle* of 24 Oct. 1958
notes that an Albert Bennett worked for barytes at
Weston Pit White Grit 'until it closed 16 or 17 years
ago'.

17. Report of the Departmental Committee (etc.) on the
non Ferrous Mining Industry 1920. Board of Trade
App'x VII table 5 Weston Mine.

18. Carruthers *et al* 1915.

19. Francis 2001.

20. An entry in his memorandum book.

21. See chapter 4, page 68.

22. Townson 1799.

23. James Whitney was taking barytes and witherite
from Snailbeach mine in 1831, see chapter 2 p.30,
where Leonard Abington intended to approach him
for some for his employer.

24. This could be a misreading for Goodrass and Co
noted paint manufacturers.

Chapter 9 Lead Mines south of the Stiperstones

1. SA 4134/2/68.

2. SA 4572/2/77.

3. Murchison 1839.

4. SA 1509/48.
5. This may be a mistake as no company of this name seems to have been registered but a South Shropshire Barytes and Lead Co. Ltd. was and Haywood was a part of it; they were involved with the barytes mill at Snailbeach.
6. Information from Powisland club transactions (Montgomeryshire Collection) Vol. Lviii Pt II p.14.

Chapter 10 Mines in the Long Mynd area
1. SA 567 box 29.
2. *Ibid.*
3. Towson 1799.
4. Plymley 1803.
5. Murchison 1839.
6. The Bentley Ford etc trials and mine correspondence is at SA D3651/B/6/5. The Company name appears in correspondence but it was not apparently registered with the Board of Trade.
7. Dewey *et al* 1958, p.59.
8. The company was registered in 1914, but no records have surfaced for whatever activity they carried out.
9. Information from Richard Jones whose father was the carpenter.
10. Shropshire Unfolded, May 2003.
11. Carruthers *et al* 1915.
12. Dines *et al* 1958: 'production at this mine is believed to have totalled 23,000 tons'.
13. Wilson *et al* 1922.
14. SA 112/5/46/10.
15. It is presumably the case at this and other mines that Mr. Butler was acting for Shropshire Lead Mines Ltd. (and at some mines, e.g. Huglith for Wotherton Barytes and Lead Co. Ltd.) and subsequently for Shropshire Mines Ltd.
16. The mine is not mentioned as being a working mine in *The Problem of Snailbeach* paper (see note 22 below), it would have been if it had held out employment prospects.
17. SCMC Account 18, p.31.
18. Jackson 1883, p.129.
19. SA 6000/13628.
20. SA 1794 on, catalogues of sales of Smythe Owen lands in various parishes including Pontesbury and Pulverbatch. A sale of 31 January 1801 includes 'The Pitts' on an unnamed farm. There is also a reference to copper being worked in Pulverbatch parish, The Pitts seeming to be the location. A Manorial survey of Condover Estate of 1767, also at Shropshire Archives, shows what seems to be the same field as part of Roberts Farm, though with no mention of any mining.
21. Who ran barytes mines elsewhere in the country as well as Shropshire, e.g. Christow Mine in Devon.
22. See *The Problem of Snailbeach,* A Ministry of Town and Country Planning paper of 1945 (which also included a suggestion that Snailbeach Village be removed and rebuilt elsewhere as it could not be brought up to a satisfactory standard). A copy of this paper is to be found in the Shropshire Caving and Mining Club Annual Journal 10.
23. Shropshire County Council Roads and Bridges Committee were informed on 23 January 1926 (in connection with the transfer of their consent to Malehurst Barytes Ltd. for the ropeways to cross the main road) that the ropeway was 'abandoned'. If this reflects the use rather than the ownership of the line then there must have been at least a short hiatus in production at this time.
24. Pers. com. E Betton, who was 6 or 7 at the time but was told by his father, Harold, who also worked at the mine.
25. Dines *et al* 1945.
26. The copper traces are noted in Dewey *et al* 1925, as they are in Lily Chitty's notes from which the Squire Hall and Butts Woods information was obtained.
27. *VCH* volume 1.
28. SA mi 6750 and Dewey *et al* 1925, respectively.
29. Murchison 1839.
30. SA 6004/184/13.
31. SCMC Account 20 volume 1.
32. Wedd *et al* 1929.
33. Murchison 1839.
34. Shropshire Sites and Monuments Records 'Ratlinghope Trials'.
35. Murchison 1839.
36. Wedd *et al* 1929.
37. Dines *et al* 1958.
38. SAC 6004/184/33. Letter of 11 Nov. 1924 from Wm. Medlicott, Solicitor of Craven Arms to Lily Chitty.
39. Much of the information on Norbury has come from Joyce Pinnock, Norbury's local historian and granddaughter of the man who filled the shafts.
40. It is odd that the mine is not mentioned as being a working or potentially working mine in *The Problem of Snailbeach* paper (see note 22 above), it ought to have been if it held out the employment prospects which a 1942 lease would seem to imply.
41. Memories of William Bricke and John Houlston collected by Lily Chitty in 1924, SA 6004/184/22.
42. Memories of William Bricke and John Houlston collected by Lily Chitty in 1924, SA 6004/184/22, it is not clear but this closure is presumably the 1894 one when barytes veins were being followed.
43. Dines *et al* 1958. This publication also states that the mine was not opened up during the First World War, which conflicts with the evidence of the promotional letter and photographs referred to below and must be incorrect.
44. SA 6000/13628.
45. SA 1709/52/-.
46. Pocock *et al* 1938.
47. Dines *et al* 1945.

Chapter 11 Lead and Copper Mines of Corvedale

1. Hamilton 1967, p.103.
2. Murchison 1839, p.188.
3. The local information was collected by C. Smout and published in *Wur bist-ee gaw'n Siree?* The dates given above are unconvincing. No mining is recorded at Westcott before 1859 though it is more than possible. An 1850 date is too early for the Shropshire's 'copper rush', it took place in the early 1860s and it is almost certain that Hayton's Bent would have been looked at then. It seems unlikely that any of the landowners cited were involved, none of them owned land at Westcott nor at that date are any of them recorded as investors in any local mine. The 1870s are also unconvincing, but an adit seems to have been dug after the 1882 OS survey but before the 1902 survey on which it appears as disused, this also begs the question of which miners were using the New Inn in 1901.
4. Information from the county Sites and Monuments Record desk top survey, via D. Poyner.
5. SA 6000/985.
6. Plymley 1803.
7. Raistrick 1989, p.189.
8. See J.H. Rhodes thesis ,The London Lead Company in North Wales 1693-1792'.
9. Like many religious houses Wenlock Priory owned land at a number of places within Shropshire and without, including in Coventry, Stow, Leominster, Clun and Sutton (Shrewsbury).
10. Précis of Plowden, 1799; contemporary report of 'the case of mines' from Donald 1955.

Chapter 12 Mines in the Breidden Hills

1. SA 3320/2.
2. Much of the primary material for this chapter is to be found in the files of Salt, the solicitors at SA D3651/B/6/5/-.
3. Torrens 2002.
4. See extracts from Thomas Orchard's diary in Anon 1987.
5. SA 261/1.
6. SA 829/35/10 uncat.
7. SA D3651/B/34/3/12/21.
8. Dines *et al* 1945, p.101.
9. Burt *et al* 1990.
10. Eddowes *Salopian Journal*, 8 April 1885.
11. Dines *et al* 1945, p.101.
12. From a report on the mine for the landowner by Messrs. Hall and Raine, March 1922.
13. *Shrewsbury Chronicle*, 6 May, 5 August and 23 December 1921.
14. Wilson *et al* 1922.
15. SCMC account 22.
16. SA 81/259.

Chapter 13 Oswestry area Mines

1. *SCMC Annual Journal* 9, 2004.
2. See SCMC library ref. PS4, these letters may have been copied from issues of a mining journal for 1857.
3. The museum is regularly open and is free, though to inspect the Woodwardian collection, still housed in its original cabinets with Mr. Woodward's own labels, it would be wise to telephone in advance.
4. In Kelly's *Directory* of 1870 there is an entry for J. Lester, manganese and copper mine proprietor and lime merchant, Llwyntidman (between Maesbury and Llanymynech). It seems a reasonable assumption that this is the same man. The copper interest is clear but the manganese one raises questions. He must have been involved at either a mine near Llanbedr, Arenig or at Llanaelhaiarn in North Wales, these were the only Welsh mines functioning at the time, though on a small scale, other UK deposits were in Devon Cornwall and Derbyshire at that date though not worked since *c*.1850. It is possible that he could have been involved at Rednal or that there were mines producing manganese in the locality of which no record has survived. UK manganese mining was very limited at this period.
5. Brown 2001.
6. Goodchild J., *British Mining* 43, pp.63-75.

Chapter 14 Copper Mines in north-east Shropshire

1. Ove Arup, Clive Mine feasibility study and Memoirs of the Geological Survey; Special Reports on the Mineral Resources of Great Britain, Vol. xxx, Copper ores of the Midlands etc.
2. Information collected by T.C. Hancox of Wellington 24 Mar. 1972, SA 2709/1.
3. Ibid., copy of 1739 letter at 1578/3/9.
4. SA 322/12/165.
5. Gough 1979.
6. Information from notes in Pradoe Church.
7. Wedd *et al* 1929.
8. See Carlon C.J., 'The Eardiston Copper Mine' in the *Bulletin of the Peak District Mines Historical Society*, Vol. 8 No. 1, June 1981.
9. i.e. a part of the Royal monopoly.
10. Rees 1968, p.652.
11. *SCMC Account* 20 vol. 1.
12. Plymley 1803.
13. Pocock *et al* 1935.

Chapter 15 Non-Mining Sites

1. Lovett letters of 1780, Chester record office TC/P/L/345 (town clerk's files).
2. See chapter 6, note 32.
3. B. Trinder, 'The lead smelters of the Ironbridge Gorge', *Shropshire Caving and Mining Club Annual Journal*, 1979.
4. Angerstein 2001.

5. *Transactions of the Flintshire Historical Society,* Vols. 18, 19 & 20.

6. Trinder 1973.

7. SA 851/292.

8. SA 851/290.

9. The list of the abbey's charters and other documents, it has been translated and published by Aberystwyth University in 1975, Ed U. Rees.

10. *VCH* Vol. 8.

11. SA lease 11786.

12. The sales of land including three sites with known coal either by or opposite the Pontesbury smelter are listed in SA D3651/B/3/6/28, being the disposal of land owned by the late Mr. Smythe Owen.

13. SA 6000/13914. There was an engine at the colliery in 1777, from Boycott correspondence, this was probably the subject of the dispute in 1778. There was also an engine from Bolton and Watt for the colliery, new in 1778.

14. See note 13 above.

15. In 1842 Lawrence owned and occupied two fields, Big Gin Croft and Little Gin Croft, between his house and the centre of Pontesbury, which may have been a small colliery; they were certainly on the coal measures and the obvious presence at some date of a gin strongly suggests mining.

16. Snailbeach Mine Co minute book.

17. A cast iron plaque for 1832 almost certainly came from this chimney. Presumably both chimneys were built in 1832 to reduce pollution or to reduce threats over pollution from influential locals, as the rector of the parish was threatening legal action over the matter, commenting that the previous chimneys were no more than ordinary steam engine chimneys. Thomas Poole's visit confirms that at least the Snailbeach smelter had its final chimney height by 1834 and White Grit's chimney was at the time of his visit 'very considerable'. It could be that the White Grit smelter over the road coming on stream *c.*1830 (see below) increased pollution to such an extent as to spur the Rector's action.

18. i.e. a condenser was being constructed in which particles of lead and zinc in suspension in the flue gases would be deposited and from whence they could be collected and sold.

19. See *The Industrial Chemist and Chemical Manufacturer*, February 1927

20. I.J. Brown, *SCMC Annual Journal*, 1980.

21. 437 box 12 uncat.

22. Henry Dennis' report of April 1878 says: 'The Reservoir is full ... notwithstanding a liberal use of it was made a short time since in flushing the Smelting Flue, collecting the Flue Dust to the Settling Pits.' (SA 5982 5/15 Longueville uncatalogued).

23. SA 6000/2877.

24. According to Merry *c.*1976 there was a fulling mill on the Rea Brook from 1581 to 1695 at this site, which may or may not have survived whole or in part.

25. Carruthers *et al* 1915.

26. Carruthers *et al* 1916.

27. See Pearson, N. 'The Rise and Fall of the Industries of Pontesbury', dissertation, Birmingham University, 2004.

28. This figure is taken from Laporte Ltd.'s centenary booklet, Laporte 1888-1988.

29. Information from a former employee, but no doubt incorrect. Other stories were that the plant was owned by the Rover Car company to produce components for spitfires and by the admiralty for naval spares.

30. Information from Esmond Betton who, with his father Harold, was responsible for keeping the plant runnable at 24 hours notice.

31. The furnace heat caused the barytes to fly apart but did not so affect any foreign matter, thus dispensing with the need for acid bleaching.

32. Information on this mill was taken from Cuckson, A., 'The Snailbeach Barytes Mill', *SCMC Journal* No 7.

33. Sutton Lower Mill, Interim report 1975, SA D27.7 v.f. and The Rea Brook SA D66.7 v.f., Alan Wharton.

34. Diary of Thomas Poole, 1834-9, SA mi 6750.

35. The information on the dimensions etc of the level have been taken from 'The Boat Level Sough', *Birmingham Enterprise Club Transactions* 2.

36. SA 1118/18 uncat.

37. Various names have been given to this company but the principal leases are to the Grit and Gravels company, see SA D3651/B/41/3/1 and 2.

38. Smith *et al* 1922, p.18.

39. see *Industrial Railway Record* No.70, April 1977.

40. See SCC records Roads and Bridges Agreements file 4689.

41. At the time of writing the last 'classic' ropeway was just about to finish, but it was to be replaced with a new one incorporating state of the art chair lift technology.

42. GWR register of private sidings.

43. Information from K. Lock.

44. From local memory.

45. Information from Esmond Betton whose father was part of the demolition crew.

46. Both of these appear in E. Tonks' excellent history of the Snailbeach railway and have been copied elsewhere. The Callow Hill line is mentioned accurately in the text but the map is less clear. The Gravels line was in the 1950 edition but corrected in the 1974 one.

Index

Taylor, John and Company 151-152, 157, 182
Tenison, Mr. 249
Thomas, John 193
Thomas, ?John 242
Thornthwaite Mining Company 169
Threapwood *see* Drepewood
Thresholds Farm 202, 204-205
Thynne family 18
Tinlie 12
tin mining 12, 38-39
Tisdall, Messrs. F.S.H. Ltd. 112, 147
tithes, lead 16
Todleth 6, 182
Tomlins, D. 121
Top Ventnor 125
Townson, Robert 186, 199, 201
Toye, W. and Company 126
transport 54-58
Treflach mine 6, 246
tributers 62
tutworkers 61

Underwood, Alt S. 161
Underwood, G. Schofield 161
Upper Batholes *see* East Roman Gravels
Upper Heath 18
Upper and Lower Lawnt 10
Upper Works *79*, 80, 86
uranium 39-40
Urwick, Mr. 184

vanadium 24, 28, 247
Ventnor 10
Venus Bank mine 6
Venus Bank Wood 98
Vessons mine 6, 10, 73
Vessons Mine Company 73
Vieille Montagne Zinc Company 101, 120

Wagbeach Level *see* Snailbeach
wages 63
Wakeman family 179
Wakeman, Sir Offley 180
Walduck, J.H. 234
Walker, Cross and company 99-100, 117, 119, 126, 129, 134, 184, 260
Walker family 201
Walker, J.B. 201, 224
Walker, J.W. 274
Ward and Lloyd 262
Wardman, Edmund 193, 196
Waring, Walter 181

Watercress Level *see* Nether Heath
Waters, Arthur 69, 111, 128, 130, 134, 137, 144, 145, 158, 159, 164, 166, 169, 180
Waters, Arthur junior 120, 128, 164
Watson, John 104
Watson, Mr. of Yorkshire 159
Watson, Peter 68-69
Watson, Robson and Ridge 132
Watson, T.H. 126
Watson, York and Shaw 128
Watts, William 234
Webb, Mr. 129
Wedgewood, Josiah 30
Wellings, Mr. 222
Wenlock mine 6, 15, 232
Wenlock Abbey 18-19
Wentnor mine 130; *see also* Ritton Castle
Westcott mine 6, 60, 196, 212, 222-223, *222*
Westcott Mine Company 222
Westcott Mining Co. Ltd. 222
West Felton *see* Rednal
West Grit 10
West Middletown mine 6, 239
Weston (Cliffdale) mine 6, 8, 9, 10, 19, 52, 70, 173, 174, 182-185, *183*
    production 185
Weston Heath mine 6, 20
Weston, John 99
Weston/Western Hill *see* Weston
Weston Hill Mining company 172, 175, 183-184
Weston Hill sett 183
West Roman Gravels mine 10
West Roman mine 10
West Snailbeach *see* Rorrington
West Snailbeach Mine Company 132
West Snailbeach Mining Co. Ltd. 179
West Stiperstones *see* Ritton Castle
West Stiperstones Mining Co. Ltd. 130
West Tankerville *see* East Roman Gravels
West Tankerville Mining Company 10, 134, 142, 144
Whalleybourne 11-12
Wixhill mine 6, 20
Whitcliffe mine 6, 198
White Grit mine 10, 22, 28, 68, 142, 148, 153, *154*, 157, 262
White Grit Company 179, 258, 259
White Grit(t) Mine Company 95, 97, *97*, 149-150, *150*
White Grit East 10, 151
White House, The 179
'white tip' 81, *82, 83*

Whitney, Jas 186
Whittall, Mr. 193
Whittall, William 237
Whittingslow mine 7, 218
Wilderley mine 7, *51*, 223-226
Wilkinson, John 67, 199, 234
Williams, Robert 187
Wilson-Barnes, W. 237
winding 49-50
Windscale Nuclear Power Station 32, 75
winze 287
Withering, Dr. William 31
witherite 24, 28, 30, 31, 52, 72, 87, 135, 179
Wixhall mine 254
Wood mine 146; *see also* East Roman Gravels
Wood and Company 172
Wood Level 7, 47, 141, 143, 149, 150, 153, 157,
        160, 166, 167, 277-278
Woodward, John 30, 245, 249
Wooton, William 121
Worthen parish 57
W(h)otherton/East Wotherton mine 4, 10, 30, 185-
        190, *186-188*, 193
    production 187-188, 190

Wotherton Barytes and Lead Co. Ltd. 190
Wotherton Barytes and Lead Mining Co. Ltd. 10,
        102, 126, 152, 161, 189, 212, 227, 268
Wotherton Barytes Mining Co. 189
Wotherton Mining Co. 189
Wrentnall Baryta Co. 228
Wrentnall mine 7, 24, 226-228, *226, 227*
Wroxeter 15
'Wynne's Patent Slimer' 107

Yelland, Boustred and Rogers 132
Yelland, James 161, 189, 245, 246
Yelland, W. & James & J. Mitchell 113
yellow spar 31
Yorton 7, 254
Young, George 187

zinc 24, 26-27, 52, 71, 101, 118, 141, 147, 219,
        241, 244, 245, 246
    production 26, 88, 108, 112, 113, 122, 135,
        155, 159, 164, 167
    uses 26
zinc-blende 26, 27, 101, 111